DIGITAL COMPUTING

DIGITAL

Fortran IV and its Applications

John Wiley & Sons, Inc.

COMPUTING

in Behavioral Science

RICHARD S. LEHMAN
Franklin and Marshall College

DANIEL E. BAILEY
University of Colorado

NEW YORK · LONDON · SYDNEY · TORONTO

Library of Congress Catalog Card Number: 68-30917
SBN 471 52400
Printed in the United States of America

PREFACE

Our objective in this book is to provide a readable and technically correct text on digital computing with Fortran IV for behavioral scientists. Our major aim is to instill a thorough knowledge of the techniques of digital computing that are useful and interesting to behavioral scientists. We make no attempt here to present research findings.

In this text we give a complete description and analysis of the widely used programming language, Fortran IV. We offer the language with a profusion of motivating examples and problems relevant to the work of behavioral scientists. Statistical computations are liberally represented and simulation techniques are given special attention. Techniques of dealing with lists and nonnumerical data, including verbal materials, are developed in detail. Eighteen projects of interest to behavioral scientists are described in an attempt to give an indication of the types of real problems that can be approached with the Fortran IV language in digital computing. Four of the eighteen are worked out in detail with complete documentation and illustrative data and output. In addition, more than thirty completely worked out and tested programs are given in the text, beginning with simple programs to calculate an average, and ranging through the treatment of verbal text.

Here, we attempt to initiate actual programming efforts on the part of the reader as early as possible. These efforts are supported in the first part of the text by giving the reader partial programs, with the hard parts already programmed, to complete and to run on the computer. The problems and examples keep pace with the material presented so that there is an increasing level of skill and knowledge to match the increasing level of complexity and difficulty.

We compiled this text with upper division undergraduate and beginning graduate students in mind. We are now using this material in laboratory courses in statistics, at both levels. There is no prerequisite for the material covered in the book. Any reasonably bright undergraduate student can master the material in the first two sections without an undue amount of difficulty in a two-semester hour course (less than thirty-six hours of instruction). It is not too much to expect most first-year graduate students in the behavioral sciences to master all three sections in thirty-six hours of instruction. We have found that small periods of personal attention to the problems students have with the material, early in the course, greatly facilitate the process of learning the later portions. The material presented here has been used, in a preliminary mimeographed form, with success in undergraduate behavioral science statistics laboratory courses and undergraduate courses in computing applications in the behavioral and social sciences.

This book may be used in several ways. The impatient student may turn immediately to Chapters 4 and 5. These two chapters contain the essentials of Fortran programming. Chapters 4 to 10 contain the complete presentation of the Fortran language and may be used as both a textbook and as a reference manual. Probably the best way to approach the book is to begin with Chapter 1, and then to proceed through the succeeding chapters in order. Then the reader will gain an understanding of both Fortran programming and some general theory of computing.

One of us (DEB) had the good fortune to be required by his professor in graduate school (Robert C. Tryon) to learn computer programming as soon as a computer was available (in 1955 at the University of California). This event resulted in a turning point for both of our careers. In 1963 we were working together on a graduate-level statistics course in psychology in which we decided to try to teach computer programming to the students. To our delight, the students thought that the programming part of the course made the rest of it worth bearing. That first year, we taught the Michigan Algorithm Decoder (MAD) language on the IBM 709. Since there were no good text materials to use in the course, we developed about 300 pages of dittoed manuscript that seemed adequate. Our efforts were futile —the Computer Center changed computer systems and we had to switch to Fortran IV. It became apparent that we would have to rewrite our original material if we were to have a good text for our students. By January 1964 we had written nine chapters of the first draft of what has turned out to be this book. That material (and a good deal of new material) has been rewritten three times, and has been used in several classes since that time. The text has been used by both of us a number of times, and graduate assistants have used it for three years in graduate courses in behavioral-science statistics-course laboratories. The experience that we gained in using the mimeographed preliminary editions contributed greatly to the published version of the book.

Many people have contributed to this book. We gratefully acknowledge their part and express our appreciation. Nearly three hundred individual students, most of them graduate students in psychology, have used our material as a text. Their comments and reactions were important in preparing the final draft. Five graduate teaching assistants and associates have had the responsibility of teaching from the preliminary version: Peter W. Lenz, Dorothy T. Monk, Dorothy K. Gerety, La Rue A. Brown, and Thomas O. Mitchell. Their comments and experience have helped, in important ways, to structure and clarify the final draft. Charles A. Phillips, Jr. performed the valuable service of proofreading the final manuscript and of helping to prepare the numerous illustrations. The University of Colorado Graduate School Computing Center ran all of the illustration programs on the IBM 7044 and on the CDC 6400. Without the help and cooperation of the Computing Center, courses such as those taught with this book would not be possible.

Special thanks must be given to Professor Bert Green, who read the manuscript at two stages and provided comment, criticism, and advice that have proved helpful beyond measure.

Our wives, Jean Lehman and Sara Bailey, deserve a large measure of credit for this book. They were initially skeptical about the entire venture and, at times, seemed to doubt that the computer even existed (or felt that the computer was a grand hoax). However, their good nature, patient support, and encouragement have seen us through.

One person, above all others, has been essential to the production of the book. Without the assistance of Barbara A. Salaman we would have found the production many times more difficult. Mrs. Salaman typed the manuscript many times. Her devotion to the book, her skill, and her efficiency exceed any measure of appreciation that we can express.

Richard S. Lehman
Daniel E. Bailey

CONTENTS

LIST OF PROGRAMMED EXAMPLES

LIST OF FIGURES AND TABLES

Chapter 8

Chapter 9

Chapter 10

DIGITAL COMPUTING

PART I

INTRODUCTION TO COMPUTING

CHAPTER 1 **BASIC CONCEPTS**

The modern electronic digital computer has become a powerful tool in behavioral science research. An understanding of computer capabilities and an ability to make use of them are essential to contemporary behavioral scientists. The uses of computers in behavioral science are varied and often remarkably novel. Not only can computers assist in the calculational and clerical tasks of the scientist but they also provide means whereby the logical power of the scientist can be extended.

This book has three basic goals. The first goal is to develop in the reader an intuitive notion of some of the fundamental principles of digital computers and digital computing. Since the computer user generally does not need to come into physical contact with the computer or to understand the principles of computer operation, this first goal can be accomplished without presenting any technical material beyond the scope of the general college undergraduate. Nevertheless, in order to communicate with computer experts when the need arises, it is important to have an intuitive grasp of some of the fundamental concepts.

The second goal is to indicate some interesting and useful ways that computers can be used in behavioral science research. This will be done in two ways. First, we approach the topics at a broad, discursive, level. Second, we present a number of suggestive projects embodying the general characteristics of applications in the behavioral sciences. These projects will be used as a basis for introducing specific characteristics of the programming language and specific methods of programming throughout the book.

The third goal is to provide a relatively complete text from which the computer programming language "Fortran" (*for*mula *tran*slation) may be learned. The arbitrary and sometimes obscure conventions, notations, procedures, etc., that make up Fortran will be imbedded in the illustrations of their use and application. We shall restrict our attention to the programming language called Fortran IV, the "fourth" version of the Fortran language (see Appendix C for a description of the many versions of Fortran IV, and the differences between Fortran II and Fortran IV).

GENERAL USES OF THE COMPUTER

It would be difficult to establish a satisfactory and exhaustive list of the types of uses to which behavioral scientists put the computer. However, to organize our thinking about uses of computers, five general types of uses are singled out: calculation of statistics, clerical work, solution of mathematical problems, aid in the design of experiments, and simulation of theories.

The drudgery of statistical calculation is relieved by the use of appropriate programs for digital computers. In fact, some analyses, such as those associated with multivariate statistics, large scale analyses of variance, survey research, and census and marketing research, are scarcely feasible without the assistance of digital computing facilities.

The computer and associated equipment can be used in a wide variety of clerical operations such as counting, sorting, tabulating, and the production of graphs. The ingenuity of the user is virtually the only limit on this type of use of the computer. The computer literally is the slave of the scientist, to use as he sees fit. To be sure, the computer does not have the initiative of a human clerical assistant, but this is an advantage to the user.

Mathematical applications are similar to those often involved in the calculation of statistics. However, no statistical aspects are necessarily implied in the solution of a mathematical problem. An example of this use of the computer is the situation in which an investigator needs the solution to an equation in order to determine a value not directly observable, e.g., normal body weight from the size of certain bones from burial sites.

The computer can be of considerable assistance in the design and preparation of an experiment. For example, it can be used to produce lists of random numbers that may be used to determine the orders of presentation of stimuli. Virtually any kind of stimulus that can be produced by printed characters on paper can be prepared on a computer at very high speed. This use can be especially valuable when randomness is needed. Many modern digital computers are equipped with visual display devices and camera attachments permitting a wide variety of image production.

One of the most important and interesting applications of computers is the simulation of behavioral processes. The essence of simulation is a program that causes the computer to "behave" as if it were a system perfectly embodying the system described in the theory being simulated. A comparison of empirical behavior and results obtained from the computer is informative about the hypothesized processes. The significant result arises when the program is constructed in accordance with hypothesized behavioral processes, i.e., a theory of behavior. The importance of simulation arises from the ability of a program written in accordance with some theory of behavior to produce results similar to observed behavior. When this is accomplished, the behavioral scientist can interpret the result as an indication that the hypothesized processes, as expressed in his program, can produce behavior similar to empirically observed behavior.

As an example of a computer-assisted investigation, consider a type of problem commonly faced in research on verbal learning. A psychologist is interested in three variables that may affect retention of learned verbal material. These variables are list length, word length, and intralist similarity. He decides to investigate the effects of four list lengths, three word lengths, and three degrees of intralist similarity. He is interested in determining the effects of each of these alone, and all of the possible interactions: a $4 \times 3 \times 3$ factorial experiment.

Stimulus materials are to be presented in the experiment by a memory drum, with each subject receiving a different list. There are to be 15 subjects under each of the 36 treatment combinations, thus requiring 36×15 or 540 different lists. The computer may be used to produce the tapes for the memory drums, each tape containing one of the lists. In addition, the computer may be employed to assign the subjects at random to the conditions of the experiment. Suppose that a total of 1500 subjects are available in a subject pool for the investigator to draw from. Each subject could be identified by name on a card. Also on the card could be information regarding the times the persons were to be available, year in school, age, sex, etc. The computer may be programmed to select 540 subjects randomly from the group, with respect to any constraints (i.e., all male) that the investigator might wish. Even more helpfully, the computer could actually set up the schedule for the experimental sessions, taking the listing of available hours into account. Output from the program could include: (1) a listing of the subjects assigned to each experimental condition; (2) a master schedule, showing all experimental sessions, the persons assigned to them, and the condition(s) to be run; and (3) a card which can be mailed to the subject stating that he has an appointment at a specific time. Thus, even before the experiment has been conducted, the computer can be of considerable assistance in matters that are clerical and routine, but time consuming.

Once the data are gathered, the computer can perform the full analysis of variance necessary for the factorial design. In addition to calculating the mean squares for all main effects and interactions, the degrees of freedom, the final F values, and the levels of significance, the computer can also produce graphs of the interactions, within-condition frequency distributions, etc., thus enabling easier interpretation of the results.

Assuming that the investigation is conducted in the general framework of a particular theory of learning, the experimenter can go one step further. He has available data that describe how human subjects actually perform in the particular learning task. He can now write a computer program that embodies the essential assumptions of the theory. The computer, when equipped with such a program becomes, essentially, a simulated "organism." This "organism" may then be confronted with a situation comparable to that presented to the human subjects. If the computer produces the same kind of data, the theory has received additional support.

The example just described illustrates the application of the digital computer in four of the capacities described previously. First, the computer was used to produce the printed lists of stimulus materials used in the experiment. Second, the computer relieved an additional burden from the clerical staff by selecting, assigning, and scheduling subjects. Third, the computer analyzed the results of the experiment. The value of the third step is obvious, especially if the data included missing observations under some conditions, or repeated measures on the subjects, e.g., if each subject learns five lists, or if more variables had been included. In addition, the plotting of interaction graphs and cell distributions again solves a clerical problem. Finally the simulation of the theory may offer additional direct support for the theory.

COMPUTERS AND THE LANGUAGE OF COMPUTING

Two basic types of computers are in general use. These types, analog and digital, operate according to different principles and have different uses. We will be concerned in later chapters only with digital computers. However, it will be valuable to distinguish the two.

An analog computer, as the name implies, computes or calculates by analogy. There is some physical quantity (i.e., length, voltage, etc.) in the computer that is analogous to the numbers being manipulated. The simplest example of an analog computer is a slide rule. Moving the slide manipulates lengths that are analogous to the logarithms of numbers. Other analog computers have been built to analyze differential equations and so forth. Analog computers find most of their applications in the biomedical sciences, the physical sciences, and engineering. As opposed to digital computers, analog computers tend to be designed for special purposes. Seldom are they general purpose machines, although recently developed machines wed analog and digital devices (hybred computers) making them useful in the control of experimental instruments and data acquisition.

Digital computers do not make use of varying lengths, voltages, etc., but compute by manipulating discrete electromagnetic states (e.g., in + and − magnetic poles) or "switches" that are in one condition or another. Combinations of these switches can be interpreted as symbols representing digits, numerical values, and logical conditions. For example, if switches one and two are both "on" it might be interpreted to represent A; if only switch one were on, B; etc. By manipulating the switches the symbols represented by them are consequently manipulated.

Probably the most important distinction between digital computers and other calculating devices is the fact that the digital computer has a large amount of internal storage space. Both data and "instructions" are stored internally in modern digital computers. Thus, the operator need not intervene at each step in computation as is necessary with a desk calculator. The fact that human intervention is unnecessary plus the speed of the electronic computer circuitry result in extremely fast computation on the digital computer. An additional distinction is the fact that the operations of a digital computer can be interpreted in logical as well as arithmetic terms. For example, we may interpret a specific condition of the machine as indicating which of two numbers is the largest, and manipulate the machine along one of two alternative courses of action depending upon the outcome of this logical comparison.

This book is concerned specifically with digital computers. However, since some analog devices have applications in behavioral science, a brief discussion of them is appropriate at this point. Many of the useful techniques in behavioral science are essentially hybrid; combining digital and analog procedures. Three examples of such hybrid approaches are given here.

Studies in auditory perception may be conducted with the aid of a digital computer. The production of sound by computer is not difficult. Since the elements of a digital computer function in an on-off or plus-minus fashion, the production of tone is relatively simple. An engineer need only attach an electronic conversion device to a single element in the system. This converter is then attached to a speaker or tape recorder. By manipulating the rate at which the state (on-off) of the element is changed, varying auditory frequencies may be produced. In this manner, tunes, scales, etc., may be formed. By using several elements and converters at the same time, simultaneous tones and chords may be generated. The speaker producing the tones is essentially an analog device, controlled by a digital computer. Green (1963) discusses the production of auditory signals by computer in more detail.

Many investigations in psychology involve manipulation of physical variables. In order to analyze the data from such research, conversion from physical dimensions to numbers is needed. Any conversion of this nature is essentially analog to digital. A variety of analog-digital (A-D) converters are available. Two examples of the use of A-D converters are given below.

One of the classical problems for the human engineer (applied experimental psychologist) is that of visual tracking. In a typical case, the subject is required to follow the movement of a point of light in an otherwise dark environment. In some cases, he actually pursues the light (the target) with another spot of light; in others, the tracking is "blind," e.g., by manipulating a lever or "joy stick" to indicate the phenomenal movement. In either case, the movement frequently can be described by reference to a hypothetical coordinate system mounted in front of the subject. Any position of the target or tracking stimulus can be defined in terms of a pair of coordinate values. In an analysis of tracking performance over time, these pairs of values would provide the basic data. An A-D converter can be attached to either the tracking stimulus or the target, or both. Such a converter would provide a digital record of the position of the stimulus in terms of numerical coordinates that can be entered into a further analysis.

A large amount of current research in behavioral science is concerned with electromagnetic potentials, as for example the basis of the electroencephalogram (EEG) or "brain wave" records. A commonly used technique for studying these phenomena is that of autocorrelation analysis. In simple terms, this analysis amounts to finding the correlation between pairs of values of the potentials, one value taken at time t and the other value at time $t + i$ where i is some time interval. In order to compute this correlation, the potentials have to be converted into numerical values.

The use of the term "analog" in this context is perhaps misleading. The electromagnetic potential at a recording electrode in the brain of a rat is not an analog of anything—it is just the potential. However, the voltage at a given meter in an analog computer is taken to be analogous to a magnitude or a value of some variable. The voltage in the analog computer and the electrode potential have one feature in common—they both are continuous processes (as contrasted with discrete processes), changing in a smooth flow over a wide range of amplitudes. On the other hand, a digital device differs in two critical ways; each element of the computer is in one state or other (on or off; + or −), and the transition from one state to the other is a discrete jump essentially without a meaningful transition state. Hence, if the EEG pattern of a patient in a tumor clinic is to be represented or analyzed by way of a digital computer, the momentary amplitudes of the electromagnetic potential over a series of discrete points in time must be captured in digital form. The conversion from the continuous form of the potentials to the discrete numerical (digital) representation of the digital computer is the analog to digital conversion. The reverse flow of information is called digital to analog conversion. A variety of machines have been developed that permit the control of instruments and the interrogation of instruments in the two modes, digital and analog. These machines are, in general, dedicated to specific laboratory use and are not encountered by the ordinary user of the computer.

The somewhat confusing use of the word analog is our first example of a common problem we shall have with the language of computing. The language of computing is strangely imprecise; "strangely," because the practice of using a computer generally is precise. The technology of computing developed almost too swiftly for a verbal nomenclature to develop with it. Language to describe the character and operation of digital computers was borrowed from the everyday and technical language of the computer developers. Unfortunately, the language describing human functioning was widely adopted to describe the functioning of the machine. In the accepted language of computing, a computer reads, writes, interprets, senses, makes decisions, translates, performs arithmetic operations, etc. We must protest! A contemporary computer does none of these things.

We must insist on a basic principle: the computer is an electromechanical device, the states of which are interpreted in terms of certain numerical and logical systems. Recent developments in engineering have produced hardware permitting easy and sophisticated control of the computer by the computer programmer. Regardless of the seeming distance between a paper and pencil program and physical control of a card "reader," the programmer who writes the computer language statement READ simply intends to close and open certain completely specifiable circuits and to supply precise amounts of electrical energy.

Having made our protest we must, of course, be realistic and recognize that an appropriate set of terms does not exist. Hence, we must use language that is descriptive or suggestive, even if it is borrowed from another domain. To do otherwise requires elaborate circumlocutions; such compulsiveness is not a service to our scientific purpose.

Throughout the previous discussion, passing reference has been made to circuits, currents, etc. Fortunately we do not have to be concerned with the engineering, the circuitry, the electrical, or the electronic aspects of computing. Additionally, we are fortunate to have sensible and efficient conventions to stand between us and the computer as a machine. Long series of technical operations of the machine are associated by conventions or rules with simple collections of holes punched on cards. Fortran IV is just such a set of conventions. These rules, the language of Fortran IV, will occupy our attention in most of the following chapters.

PARTS OF A DIGITAL COMPUTER SYSTEM

In most contemporary digital computers, there is no single piece of equipment that may be designated as the "computer." Thus, it is more correct to speak of a computer system, since the "computer" is made up of a group of interrelated pieces of equipment, each serving a distinct purpose.

In the following discussion of the parts of a computer system, it will be convenient to point out similarities between the computer and a calculating device well known to most behavioral scientists—the desk calculator. The calculator has certain functional similarities to the computer system, since both operate on a digital basis. There are also certain differences between the two devices, and these form the basis for our discussion.

Basic Description of the Desk Calculator. The commonly used forms of the desk calculator all have certain features in common. These include a keyboard (sometimes two keyboards) for entering numerical data, a carriage that generally contains two or three rows of dials for displaying and storing numbers, and a set of operation buttons, which cause the calculator to add, subtract, multiply, etc. To provide an example that will be useful in discussing computer operations, consider the problem of finding the mean of a set of scores, i.e., the sum of the scores divided by the number of scores that were added together.

To start the process, assume that the investigator has listed N scores on paper. These might be scores from IQ tests, records from a learning experiment, or from any of a wide variety of sources. As a first step, the operator presses the button labeled CLEAR which sets all of the dials on the carriage to zero. Next, the first data value is entered into the keyboard and the ADD key pressed. This transfers the data value from the keyboard to one of the rows of carriage dials by adding the data value to the zero in the dials. Next, the second data value is entered into the keyboard, and the ADD key again pressed, thus adding the value in the keyboard to the contents of the row of dials and forming the sum of the first two values. This process is repeated, forming the sum of the first three values, then the first four, and so on until all N values have been entered. The quantity in the dials at that point is the sum of the N numbers. This sum is entered in the keyboard and the ENTER DIVIDEND key pressed to start the division stage of the operation. Finally N, the number of observations, is entered into the keyboard and the DIVIDE key pressed, causing the division to take place and the quotient to be displayed in the dials.

There are several parts of the desk calculator that are analogous to parts of the computer. First, there is a section of the calculator that is specialized to receive data—the keyboard. Another part of the calculator receives instructions from the operator—the various operation buttons. Finally, there are devices that perform arithmetic operations and display results—the dials on the carriage. All of these functions, and several others, are served by parts of the digital computer system. An input device in the computer system, for example, receives both data and instructions from the programmer. An output device displays the results of the calculations performed inside the system. Inside the computer system there are hardware items that function like the dials on the calculator—locations where the arithmetic work is done. These are generally called registers, or working registers.

In addition to the similarities, there are important differences between the calculator and the computer system. One of the most important, and obvious, of these differences is speed of operation. The computer, since it calculates by means of varying electronic states rather than mechanically as does the calculator, operates at a fantastically greater rate of speed. Another distinction is that the computer is usually a much larger piece of equipment than is the calculator. However, with the current trend to extreme miniaturization of computer components, this may soon become an invalid comparison.

Besides the speed and size of the computer, the most important distinction between the two devices is in terms of storage or "memory." A calculator typically cannot store any number other than those in the carriage dials. Some calculators, however, are provided with one or more rows of dials called "memory" for storing intermediate answers during a sequence of operations. Even with these machines, each individual piece of the data must be entered manually into the keyboard when it is needed for use. In the computer system, on the other hand, the data are stored internally in some form of storage device, thus eliminating the need for individual entry of each piece of the data at the time it is used.

Not only are the data stored inside the computer system, but also the instructions are stored internally. In using the calculator, the operator is required to press a button to "instruct" the machine to perform each addition, division, etc. In the computer system all of the instructions (called the *program*) are stored internally. Indeed, the programmer or operator need not even be physically present when the computer is running. Once a program is started, there need be no additional human intervention.

An important distinction between the computer system and the desk calculator is the computer's ability to make "decisions." A decision in computer terminology is a simple yes-no decision, based upon some state of the system. For example, at one point in the program, it may be desirable to have available two alternative courses of action depending upon the value of some number inside the computer; if the number is positive, one series of operations is performed, and another if the value is negative. This kind of branching or decision making makes the computer a flexible device, capable of following alternative courses of action. Of course, the specification of those courses of action and the states of the computer that produce them are the responsibility of the programmer.

From this general discussion of the components of a computer system, we turn to a more careful consideration of those parts. A computer system may be divided into five kinds of components as follows:

1. *Storage devices.* Those devices specialized to store information (both data and instructions).
2. *Central processor.* The unit where instructions are executed; performs simple arithmetic and logical operations.
3. *Control unit.* The unit that, by means of buttons and display devices, permits the operator to monitor and operate the system.
4. *Input-output units.* The various devices that provide for the transfer of information (both data and instructions) between the user or programmer and the computer system.
5. *Peripheral systems.* Collections of equipment that are helpful in many uses of the computer, but not essential to its operation.

Storage or Memory Components. A central part of a computer system is the storage system. There are several varieties of storage units in general use, but all have at least one feature in common: storage of information. This information is the representation of both the programs—instructions to the computer—and the data.

Storage devices may be classified as internal or external. An external storage device may be compared roughly to a filing cabinet, in which information may be kept for a long period of time. External storage systems are generally characterized by two features, large capacity and relatively slow access time. That is, a great deal of information may be stored but it can take a relatively long time to locate one particular piece of data. The information from an external storage device must be transferred to an internal device before it can be utilized by the computer. Internal storage devices are directly accessed by the arithmetic processing and control units of the system. Therefore, the access time is small.

The basic unit of the capacity of a storage device is the bit. A bit is a binary (two valued, 0 and 1) digit. Bits are grouped together in strings to form the functional units of storage devices, characters, and words. The number of bits making up characters and words varies with the computer, but a common number is 6 bits per character and 36 bits per word or 6 characters per word. The storage capacity of a system is usually described in terms of words. The IBM 7094 computer, for example, has internal storage for approximately 32,000 words of 36 bits each. Hence, the 7094 is sometimes referred to as a 32K (32,000) system. Table I.1 gives the storage capacity and other characteristics of some representative large scale computers.

Magnetic Core Storage. Magnetic core is at present the most widely used internal

Table I.1

Some characteristics of some representative large scale computers

	CDC 3600	CDC 6600	UNIVAC 1108	Burroughs B 5500	IBM 7094	IBM 360/50
Primary storage (thousands of words)	32-262	32-131	65-262	32	32	32-131
Word length (bits)	48	60	36	48	36	32
Access to primary storage in microseconds	.7	.5	.75	4	1.4	2.
Add time in microseconds	2.	.4	1.75	2.	2.8	1.68
Multiply time in microseconds	2.12-6.5	1.	2.6	13.-26.	2.8-5.6	4.05
Tape characters per inch	800	800	800	556	800	800
Tape speed, in inches per second	7.5-120	120	120	120	15-170	75
Cards read per minute, per reader	1200	1200	615	800	250	1000
Lines printed per minute, per printer	1000	1000	600	700	1100	1100

storage system. A core is a tiny ring of ferrous material, some less than a fiftieth of an inch in diameter. When an electric current is sent along a wire passed through the center of a core, the core is magnetized in a particular direction. If the current is sent from the other direction, the polarity of the magnetization is reversed. A core can therefore be magnetized with its polarity in either of two directions, providing the basis for storing one bit of information.

In reality, several wires pass through the center of each core. These wires are connected to a frame, which holds a large number of cores. The number of cores per frame varies with the system, but a common number is about 4000. The wires passing through the cores make possible the selection of any given core for "reading out" of the binary digit contained there or the placing of a binary digit at that position.

Magnetic Drum Storage. Drum storage is another common form of memory. This system uses a rapidly rotating ferrite drum that can be magnetized in discrete spots, each spot representing a binary digit, again depending upon magnetic states. Drum storage has several weaknesses. First, the physical size of a drum is not practical at times. Second, a word of information can be read or written only when the drum is in a particular position, namely, under the read/write head. Thus, the speed of access to a given word depends upon the position and size of the drum. Magnetic drums of high speed have been developed and are coming into use as an aid in storing large blocks of information that are used over and over again by the system.

Magnetic Disc. Disc storage is similar to the drum. It, too, operates on the principle of magnetized spots. A magnetic disc is shaped like an ordinary flat phonograph disc but it is coated with a ferrite material so as to maintain local magnetic charges. Each side of a disc might contain 100 concentric tracks in which information may be stored as magnetized spots. Generally, a number of discs are mounted on the same rotating vertical shaft. The recording and reading heads are mounted on an access arm that can reach any track, any piece of information on any track, on any of the discs. Disc storage is quite widely used, although the access speed is dependent upon the position of the desired data relative to the read/write heads. Disc and drum storage generally is very much larger than core storage (or other primary storage devices).

Both disc and drum storage devices are usually classified as external storage media, because the information stored there is not directly accessible by the arithmetic and control units.

Magnetic Tape. Magnetic tape operates on much the same principle as disc and drum. The physical vehicle for the magnetic records is a plastic tape similar to audio tapes. The tape is wound onto reels that may be mounted on "tape drives" that feed the tape through a device that reads ("playback") and writes ("records") the magnetic records. The information on magnetic tape is permanent unless "erased."

Access to information on magnetic tapes is comparatively slow—much more rapid than punched cards, much less rapid than disc or drum. One of the outstanding features of magnetic tape is the vast quantity of data that can be stored on single reels of tape. A full reel contains up to 2400 feet of tape. Some tape drives read and write more than 100 characters (usually six binary bits) per inch of tape at as much as 170 thousand characters per second.

Thin Film. A recent development in storage components is very thin magnetic film. A film of magnetic material (usually a micron or less in thickness) is deposited in small areas on some base material such as glass or plastic. The spots of film may then be magnetized with one of two polarities, providing the basis of binary storage.

Access time for contemporary thin film

memories is comparable to magnetic core. As they are a relatively new kind of device, the cost per bit of storage is higher than core but will decrease as mass production techniques are improved. It may happen that thin film will replace core as the principal internal storage medium in most new computers.

Photographic Storage. A promising new storage technique is the use of extremely high resolution photography. Binary information can be stored compactly on small chips of photographic film as tiny exposed or nonexposed points. The technique is being employed in some bulk storage devices under development. When these devices are perfected, it is expected that they will have a capacity of up to a trillion bits, with an average access time of a few seconds or less. They will be useful as secondary storage media.

Miscellaneous. There are two other kinds of storage that should be mentioned briefly for sake of completeness. These are electrostatic memory and acoustical delay. In electrostatic memory, binary information is stored as points on the surface of a cathode ray tube. In acoustical delay, binary information is stored in a recycling electronic circuit that introduces a temporal delay, thus allowing for the storage of information over time.

Finally, it should be mentioned that some external storage devices frequently serve another purpose in the computer system. Since externally stored information must be transferred to internal storage, these devices are frequently used as methods for input of information to the computer from a user and output to a user.

Data stored in any of the various storage devices are called upon by other parts of the computer system by means of an addressing operation. That is, every word in internal storage is assigned a unique label or address. The analogy of a large post office may be helpful here. Each word in storage is analogous to a post office box, the box containing a number of pieces of information (binary bits). The *contents* of a given box may be symbolically designated as $C(a)$ where a is an address or post office box number. Thus, for example, the contents of core storage location 5560 could be symbolically designated as C(5560). This distinction between a location and the contents or information at that location is a crucial one to which we shall have frequent occasion to refer.

The Central Processing Unit. This unit of the digital computer system contains the circuitry capable of performing arithmetic operations (e.g., addition and multiplication) and logical operations (e.g., stop if a certain number is equal to zero). The operations to be carried out are determined by the program, i.e., by instructions stored in the machine.

Also located in the central processing unit are a number of "working registers." In essence, a working register is no different than a word of storage in central storage. It is in the working registers, however, that arithmetic and other operations are performed. The registers are analogous to the dials on a desk calculator. Computer systems vary in how many working registers they use, and the names used to refer to them.

Control Unit. The control unit serves three functions. First, timing of operations is carried out here. Since the computer operates at very fast speeds – generally on the order of several hundred nanoseconds to a few microseconds (a nanosecond is a billionth of a second – 10^{-9} second – while a microsecond is 1/1000,000 second, and a millisecond is 1/1000 second) per machine operation – timing is a critical problem. A timing mechanism in the control unit synchronizes operations of the system. Second, the control unit decodes and interprets instructions. The stored machine instructions are brought from storage to the control unit. They are decoded and the control unit, in effect, sets up the circuitry in the processing unit that executes the instruction. Finally, the control unit provides a means of communication between the computer system and the operator. The operator starts and stops the system, controls the input and output devices, examines contents of the working registers, and in some cases, enters a small amount of data. The computer, by means of lights, printers, typewriters, and other devices, can communicate to the operator such information as where it is in a program, errors, and kinds of errors.

Input-Output Units. Although the operator can give instructions and sometimes enter data to the computer via the control unit, this method of getting material into and out of internal storage is not generally used. Special devices for handling the input and output of information in a more efficient way have been developed. Three of the most common methods are punched cards, punched paper tape, and magnetic tape. Punched cards are rather slow to manipulate and are rarely used as direct input to the computer. Cards are often converted to magnetic tape (or disc or drum) form by a peripheral system (see below) before they are input to the system. Nevertheless, the punched card remains a versatile tool in data analysis. Most programming and data recording operations use punched cards extensively.

Magnetic tape is a very efficient input-output medium. Punched paper tape is often useful for input. Many automated laboratories record their data directly on paper tape that can be read directly by the computer, thus eliminating the possibility of clerical errors and the expense of clerical transcription. Tape and cards serve both as input and output media.

There are several devices designed specifically for output. The most common of these is the printer. It is capable of producing pages of printed material consisting of letters, numerals, and a variety of other special characters (i.e., +, =, .) depending upon the system. Printers generally operate at speeds up to about 1000 lines per minute with 120 to 136 characters per line. The input analog to the printer, an optical scanner which can read printed documents, is being developed by several manufacturers. It is not generally available presently.

Other methods of output include the cathode ray tube (CRT), which is like a television tube. The CRT may be photographed, producing permanent visual displays in either still or moving pictures. Another output device sometimes available is the plotter that can produce graphs and other illustrations.

Figure I.1 summarizes the parts of a typical computer system made up of the components discussed above. Also shown on the illustration are lines representing

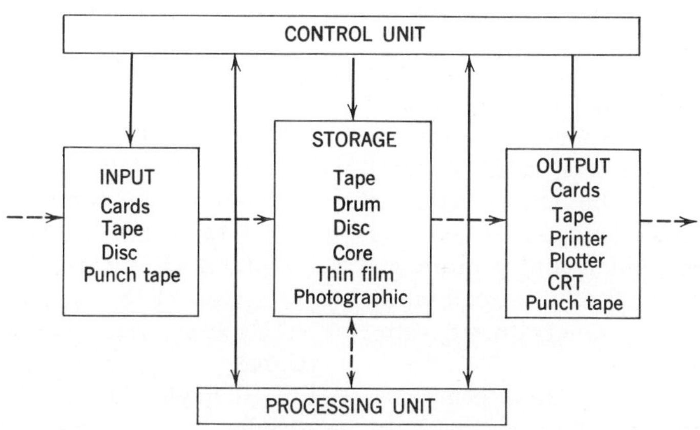

Figure I.1 Parts of a digital computer system. Key to connecting lines: ----- implies data flow; ——— implies flow of control.

the flow of data and control information. The complete picture of the modern computer system is often considerably more complex due to two principal kinds of modifications that do not appear in the figure: peripheral systems, and multiprocessor systems. Also, the appendage of communications equipment to a computer (to service remote input-output devices and other computers) would complicate the system shown.

Peripheral Systems. Large scale computer systems operate at such high speeds that if the processing were to wait for the slower input-output operations (i.e., reading cards and printing), a great deal of valuable computer time would be wasted. To avoid this problem, some separate device or peripheral system, frequently a smaller computer, is used to prepare information for the large computer. In general, most of the input to and output from the major computer system is by means of one of the fast external storage media such as tape or disc. Input to the peripheral system is frequently by means of cards. The peripheral system transfers the information to a tape or a disc which serves in turn as the input unit to the major computer. Output from the main computer is likewise usually on tape or disc. The information on that tape or disc is then translated to one of the other means of output (i.e., cards, printed paper, CRT output, etc.) by the peripheral system.

Any input-output equipment that is connected directly to the main computer is referred to as "on-line" while that connected with the peripheral system is called "off-line." For the sake of completeness, it should be stated that in most installations there is an on-line card punch, card reader, and printer, although these are for use by the computer operators and not for general use by programmers and users.

Multiprocessor Systems. Many computer systems are presently designed by linking together two or more separate computer systems. For example, in a multiprocessor system, there may be two or more central processors, operating simultaneously, and sharing storage and input-output devices. A multiprocessor system may operate on several programs simultaneously in one of two ways: multiprogramming and parallel processing.

In a parallel processing system, several programs are actually executed simultaneously, one by each of the several central processors. Some of the large computing systems (e.g., CDC 6600) are designed specifically as parallel processing systems.

A multiprogramming system may operate by interleaving several programs —working on one, leaving it, working on another, coming back to the first, etc. Multiprogramming and multiprocessing are features found only in the largest and most sophisticated computer systems. Quite often, these systems are also capable of demand or "time-shared" operation. This concept will be discussed in more detail in Chapter 12.

For most of the material presented in this book, we need not be concerned with the complexity of the computer with which we are dealing. The system operates on a Fortran program according to the rules developed in the following chapters, and it makes little difference, to the programmer in most cases, whether the computer is a single system, a multiprocessor system, or whether a peripheral system is involved.

REPRESENTATIONS OF DATA EXTERNAL TO THE COMPUTER

There are three primary methods for representing data and other information external to the computer—punch cards, punch tape (paper), and magnetic tape.

Punch Cards. Cards read by most computers are of the 80-column, rectangular punch type. Each column is defined by twelve row positions in which a punch can be made. The top two rows serve as so-called "zone" rows. The rest of the rows represent the digits 0 through 9. A single punch in the digits rows of a column represents to the computer the code for that numerical value. Alphabetic and special (e.g., /, $, *, ...) characters are represented by two or more punches in a column. Figure I.2 shows a standard general-purpose punch card with all the characters included in the Fortran repertoire. The printing at the top of the card is produced by the card punching machine, the keypunch. The printing is not read by the computer.

The holes punched by a keypunch can represent any variety or form of data. The data may be coded or simply a representation of data values. In any case, the column where a given datum is punched is systematically assigned by the computer user. This simple fact has led many computer users astray in their first attempts to use the computer. As we shall see, cards must be punched as required by the program, and there must be a complete and exacting agreement between the way the data are punched and the description of the cards in the program. The computer user should know how his data are to be punched prior to collecting the data. This information often can be used in setting up observation sheets, etc., in such a way that the keypunching can be done from them directly. For example, a program may reserve the last 8 columns on each card (73 – 80) for an identifying name or number (e.g., a subject's name or the number of the card in the card deck) and these columns are not input as data. Other programs may require the data to be punched in all 80 columns of the cards. Any arbitrary collection of columns can be used for any arbitrary purpose as long as the program reading the cards is designed accordingly.

The conventions for punching are not standardized. However, several points can be made. First, adjacent columns are used to punch data requiring more than one column. The set of columns used to punch a datum is called a field (e.g., a three-column field). Second, only one character (i.e., a keypunch symbol) per column is punched. Punching several numbers or characters in a given field or column is called multiple punching and generally leads to problems for the computer user whose program is written in Fortran because the punches do not correspond to the Fortran code conventions. Third, if several replications of the observations are made, the corresponding data are punched in identical fields on the cards representing the replications. Fourth, if the data for a given replication require more than 80 columns, a second

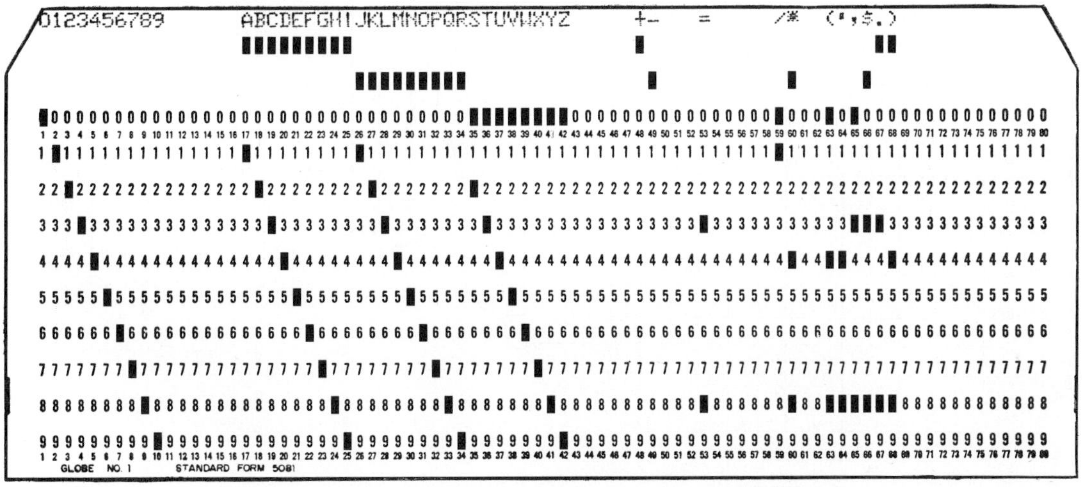

Figure I.2 Standard punch card showing Fortran characters.

(or more) card follows the first card. These and other statements about card punching are not universally observed. However, the way cards are read by a program is part of the program, and therefore discoverable by inspecting the program. The detailed rules of card reading will occupy a good part of two of the following chapters.

In order to present a keypunch operator (often oneself) with a clear record to follow in punching cards, the data should be recorded on special forms. These forms vary from computing center to computing center. An example of such a form appears as Figure I.3. Some sample data to which we shall later refer are recorded on this form. When cards are punched from this form, each line will appear on a separate card.

Special forms are used to indicate the punch cards for a program. The basic concept is the same: instructions and control commands are punched on cards. Since the computer "translates" these into a set of instructions they must be punched according to fixed rules. The rules are discussed in detail in the following chapters. An example of the special form used to write out the Fortran instructions is given in Figure I.4, which shows a form filled out with a simple Fortran IV program.

The punched cards for a set of data make up a deck. The cards must be in the order required by the program that is to read the cards. When a large number of cards are required, the bulk of the deck becomes a nuisance and a hazard (don't drop the deck!). In order to avoid hav-

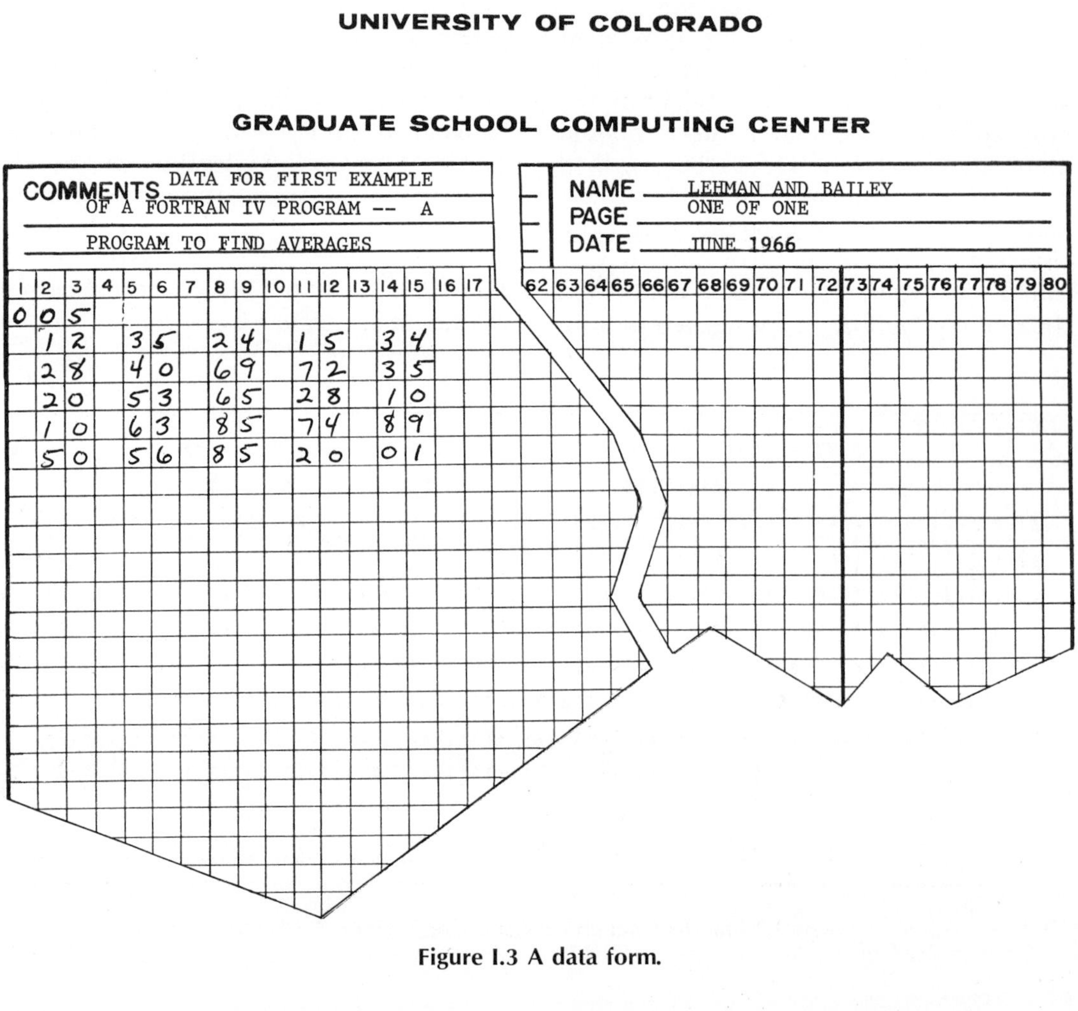

Figure I.3 A data form.

UNIVERSITY OF CALIFORNIA — FORTRAN CODING FORM — COMPUTER CENTER BERKELEY

Program MEAN
Coded By BAILEY
Checked By LEHMAN
Identification (73–80)
Date 7-22-67
Page 1 of 1

C FOR COMMENT | STATEMENT NUMBER (1–5) | Cont. (6) | FORTRAN STATEMENT (7–72)

```
CTHIS PRØGRAM CALCULATES THE MEAN ØF FIVE NUMBERS READ BY THE PRØGRAM .
C     K SETS ØF VALUES ARE INPUT AND THEIR MEANS FØUND.
C     K IS DETERMENED BY THE NUMBER ØF SETS ØF DATA TØ BE AVERAGED

      READ 100, K
      I = 0
    1 READ 101, X1, X2, X3, X4, X5
      SUM = X1 + X2 + X3 + X4 + X5
      AVER = SUM/5.
      PRINT 102, AVER
      I = I + 1
      IF(I.LT.K) GØ TØ 1
      STØP
  100 FØRMAT(I3)
  101 FØRMAT(5F3.0)
  102 FØRMAT(F6.2
      END
```

Series 3502

Figure I.4 Fortran coding form.

ing to handle the cards, they may be recorded on a magnetic tape which may then be treated as a permanent depository of the data.

Magnetic Tape. In the process of computing, data may be generated from other data, e.g., the correlation matrix for a set of multivariate observations. If these derived data or the original data are of use in an analysis to be done at a later date they may be recorded on a magnetic tape, the tape "saved" and used later as input. These procedures are discussed in greater detail in Chapters 9 and 12.

Punched Paper Tape. Most computer systems have as optional equipment a special unit to read punched paper tape. When data are generated in an experimental setting it is often possible to punch these data as code onto a paper tape by way of a paper tape punch. This is a very convenient way of entering data to the computer—permanent, economical of bulk, quickly read by the computer, etc.

Unless punch equipment of the appropriate specifications is available, this mode of data recording and representation is not of interest. Availability in the computing center of punched paper tape reading equipment is, of course, also necessary. The user should consult the appropriate officials at his computing center regarding the availability and specifications of the equipment.

A FORTRAN PREVIEW

Before going any further, we shall work out a simple Fortran program. We shall take the example used earlier to compare the desk calculator and the computer. We wish to calculate the average of a set of numbers. Take a very simple case—we want the average of five numbers that we have observed in an experiment. Ordinarily this problem would be done with the desk calculator or by hand. However, imagine that we find ourselves with many such calculations all at one time and have the same problem cropping up every now and then. We can write a simple Fortran program to do the job for us. Since we may not know how many five-value calculations we shall have on any specific application of the program we shall write the program so that part of the data it receives is the number of averages it is to find. We shall want the computer to read the five numbers for a given problem, calculate their average, print out the value of the average, and keep track of the number of problems solved so that the program can stop after the last problem.

Before writing the program we shall draw out the logic or flow of the program. This step is called flow charting the program. We shall discuss flow charting and flow charts in detail later. Right now all we need is the simple logic of this elementary program. To begin with we need a start and a stop. The start always is taken as the first command in the program but the stop has to be signaled explicitly. In the middle of the program there are five stages: (1) determine the number of problems to be dealt with in this use of the program, (2) read in the five values for the problem to be solved, (3) calculate the average, (4) print the average, and (5) determine if there are more problems to do. The fifth stage requires setting up a "counter" or tally to keep track of the number of problems calculated. This counter will have to be established early in the program with a known value, say zero.

In order to be clear in this development, a notation for the variables and constants we shall use must be specified. We shall specify them at this point with more detail than usual.

X1	The first of the five values
X2	The second of the five values
X3	The third of the five values
X4	The fourth of the five values
X5	The fifth of the five values
K	The number of five-value problems to be solved on any run of the program
I	The number of problems already solved at any given time by the program
SUM	The sum of the five values
AVER	The average of the five values

Each stage of the flow of the program is represented in the flow chart diagram by a box of a given shape (more about these conventions later). The boxes representing the stages are connected in such a way as to indicate the flow from one stage to another. At one point there is a choice of flow—before the end of the problems as the program recycles through stages two through five; after the last problem the program comes to a stop.

The flow chart of the program is given as Figure I.5. The Fortran IV coding can

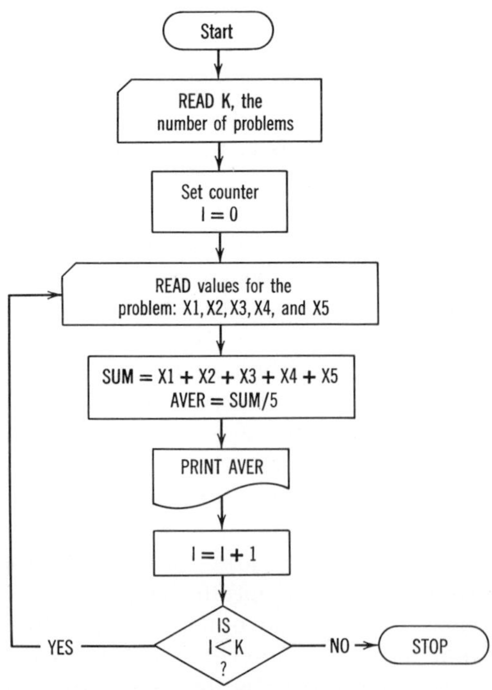

Figure I.5 Flow chart for a program to average K sets of five numbers.

be written very simply following the flow chart. The program written by the authors appears on the Fortran coding form of Figure I.4. Each line of the program, of the coding form, is a separate Fortran statement. The first three are simply comments and have no effect on the calculation but are useful in identifying the purpose of the program and the meaning of symbols used in the program. The value of K is read immediately, the 100 following the word READ refers to the Fortran statement number 100 four lines from the bottom. Statements 100, 101, and 102 are used by the program to determine the places on data cards where the data to be read will appear (and the form in which they will appear) or how the data to be printed will appear on the printed output page. Next we establish the counter I, and set the value of the counter to zero. Statement number 1 is the input statement causing all five values of a problem to be read. The next two lines give the algebraic instructions—calculate the mean of the five values. The meaning of these lines is self-evident. At this point in the flow of the program we have done one of the problems and we indicate this by adding 1 to the counter I. The equal sign in Fortran is not to be interpreted in the way the equal sign in algebra is interpreted (such an interpretation will lead you astray part of the time). Rather "=" is taken to mean "replace the quantity on the left by the quantity on the right." Therefore the statement I = I + 1 means "replace the value of I with a value one larger than the value of I." The new value is still called I but it will be one larger than the previous value of I. The next statement causes the value of the average to be printed. The statement IF(I.LT.K)GO TO 1 may be read: "if the current value of I is less than K, start executing the statements beginning with statement number 1." This causes the statements beginning with statement number 1 to be executed again. This cycles through over and over again until there have been K problems solved (I is increased by one every time a problem is solved and there are K problems to be solved). Once I is not less than K, i.e., as soon as K problems have been solved, the flow is to the next statement in the program, STOP, which causes the program to come to a halt.

The FORMAT statements provided after the STOP are not a part of the "working" program but provide information to the program regarding input and output. These will be discussed in detail later. After all of the program statements, and information provided by the programmer, e.g., the FORMAT statements, the END card signals the last of the statements for this program.

There is a sequence of events that defines the procedure for using the program. The deck of cards into which the statements have been punched is called the Fortran *source deck.* A part of the source deck for the program is illustrated in Figure I.6. The first statement is the first card (top) and so on until the last card (bottom) is the END card. Several conventional preliminary cards are placed in front of this deck and it is input to the computer under the control of another program called the *Fortran compiler.* The Fortran compiler takes these statements one at a time and converts them into the cryptic machine language of the computer. The result of this analysis of the Fortran program is a program in machine language called the *object program.* In the modern computing center all of this is done as a routine matter and all that the programmer needs to do is to submit his program with the necessary preliminary cards to the computing center. Two options generally are available—the program as compiled by the Fortran compiler can be run immediately, or the object program can be punched on new cards to be submitted to the center to be run at a later date. In the former case the data to be analyzed are placed at the back of the source deck. They must, of course, be punched appropriately for the program. Figure I.3 shows data

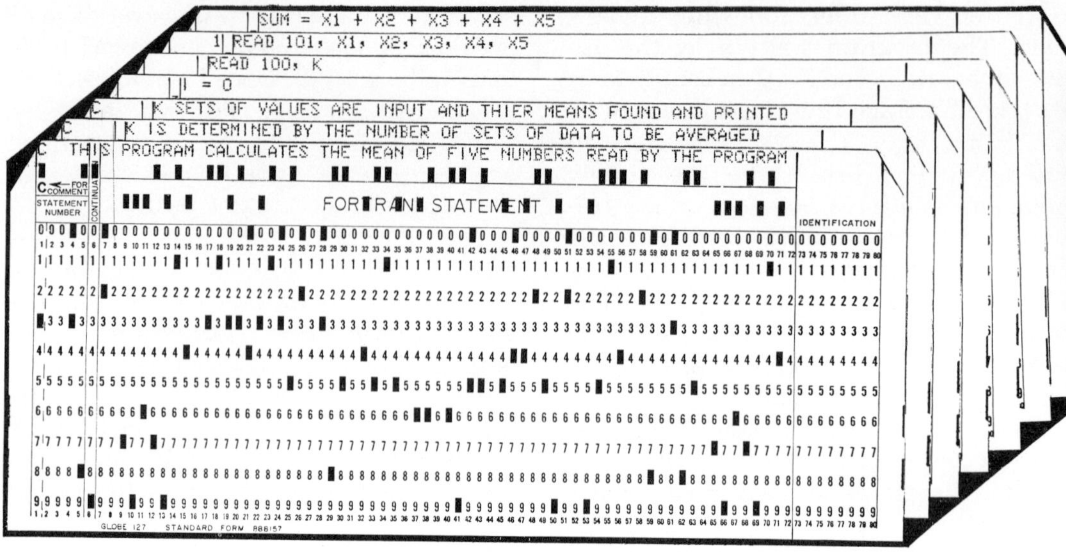

Figure I.6 A part of the source deck for the averaging example.

for the example program. If an object deck is obtained from a compilation and data are to be analyzed by the use of the program, the object deck is followed by the data cards and the complete deck is submitted with the appropriate conventional cards in front of it. This process may be summarized by the flow of the diagrams in Figure I.7.

The reader is encouraged to obtain Fortran coding forms from the computing center, write out the program as it appears in Figure I.4, and submit the form to the center for keypunching. Before doing this he should consult a programming advisor or programming consultant in the computing center about the required project or account designation, identification cards, the cards the center requires in front of the Fortran program, and the cards needed before and after the data cards. These extra cards will vary from center to center. Generally they will be punched by the keypunch operator if they are indicated on the coding form. After having made arrangements at the computing center to have your program processed on the computer, submit the source deck and data according to the local conventions.

The data of Figure I.3, when input to the program of Figure I.4, result in the means shown in Figure I.8, which is a reproduction of the actual computer printed output.

Gaining experience with the mechanics of submitting programs for processing, locating programming advisors, finding the location for picking up output, etc. is valuable at this stage of learning about computing. When you visit the computing center inquire about general guides to local conventions and regulations. Most computing centers have a written description of standard procedures and are eager for their users to read it thoroughly before approaching the center for use of the computer.

BINARY AND OCTAL NUMBERS*

It is fortunate that modern computing systems and programming techniques relieve the programmer of the necessity for understanding the technical aspects of the electronics and the logical-mathematical basis for the computer. Since most behavioral scientists are not very well trained in mathematics and formal logic this is especially important. Many

*This section may be bypassed on first reading. Any reader familiar with the "new" mathematics will have already become acquainted with the material.

behavioral scientists, we suspect, have avoided using the computer because of the misconception that using a computer requires a high level of knowledge and skill in mathematical analysis. While some familiarity with mathematical thinking and notation is a definite asset in computing it is by no means a requirement.

In this section we introduce some of the simple mathematical concepts dealing with the number systems commonly found on modern digital computers. This material is not required for most programming applications, but will facilitate understanding of some of the more advanced techniques.

The digital computer takes advantage of two states of an electronic circuit. The technical character of these states is unimportant and we can call one state 0 and the other state 1. In order to use the

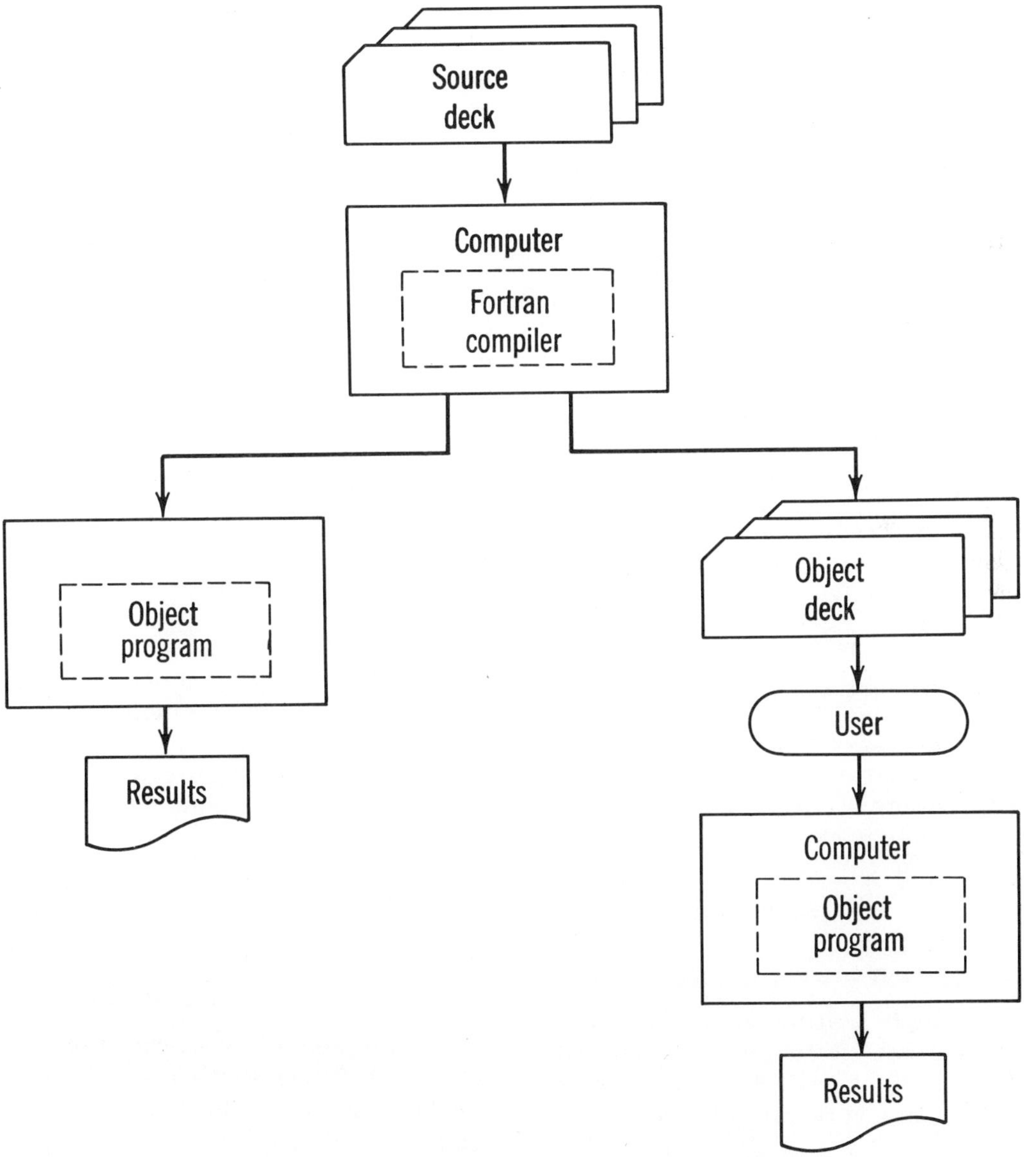

Figure I.7 Steps in processing a Fortran program.

```
24.00
48.80
35.20
64.20
44.20
```

Figure 1.8 Output from example program to calculate means.

basic two state characteristic of electronic computing circuits, it is convenient to express all numbers by using the two numerals 0 and 1. One state represents the number 1, and the other state represents zero. In this way, any value can be represented by a series of states (or zeros and ones) of circuits in the computer. Such a system of numbers is known as the base 2 or *binary* number system as contrasted with the familiar base 10 or *decimal* system of numbers.

In order to learn another system of numbers, it helps to understand clearly what is meant when we write a number in the usual (decimal) manner. Consider the number 942. It may be written as

$$942 = 9 \times 100 + 4 \times 10 + 2 \times 1$$

Since 100, 10, and 1 can also be expressed as powers of 10,

$$942 = 9 \times 10^2 + 4 \times 10^1 + 2 \times 10^0$$

Thus, when we write 942, we are writing an ordered series of coefficients of successive powers of 10. A few more examples may help to clarify the process.

$$1965 = 1 \times 1000 + 9 \times 100 + 6 \times 10 + 5 \times 1$$

$$= 1 \times 10^3 + 9 \times 10^2 + 6 \times 10^1 + 5 \times 10^0$$

Again, simply writing the coefficients of the successive powers of 10, we have the number 1965 expressed in our ordinary notation. An additional example:

$$508 = 5 \times 100 + 0 \times 10 + 8 \times 1$$
$$= 5 \times 10^2 + 0 \times 10^1 + 8 \times 10^0$$

Note that in writing the coefficients of the powers of 10, it is necessary explicitly to indicate zero coefficients. In this example, the zero indicated that no "tens" are to be added to make up the number but 5 "hundreds" are a part of the number. In general, a zero coefficient indicates that it is not necessary to include any of that particular power of 10 to make up the number. But the zero coefficients must be included, since confusion would otherwise result. In the above example, if the zero were omitted, it would be easy mistakenly to write 58 instead of 508.

The reader may see that there is a general rule implicit in these examples: the fact that 10 numerals (the coefficients) are needed to express decimal numbers is related to the fact that the number 10 is used as the base of the number system. In order to generate a system of numbers using only two numerals, the number 2 is used as the base of the system, in place of 10. That is, coefficients of powers of 2 are involved, instead of powers of 10. The coefficients will be the numerals 0 and 1.

It is convenient to introduce some terminology that will help keep things straight in dealing with number systems. A subscript number is used to indicate the base of a number system. Thus, the number 583_{10} means the number five hundred and eighty-three expressed in the base ten number system.

The base 2 or binary number system is developed and used in the same way as is the base 10 system. Converting the number 13_{10} to its base 2 equivalent:

$$13_{10} = 1 \times 8 + 1 \times 4 + 0 \times 2 + 1 \times 1$$

Again, the numbers 8, 4, 2, and 1 may be expressed as powers of 2, the base of the number system. Thus

$$13_{10} = 1 \times 2^3 + 1 \times 2^2 + 0 \times 2^1 + 1 \times 2^0$$

If just the successive coefficients of the powers of 2 are written, we have the number 13_{10} in the binary number system:

$$13_{10} = 1101_2$$

Table I.2 gives the binary equivalents of a number of decimal numbers.

Arithmetic operations can be carried out on binary numbers. Just as there are rules governing arithmetic in base 10 numbers, there are rules governing binary operations. As an example, consider addition. The rules of binary addition are:

$$0 + 0 = 0$$
$$0 + 1 = 1$$
$$1 + 0 = 1$$
$$1 + 1 = 0, \text{ carry } 1$$
$$1 + 1 + 1 = 1, \text{ carry } 1$$

Addition takes place from right to left and carrys are to the left. Consider the problem

$$\begin{array}{r} 38_{10} \\ +15_{10} \\ \hline 53_{10} \end{array}$$

In binary,

$$\begin{array}{r} 100110_{2} \\ +001111_{2} \\ \hline 110101_{2} \end{array}$$

Working from the right, we first have 0 + 1, which by the rules equals 1. The next column gives 1 + 1, which equals 0, carry 1. The third column gives 1 + 1 + 1, which is 1, carry 1. The final answer, obtained by following the addition rules, is 110101, which is the binary equivalent of decimal 53, e.g.,

$$\begin{aligned} 53 &= 1 \times 2^5 + 1 \times 2^4 + 0 \times 2^3 + 1 \times 2^2 \\ &\quad + 0 \times 2^1 + 1 \times 2^0 \\ &= 32 + 16 + 0 + 4 + 0 + 1 \end{aligned}$$

Similar rules may be stated for performing all other arithmetic operations on base 2 numbers. We need not consider them in detail or be concerned about how such operations are carried out by elec-

Table I.2

Decimal-binary-octal equivalents

Base 10	Base 2	Base 8
$0 = 0 \times 2^0$	= 0000	= 0
$1 = 1 \times 2^0$	= 0001	= 1
$2 = 1 \times 2^1 + 0 \times 2^0$	= 0010	= 2
$3 = 1 \times 2^1 + 1 \times 2^0$	= 0011	= 3
$4 = 1 \times 2^2 + 0 \times 2^1 + 0 \times 2^0$	= 0100	= 4
$5 = 1 \times 2^2 + 0 \times 2^1 + 1 \times 2^0$	= 0101	= 5
$6 = 1 \times 2^2 + 1 \times 2^1 + 0 \times 2^0$	= 0110	= 6
$7 = 1 \times 2^2 + 1 \times 2^1 + 1 \times 2^0$	= 0111	= 7
$8 = 1 \times 2^3 + 0 \times 2^2 + 0 \times 2^1 + 0 \times 2^0$	= 1000	= 10
$9 = 1 \times 2^3 + 0 \times 2^2 + 0 \times 2^1 + 1 \times 2^0$	= 1001	= 11
$10 = 1 \times 2^3 + 0 \times 2^2 + 1 \times 2^1 + 0 \times 2^0$	= 1010	= 12
$11 = 1 \times 2^3 + 0 \times 2^2 + 1 \times 2^1 + 1 \times 2^0$	= 1011	= 13
$12 = 1 \times 2^3 + 1 \times 2^2 + 0 \times 2^1 + 0 \times 2^0$	= 1100	= 14
$13 = 1 \times 2^3 + 1 \times 2^2 + 0 \times 2^1 + 1 \times 2^0$	= 1101	= 15
$14 = 1 \times 2^3 + 1 \times 2^2 + 1 \times 2^1 + 0 \times 2^0$	= 1110	= 16
$15 = 1 \times 2^3 + 1 \times 2^2 + 1 \times 2^1 + 1 \times 2^0$	= 1111	= 17

tronic circuitry in a computer. It suffices to say that instructions to the computer (the program) set up the circuits necessary to carry out the operations.

In the base 2 number system, we have everything that is necessary to express all numbers in terms of only two numerals, zero and one. This enables the computer to represent any number by a series of two-state operations. Thus, to store a number in the computer we might use a series of switches, each switch representing a power of 2. If a given switch were "on," it could indicate a coefficient of one for the corresponding power of 2, if "off," a zero coefficient. This ability to utilize only two symbols, zero and one, enables us to store numbers in the computer.

In spite of the ease with which electronic circuits can deal with base 2 numbers, they are extremely inconvenient for us to use. In the first place, we are not accustomed to working with powers of 2, or with numbers expressed in terms of powers of 2. Second, the physical size of the numbers, that is, the length of the string of ones and zeros, gets long with large numbers. Fortunately, we rarely have to deal with numbers in their binary form. All modern digital computers have prearranged sequences of operations that translate from base 10 into, and from, the computer's base 2 equivalences. At times it is necessary to "look inside" the computer and see what is there. What is "there" consists of strings of binary digits. In order to save space and make the numbers more manageable, binary numbers frequently are expressed by converting them into yet another number system. This system is the base 8 or *octal* number system and is closely related to the binary in that conversion from one system to the other is very easily done.

The basic structure of the base 8 system is exactly like that of the other systems, namely, numbers are expressed as the successive coefficients of powers of the base of the system, in this case 8. For example,

$$\begin{aligned} 10_{10} &= 1 \times 8 + 2 \times 1 \\ &= 1 \times 8^1 + 2 \times 8^0 \\ &= 12_8 \end{aligned}$$

Or another example,

$$\begin{aligned} 205_{10} &= 3 \times 64 + 1 \times 8 + 5 \times 1 \\ &= 3 \times 8^2 + 1 \times 8^1 + 5 \times 8^0 \\ &= 315_8 \end{aligned}$$

The importance of the octal system is that it is extremely easy to convert from binary to octal. To see how this works, a number in all three number systems shows the translation from binary to octal and *vice versa.*

$$371_{10} = 101110011_2 = 563_8$$

The procedure for the base 2 to base 8 conversion is as follows. Break the binary number down into groups of three digits, starting from the right (just as we frequently do with commas in decimal numbers). This gives

$$101\ 110\ 011$$

Now convert each group of three digits to its decimal equivalent by consulting Table I.2. For example, the decimal equivalent of 101 is 5. Now we have

$$\underbrace{101}_{5}\ \underbrace{110}_{6}\ \underbrace{011}_{3}$$

and the octal equivalent of 371_{10} is 563. Thus for a very simple conversion between binary and octal, it is only necessary to consult a table, or memorize the binary equivalents of the decimal numbers 0–7.

Appendix D contains an octal to decimal conversion table for decimal numbers from $.000001_8$ to 7777_8.

Suggested Reading

This chapter has touched on a wide range of topics. Such a brief treatment is inadequate to convey any but the most superficial information about those topics. The interested reader will find more extensive discussions of all of the topics introduced, and more, in the books and journals listed below. Many of these books and journals also contain bibliographies that will help the reader discover additional secondary sources as well as the primary source publications.

American Federation of Information Processing Societies Proceedings (AFIPS), Vol. 1 through Vol. 30 (1967). Washington, D.C.: Thompson Book Company.

Borko, H. (ed). *Computer Applications in the Behavioral Sciences.* Englewood Cliffs, N.J.: Prentice-Hall, 1963.

Communications of the Association for Computing Machinery. Published monthly by the Association for Computing Machinery, 211 East 43rd Street, New York, N.Y., 10017.

Computing Reviews. Published bimonthly by the Association for Computing Machinery, 211 East 43rd Street, New York, N.Y. 10017.

DATAMATION. Published monthly by F. D. Thompson Publications, Inc., 35 Mason Street, Greenwich, Connecticut 06830.

Feigenbaum, E. A., and J. Feldman. *Computers and Thought.* New York: McGraw-Hill, 1963.

Flores, I. *Computer Programming.* Englewood Cliffs, N.J.: Prentice-Hall, 1966.

Flores, I. *Computer Software.* Englewood Cliffs, N.J.: Prentice-Hall, 1965.

Green, B. F. *Digital Computers in Research.* New York: McGraw-Hill, 1963.

Information, A Scientific American Book. San Francisco: W. H. Freeman, 1966.

McMillan, C. and R. F. Gonzalez. *Systems Analysis, A Computer Approach to Decision Models.* Homewood, Ill.: Richard D. Irwin, 1965.

Naylor, T. H., J. L. Balintfy, D. S. Burdick, and K. Chu. *Computer Simulation Techniques.* New York: Wiley, 1966.

Ralston, A., and H. S. Wilf, (eds.). *Mathematical Methods for Digital Computers,* Vol. I. New York: Wiley, 1960.

Veldman, D. J. *Fortran Programming for the Behavioral Sciences.* New York: Holt, Rinehart and Winston, 1967.

CHAPTER 2 ELEMENTARY MACHINE AND SYSTEM OPERATIONS

This chapter has two major aims. First, we hope to acquaint the reader with a few of the elements of "machine language" programming. With languages such as Fortran, there is little need to understand machine code in detail. A little knowledge is not dangerous in this case—rather, it is helpful in developing an insight into the operation of the computer system. The second major aim is to demonstrate that programming is really quite simple, especially with the assistance provided by the computer itself. The section "Programs to Help the Programmer" discusses the assistance in developing programs that a computer user can expect from the computer.

The material in most of this chapter is not essential in understanding Fortran IV programming. The impatient reader, or the reader with some knowledge of computing, may jump immediately to the last section of this chapter entitled, "Programs to Help the Programmer," and then to Chapter 4. For other readers, this chapter provides a more intelligible presentation of what the computer does than emerges from a discussion of Fortran. Fortran tends to "hide" the fundamental properties of a computation. The gain associated with this obfuscation is a facilitation in writing computer programs. The language of Fortran is much more like natural language than the "machine" language of computers. Fortran requires less detail in expressing a program than does machine language. Fortran is therefore easier to learn and use.

Before introducing the explicit notions of machine language programming, we shall develop an analogy in simple story form.

THE FEEBLE-MINDED CHILDREN

Imagine a teacher who had the task of working with feeble-minded children. To promote the understanding of simple commands and the identification of simple objects, she devised special teaching techniques. Some of the children could read and understand a few words, particularly verbs. In addition, the children were somewhat familiar with numbers and could recognize them. However, it was difficult to get the children to show their knowledge. In order to capitalize on their rudimentary skills, the teacher devised a game that the children enjoyed playing. The game permitted the teacher gradually to introduce new words into the children's vocabularies.

The teacher built a set of 20 "mail boxes," each box identified by a number. The boxes were arranged in a row in numerical order. The teacher placed into each box a note containing a word. A child playing the game began at box 1, retrieved the note from the box, and acted out whatever was signified by the word on the note. Then the child would go to the next box, and so on, working through the boxes in order. When she first started the game, the teacher used the following five words:

Word	*Activity for the child*
JUMP	Jump up and down
RUN	Run around the room once

WALK	Walk around the room once
COME	Return to the teacher for something else to do
GO TO ______	Instead of taking the next instruction from the next box, go to box ______ and follow the instruction there

A typical listing of some of the boxes and the notes the teacher placed in them might be

Box	*Word*
1	WALK
2	JUMP
3	RUN
4	GO TO 9
.	.
.	.
.	.
9	JUMP
10	COME

The children enjoyed this game and were willing to display their understanding of numbers and action words. In order to introduce more words the teacher demonstrated the action required by a word and included it in the game. In the course of playing the game the children quickly learned the action meaning of a word. This permitted the teacher to introduce a more complex pattern of activity for the children. For example, the teacher introduced two new words, LAUGH, meaning to laugh out loud, and SIT, meaning to sit down and then to get up again. With this increased vocabulary the teacher placed the words in the boxes in the following order

Box	*Word*
1	LAUGH
2	JUMP
3	GO TO 10
4	LAUGH
5	SIT
6	SIT
7	RUN
8	GO TO 12
9	COME
10	RUN
11	GO TO 8
12	SIT
13	GO TO 5

When the teacher tried out this new combination of words and boxes the child playing the new game would not quit but continued to run, sit, etc., for a time far longer than the teacher imagined that the game called for. Something was wrong with the order of the words in the boxes. (The reader should discover why the game had no end.)

The process of programming a computer in machine language is not unlike the process of placing words in boxes for feeble-minded children. The computer, in fact, is not unlike a feeble-minded child. A program containing the same kind of error as that contained in the last example would cause the computer to "continue to play the game" until someone intervened.

The hardware of the computer system, the electronic circuitry, is constructed so that it "recognizes" certain instructions that are placed in certain locations, the "boxes," of the system. These instructions are presented to the computer as strings of binary information. Each computer system has a certain "vocabulary" of instructions that it can "recognize" and execute, such as ADD, SUBTRACT, and MULTIPLY.

BASIC PROGRAMMING

The step from feeble-minded children to computers is a small one, requiring only a little additional discussion and the definition of a few terms. Whereas we do not know how the child "understands" or keeps track of what he is doing we may specify this quite precisely for the computer.

In order to facilitate this discussion, we describe an imaginary machine with very simple properties. The machine has a set of operations to perform, like the numerical operations of add, subtract, etc. Additionally, it is useful to build into our imaginary machine ways of keeping track of the values of numbers and of keeping track of the location (box) of the next instruction. These three functions are represented in several "registers," or special storage locations in the machine. The registers are maintained by the computer as an automatic process of its operation.

The instructions for the computer are stored in individual locations in the primary storage of the computer. The instructions, as in the case of the feebleminded children, are carried out sequentially unless there is some rerouting instruction like the GO TO in the children's game. The location number of the next instruction to be executed is stored in a register called the Instruction Counter (IC).

At the start of an operation cycle in the computer, an instruction is moved from the location specified by the IC to the second register, the Instruction Register (IR). In the IR, the instruction is decoded, the necessary circuitry is established, and the operation is carried out. After this, the IC is advanced by 1 (unless it was changed by the instruction just executed) and the instruction from the next location (the address given in the IC at this time) is brought into the IR, and so forth.

Operations in the computer generally deal with numbers (e.g., data) that are stored at some specified locations in memory. For this reason, an instruction will consist not only of an operation to be executed but also the memory address of the number that is to be operated on. For example, when two numbers are added together, the actual addition takes place in a third register called the *ac*cumulator (AC). First the AC is cleared (all the binary places set to zero). Next, the first number is added to the AC, and finally, the second number is added to the AC, leaving the contents of the AC as the sum of the two numbers.

We speak of the contents of registers just as if they were boxes with things in them. This is not literally true. A register is a collection (string) of electronic devices each of which has two states. Interpreting one of the states as a 0 and the other state as a 1 leads to the interpretation that the register contains a binary number. The string of two-state devices making up a register, with each device in one state or another, thus corresponds to a specific binary number. In the IR the string is composed of two parts, an operation part and an address part. The operation part indicates the operation to be performed and the address part indicates the location in primary storage containing the datum to be operated on. In order to be precise we would have to speak of the operations in machine language as the strings of device states in the IR leading to a given operation, and the strings of device states in the address part of the IR indicating the address of the datum. However, we take a couple of conceptual leaps and substitute operation codes and decimal numbers for the locations in memory.

As an example of basic programming, imagine a program to find the mean of five numbers (e.g., 19, 18, 25, 32, and 24). This is the problem for which we developed an illustrative Fortran IV program in the first chapter. In the example here we ignore the programming to input the necessary data and to output the results of the computation. We deal only with a single set of five numbers. The program developed is equivalent to the statements

```
SUM = X1 + X2 + X3 + X4 + X5
AVER = SUM/5.
```

in the Fortran program.

The example program has a great deal of similarity to a "program" a person would follow if he were working with a desk calculator that we shall outline first. Assume that a person has a calculator and a sheet of paper listing the five values from which he is to calculate an average. The "program" he follows can be written out as 17 steps or simple operations performed by the operator of the calculator. In order to illustrate the parallel with the computer, computer instructions and desk calculator steps are listed side by side in Table II.1.

The desk calculator routine is parallel to the computer routine in the following ways. All of the instructions are stored at specific locations, namely, at a given numbered step in the instruction list. Each instruction is identified by a unique number (address) in the list. Likewise, each of the five values to be added are "stored" on a piece of paper in a given sequence or in specified places. Addition is carried out in a row of dials on the calculator (the accumulator) and the result of the division appears in another row of dials. The calculator operator serves as both the IC and the IR, keeping track of his place in the program, reading and executing the operations.

Now, turn to the same program for the

Table II.1

Desk calculator "program" to calculate an average, with some parallel computer operations

Desk Calculator Step	Desk Calculator Operation	Computer Instructions Operation	Computer Instructions Address
1	Clear dials	CLA	10
2	Enter first number in keyboard		
3	Press +		
4	Enter 2nd no.	ADD	11
5	Press +		
6	Enter 3rd no.	ADD	12
7	Press +		
8	Enter 4th no.	ADD	13
9	Press +		
10	Enter 5th no.	ADD	14
11	Press +		
12	Enter total	DVD	20
13	Press ENTER DIVIDEND		
14	Enter divisor		
15	Press ÷		
16	Enter quotient on summary sheet	STQ	50
17	End of routine	HLT	

computer. Assume that the values of the numbers to be added are stored in memory locations numbered 10, 11, 12, 13, and 14. Location 20 contains the number 5, the divisor, and location 50 is set aside for the purpose of storing the average. Locations numbered 100 through 107 contain the instructions making up the program. We are not concerned here with the process by which the data and instructions are placed in memory—a problem in input-output programming that is considered in our discussion of Fortran IV.

When the execution of the program begins, the IC is set to 100 so that the first instruction is moved to the IR and executed. When the first instruction is executed, the IC is increased to 101, causing the second instruction to be moved to the IR, and so on.

The AC may have a number left in it from some previous operation or program. The first instruction must therefore clear the AC (that is, set it to zero). We also wish to add the first number, stored in location 10 (i.e., 19), to the cleared AC. The instruction that accomplishes this is:

CLA 10

Or, in words, *cl*ear the AC and *a*dd to it the number found at location 10. This accomplished, the IC advances to 101 and brings the next instruction to the IR. This instruction will cause the second number to be added to the number which is already in the AC, leaving in the AC the sum of the first two numbers. The appropriate instruction is

ADD 11

This step leaves 37 (i.e., 19 + 18) in the AC when the addition is finished. Again the IC advances, bringing the instruction from location 102 to the IR. This is another ADD, with the address specifying the third data number:

ADD 12

Two more ADDs complete the summation:

ADD 13
ADD 14

At the end of the execution of the last instruction the AC contains the sum of the five data values. All that remains is to calculate the average and store it in location 50.

The value of the divisor is 5, which is stored in location 20. The operation DVD causes the division of the contents of the AC by the contents of the location specified by the address in the DVD instruction. Since the divisor is stored in the location numbered 20, the full instruction is

DVD 20

The execution of this instruction causes the quotient to be placed in a register called the Multiplier-Quotient (MQ) register. The contents of this register may be transferred to a specified location by the command STQ, meaning to *st*ore the contents of the M*Q* in the location specified in the address part of the instruction. We reserved location 50 for the average and thus the store instruction is

STQ 50

Finally, the computation is ended with the instruction to *halt*, HLT. Since the instruction HLT does not refer to any particular register or data there is no address part of the instruction.

The complete contents of memory for this program segment are listed in Table II.2. Memory essentially is divided into two parts, a program area and a data area.

An important operating characteristic of most computers is employed in the next example. This characteristic is known as "destructive read-in and nondestructive read-out." That is, when information is placed in (read into) some working register or internal storage location, the previous contents of that location are destroyed. When information is read out of a location, e.g., when a number is placed in the AC, the content

Table II.2

Contents of primary storage before calculation of mean of five numbers

Address	Contents	Kind of word
1		
.		
.		unused storage locations
.		
10	19	data
11	18	data
12	25	data
13	32	data
14	24	data
.		
.		unused storage locations
.		
20	5	data (a constant)
.		
.		unused storage locations
.		
50	—	data (for the mean)
.		
.		unused storage locations
.		
100	CLA 10	instruction
101	ADD 11	instruction
102	ADD 12	instruction
103	ADD 13	instruction
104	ADD 14	instruction
105	DVD 20	instruction
106	STQ 50	instruction
107	HLT	instruction

of the storage location is unchanged. Reading a number out of, for example the AC, does not change the content of the AC. Rather, the operation duplicates the number so that it is in both the AC and the storage location to which it was moved. In reading a number into the AC and some of the other working registers, the destruction of the previous contents can be controlled by the programmer through his choice of instructions. For example, a CLA clears (sets to zero) the AC and adds a new number to it while the ADD instruction does not clear the AC but causes the sum of two numbers to be formed there.

Imagine that the five numbers averaged in the program are a diagnostic indicator or a critical value of some sort. For every average calculated we make a decision as to whether it is indicative of a diagnostic category or not. Instead of having the computer print the value of the average, we want the computer to print an indication of whether the average is above a critical point or below it. We indicate the instance of the value being below the critical point by placing the value 1 at a given location and the instance of the value being equal to or above the critical point by storing a 0 at the same location. Imagine that the critical value is 20—any average value of 20 or more causes the indicator to have a value of 0 and any value less than 20 causes the indicator to have a value of 1. For simplicity, assume that all of the averages are greater than zero.

The program listed in Table II.2 can be expanded with new instructions, beginning in location 107 and moving the HLT instruction to the end of the expanded program. Imagine that the cutoff value, 20, is placed in location with address 21. We also need the possible values, 0 and 1, for the indicator, and a place to store the value of the indicator when it has been determined. Store 0 in location 22, 1 in 23, and let the location numbered 51 be reserved for the indicator assigned to the calculated average. The lines that must be added to the data storage portion of Table II.2 are

Address	*Contents*	*Kind of Word*
21	20	Data (a constant)
22	0	Data (a constant)
23	1	Data (a constant)
51	—	Data (to be determined, i.e., the indicator)

The first step in the decision process is to compare the value of the mean, now stored in the location numbered 50, with the cutoff value in the location numbered 21. This is executed by placing the mean in the AC:

```
107  CLA  50
```

and then subtracting the cutoff value by

```
108  SUB  21
```

The instruction SUB means to *sub*tract the contents of the location specified in the address part of the instruction from the contents of the AC. The result of the subtraction, the remainder, is left in the AC. If the result of this subtraction is positive (including zero), the cutoff point value must have been no larger than the average. Therefore a positive remainder is indicative of a non-critical case, i.e., the indicator should be set to 0. If the result of the subtraction is negative the cutoff point value must have been larger than the average and the indicator should be set to 1. Two program segments are now defined, the first to store a 1 in the location numbered 51 and the second to store a 0 in the location numbered 51. The first segment will be executed only if the remainder in the AC is negative. The second segment will be executed only if the remainder in the AC is nonnegative. The mechanics of this selective execution depend on instructions that permit branching, or skipping specified instructions.

The instruction TPL (*t*ransfer if *pl*us) causes a skip to the instruction the address of which is given in the address part of the instruction, *if* the contents of the AC are positive (including zero). If the contents of the AC are negative the next instruction is executed—no instructions are skipped. Another transfer instruction is needed—an absolute transfer that causes a transfer to a specified instruction location regardless of the AC. TRA, or *tr*ansfer *a*bsolute, causes a transfer to the location specified in the address part of the instruction. These two transfer instructions complete the program since the STO command stores the content of the AC:

```
109  TPL  112
110  CLA   23
111  TRA  113
112  CLA   22
113  STO   51
114  HLT
```

If the contents of the AC are nonnegative the program skips over instructions in locations 110 and 111 to execute the instruction in location 112. If the contents of the AC are negative the instruction in location 110 is executed and the instruction in location 111 causes a transfer to execute the instruction in location 113. Hence, both of the transfer instructions end eventually with an execution of the instruction in location 113, causing the contents of the AC to be stored in location 51. By the time the program executes the instruction in location 113, a zero or a 1 has been stored in the AC, either by the instruction in location 100 or that in location 112. The new portion of the expanded program now looks like:

Address	*Contents*	*Kind of word*
107	CLA 50	Instruction
108	SUB 21	Instruction
109	TPL 112	Instruction
110	CLA 23	Instruction
111	TRA 113	Instruction
112	CLA 22	Instruction
113	STO 51	Instruction
114	HLT	Instruction

As a final example of machine language programming, consider the problem of adding N numbers. We could do this with a sequence of N ADD instructions, each specifying a different address, but this would be laborious and would work only if N were some specific value. The problem can be simplified, and at the same time the solution made quite general, by taking a somewhat different approach. We construct what is known as a loop; a sequence of operations repeated several times, in this instance N times. The loop contains a single ADD instruction that is executed N times, each time with a different address. That is, the same sequence of operations is executed for every number to be added, each time changing the address on the ADD instruction so that data at different addresses are added.

The process of changing the address of an instruction is related to the fact that the contents of memory are strings of binary digits. The computer has no general way of distinguishing between instruction and data words except in the manner in which they are used. If a word is brought into the IR it is interpreted as an instruction. On the other hand, any word appearing in the AC may be operated on as data. The address part of an instruction may be changed by placing the instruction in the AC and modifying the address portion of the word arithmetically. Thus to change the address of an ADD instruction, for example, it is placed in the AC just as if it were a data word. Once the binary information that is the representation of the ADD instruction is in the AC it is treated as a data word and the appropriate magnitude is added to or subtracted from it in order to change the address. Once the address is changed, the instruction can be returned to its position in the program. When it is used, the instruction is placed in the IR and the modified address is used.

The looping procedure results in a very general sequence of machine instructions. The terminating condition of the loop (that is, when it stops) depends only on a single number N, which could vary with different executions of the program. Since the loop could be a part of a larger program, it is not ended by halting the machine, as in previous examples, but by transferring to another location (200) which is the beginning of the next part of the program. Table II.3 gives the locations of various numbers in the program. The numbers in locations 501, 502, and 503 will be explained below.

There may be numbers stored in several of the locations we want to use, and because of the way we want to use them, we should make sure that these locations initially contain zero. Location 501 is used as an index or counter, indicating how many times we have been through the loop. Location 501 is set initially to zero. The contents of location 501 will be augmented by one each time through the loop. The terminating condition is satisfied when locations 501 and 504 contain the same numbers since 504 contains the number of values to be added. Location 999 will store the final sum, and partial sums as we go through the program. That is, we first place the first data number in location 999. The next time through the loop we place the sum of the first two numbers in location 999, and so

Table II.3

Storage locations for addition loop

Location	Content	Purpose
100 . . . 114	Program statements	
200	First location containing next part of program	
501	—	Counter (or index)
502	0	Zero for initial setting
503	+1	For counting and changing
504	—	Criterion value (N--number of numbers to be added) to be set by earlier part of program, perhaps by input.
999	—	To store result
1000 . . . xxx	Numbers to be added (data). Provision for N locations are made elsewhere in the program. The location indicated by xxx has a location number equal to 1000 + N - 1	

on, until, when we have completed the loop, location 999 contains the sum of all N numbers. The initial value in location 999 must be zero.

The instructions to place zeros in locations 501 and 999 move the zero from 502 to the AC, and from the AC to 501 and 999.

```
CLA 502
STO 501
STO 999
```

These instructions are stored at locations 100, 101, and 102, respectively.

The next instruction, stored at location 103, moves the partial sum from location 999 (a zero the first time through the loop, partial sums each succeeding time) to the AC and marks the start of the loop:

```
CLA 999
```

Location 104 contains the important ADD instruction that does the addition in the loop. The first time through the loop, it has the address of the first piece of data to be added. By the time this instruction is executed again, its address will have been changed so that it refers to the second piece of data, and so forth:

```
ADD 1000
```

Next, the partial sum (zero + the first datum the first time through, zero + first datum + second datum the second time, etc.) is returned to location 999:

```
STO 999
```

The next several instructions change the address of the ADD instruction so that it refers to the next successive piece of data. The ADD instruction is moved to the AC, one is added to it, and it is replaced where it was. Remember that the ADD is in location 104 and the number one in location 503:

```
CLA 104
ADD 503
STO 104
```

Thus, the ADD is placed back where it was with its address increased by one. The ADD part of the contents of 104 is not changed by this operation. Only the address part of 104 is changed.

Two steps remain. First, count the number of times that we have been through the loop. Then, if the number of times is equal to *N* (the criterion value stored in 504), we are finished and go to the next part of the program. If we are not finished, transfer back to the start of the loop (the instruction at location 103).

To count the number of times through the program, we bring our index from location 501 to the AC (remember that the first time through this has the value 0), add one to it, and replace it at 501. This replacement leaves the value of the index in the AC, so we start the end-of-loop test by subtracting the criterion value (location 504) from it:

```
CLA  501
ADD  503
STO  501
SUB  504
```

If, at this point, the AC is negative, it means that not all numbers have been added and we must return to the start of the loop at location 103. If, on the other hand, the AC is zero or positive, we transfer to the next part of the program at location 200. This time we *t*ransfer if *mi*nus, i.e., if the contents of the AC are negative the next instruction to be executed is located at the address indicated in the transfer instruction.

```
TMI  103
```

If the AC is positive the instruction following the transfer instruction is executed. In this example, the absolute transfer

```
TRA  200
```

is executed to complete the looping. Locations 200 and beyond would contain instructions to complete the data analysis intended, perhaps to divide the sum by the number of elements summed in order to determine the average, etc. The complete program just written appears in Table II.4.

Table II.4

Addition loop program

Location	Instruction word: Operation	Instruction word: Address	Comment
100	CLA	502	Zero to AC
101	STO	501	Set result to zero
102	STO	999	Set counter to zero
103	CLA	999	Result to AC. Start loop
104	ADD	1000	Add next number
105	STO	999	Save result so far
106	CLA	104	ADD instruction to AC
107	ADD	503	Add 1 to address of ADD
108	STO	104	Put ADD back
109	CLA	501	Counter to AC
110	ADD	503	Increase count by one
111	STO	501	Put counter back
112	SUB	504	See if we are done
113	TMI	103	If minus, not done, go to start of loop
114	TRA	200	Go to next part of program

The machine language method of programming is long, tedious, and very exacting. A great deal of time is spent to program a simple loop for the addition of numbers, especially when it is considered that most computers will execute this series of operations for forty numbers in less than a millisecond.

Before the science of computing was very old it was discovered that the computer itself could be of considerable assistance in programming. Several advances were made over a very short period of time, both in machinery and in means whereby the user could communicate with the machine. In the latter respect the computer itself became instrumental in helping the programmer. Basic machine language programs were written in order to do most of the clerical work for the programmer.

PROGRAMS TO HELP THE PROGRAMMER

In the addition loop illustrated above, it was necessary for the programmer to keep careful track of the numerical addresses of a variety of pieces of information. Were the program much longer than that illustrated, the "housekeeping" tasks would be critical. One means of simplifying this task is to introduce mnemonic symbols standing for addresses. Each mnemonic symbol is made to stand for a location but the programmer would have to remember only the more easily remembered mnemonic. To implement this scheme the computer can be programmed to make a simple "translation" of mnemonics to numbers.

Symbolic Programming. In the coding illustrated above, the absolute numerical addresses of words in memory were employed. A program written in this manner is generally called an *absolute* program. (Actually, the example developed is a cross between absolute programming and symbolic or mnemonic programming. In true absolute programming octal equivalents of the operation codes and octal addresses would be used.)

A program can be written in absolute code to translate symbolic representations of operations and locations into absolute code. The data of such a translation program would be other programs written or coded in a symbol set more easily remembered or constructed by the programmer. The translator is generally called an assembly program or *assembler.* The assembler is programmed to establish equivalences between symbolic notation in programs and actual addresses within the computer system. In this way, the programmer may work with symbols more readily understood. The assembler establishes the linkage between symbol and actual address.

A language using symbolic notation for addresses is called a symbolic language or an *assembler language.* The assembler constructs a table of symbols used, establishes the amount of storage needed, etc., and defines the equivalences between symbol and address. Table II.5 gives a possible assignment of symbols for the locations involved in the looping program. In writing such a symbolic program the actual addresses would not be specified; that would be done by the assembler. In Table II.5 each of the locations referred to in the program is given a symbolic name. Thus, whenever the symbol I appears in the symbolic program the assembler establishes the equivalence between I and 501 (or whatever address is assigned at the time the assembler makes up the symbol table). Imagine that the symbol DATA is assigned a value of 1000. When the symbolic statement

ADD DATA

(see Table II.6) is assembled, it is exactly as if we had written

ADD 1000

and the address is modified in the original example. Using the notation of Table II.5, the program would appear like the one listed in Table II.6.

Writing a program in an assembly language is still long and tedious, since each

Table II.5

Symbol table for looping program

Symbol	Address	Meaning of location
I	501	index for counting
NULL	502	zero for initial setting
INCR	503	one for incrementing
N	504	number of scores
SUM	999	to store sum and mean
DATA	1000	first data value
LOOP	103	first instruction in loop
INST	104	location of ADD instruction that must be modified
NEXT	200	next instruction

step in the computation must be coded individually. However, it is a considerable improvement over absolute programming.

The next development reflects the fact that an active programmer finds himself writing the same strings of instructions, over and over, often in programs to do very different things. For example, many computations involve simple loops—doing the same set of operations N times, each time changing the address of an instruction by a fixed amount. Why not let the computer do the clerical job of specifying the details of the loop when the programmer wants a loop in his program? All the programmer need do is to specify the operation to be performed, how many times it is to be performed, and where the data are located; the computer can do the clerical tasks of constructing the tests, address changes, etc. Of course the computer must be programmed to do this. The program that does such a job is called a *compiler* program and the conventions of specifying what is to be done is called a compiler language. Fortran IV is a compiler language and it is processed by the Fortran IV compiler.

Table II.6

Looping program in symbolic language

Operation	Address
CLA	NULL
STO	SUM
STO	I
CLA	SUM
ADD	DATA
STO	SUM
CLA	INST
ADD	INCR
STO	INST
CLA	I
ADD	INCR
STO	I
SUB	N
TMI	LOOP
TRA	NEXT

Compiler Languages. A compiler language is a set of rules for writing programs that are translated into machine code by a program called the compiler. The compilation of a program is a one statement to a many statement translation as compared with the one-to-one nature of assembly—a single program statement in compiler language may give rise to many program statements in assembler code.

One of the aims in the development of

compiler languages is to make them closer to natural language. In particular, the Fortran languages are similar to ordinary algebra. "Fortran" is an acronym for *for*mula *tran*slation. The Fortran program corresponding to the summating loop in the symbolic program developed above is composed of three statements (recall the example in Chapter 1):

```
   SUM = 0.0
   DO 10 I = 1, N
10 SUM = SUM + DATA(I)
```

The first statement sets the location SUM to zero. The next statement starts the loop, sets the initial value of I to 1, arranges to have I increased by 1 each time through the loop, and sets the terminating condition ($I > N$). The final statement carries out the addition.

The following chapters develop the Fortran language in detail. Before we get into this a few comments about the computing system are necessary.

EXECUTIVE SYSTEMS

In addition to programs written to translate from compiler or assembler languages into machine language, programs have been written to perform a wide variety of other functions. Those with which we shall be concerned in this section are called executive programs, executive system, or monitor system. These programs, or sets of programs, cause the computer to perform many operations (e.g., accounting for who used the computer for how long) that would otherwise have to be done by humans. That is, these programs allow the computer automatically to perform many operations that otherwise would have to be done manually.

Most computer installations have at least one executive system, many have more than one executive system. Where more than one executive is used, part of each working day is run with one executive system, and part with the other. Each executive system has its own idiosyncracies. Most executive systems, however, have certain features or operations in common. To illustrate an executive system, we shall here follow the progress of a Fortran program through the typical installation.

The deck of cards making up the program and data (see Figure II.2) are referred to collectively as a "job." The job deck consists of four types of cards: (1) identification cards giving the programmer's name, account number, etc.; (2) system instruction cards giving instructions to the executive system; (3) program cards in Fortran, machine language, or some other language; and (4) data cards for the program.

A job deck is placed on the card reading system and written on magnetic tape (or disk). All cards in the job deck (identification, data, program, and all) are placed on tape. The tape prepared in this fashion is mounted on one of the tape units of the computer and is called the input tape. Now the executive system takes over. It reads the image of the identification card on the tape and finds the account number so that the correct amount of time may be charged to that account. It also determines the time of day and date that the program is run and makes a note of that information on another tape called the output tape.

The executive system next determines what must be done to the program that is on the input tape. That is, there are cards giving instructions to the executive system to do such things as compile a program, and so forth. In order to carry out some of these instructions, the executive system calls upon its component programs. If, for example, the job requires compiling a Fortran program, the Fortran compiler program must be called upon to do the actual translation.

After the program has been translated successfully into machine language, i.e., compiled, the executive system calls on another of its component programs to place (load) the machine language program into primary storage so that it is ready for execution.

Finally, the control of the computer is turned over to the loaded program which carries out the work for which it was intended. At the conclusion of the program, control of the computer is returned to the executive system which then calls in (looks at) the identification card, the system control cards, etc., for the next job on the input tape and the process is repeated.

The programmer communicates with the executive system by means of cards in his input deck. The executive system recognizes certain cards as instructions to it, while others are utilized by the compiler or other programs. Figure II.1 presents a complete listing of a deck which is to serve as an input to a computer system. Each line in this listing represents a single card. The cards are identified as one of the four types of cards indicated above.

The cards of type 1 are recognized by the executive program and are the basis for determination of the legitimacy of the account number indicated by the user, the amount of time the user estimated he would use, etc. The cards of type 2 are instructions to the executive. In Figure II.1 the cards indicate that a Fortran program is to be compiled and executed.

The third type of card is the program card. The statements of the Fortran program are punched on cards as indicated in Chapter 1 and included in the total deck.

At the end of the Fortran deck a card of type 2 occurs to indicate that there are cards following to be dealt with as data by the compiled program. The type 2 card here is taken as a signal to the compiler not to try to deal with the cards following—they are data for the compiled program.

Finally, data cards are included in the deck as a fourth type of card. These cards contain the data to be dealt with by the compiled program. If there were no data needed by the program the $ENTRY card and the data cards would not be included in the deck.

Figure II.2 shows a card deck that might be submitted to the Computing Center at the University of Colorado for

```
                                                                          Card Type
$ID      BAILEY      PSYCH 587      R900N      002      005      000           1
$ID      BAILEY      PSYCH 587      R900N      002      005      000           1
$IBJOB                                                                         2
$IBFTC AVER                                                                    2
      READ 100,K                                                               3
      I=0                                                                      3
    1 READ 101,X1,X2,X3,X4,X5                                                  3
      AVER=SUM/5.0                                                             3
      I=I+1                                                                    3
      PRINT 102,AVER                                                           3
      IF(I.LT.K) GO TO 1                                                       3
      STOP                                                                     3
  100 FORMAT(I3)                                                               3
  101 FORMAT(5F3.0)                                                            3
  102 FORMAT(F6.2)                                                             3
      END                                                                      3
$ENTRY           AVER                                                          2
005                                                                            4
012035024015034                                                                4
028040069072035                                                                4
020053065028010                                                                4
010063085074089                                                                4
050056085020010                                                                4
```

Figure II.1 Example of a complete input deck.

compilation and execution on the IBM 7044. The cards with a $ in column 1 are specialized for the particular computing system and computing center. Other cards in the place of those illustrated may be required in another computing center. The computer being operated by a computing center and the conventions of that center determine the specific cards of types 1 and 2 and their sequence.

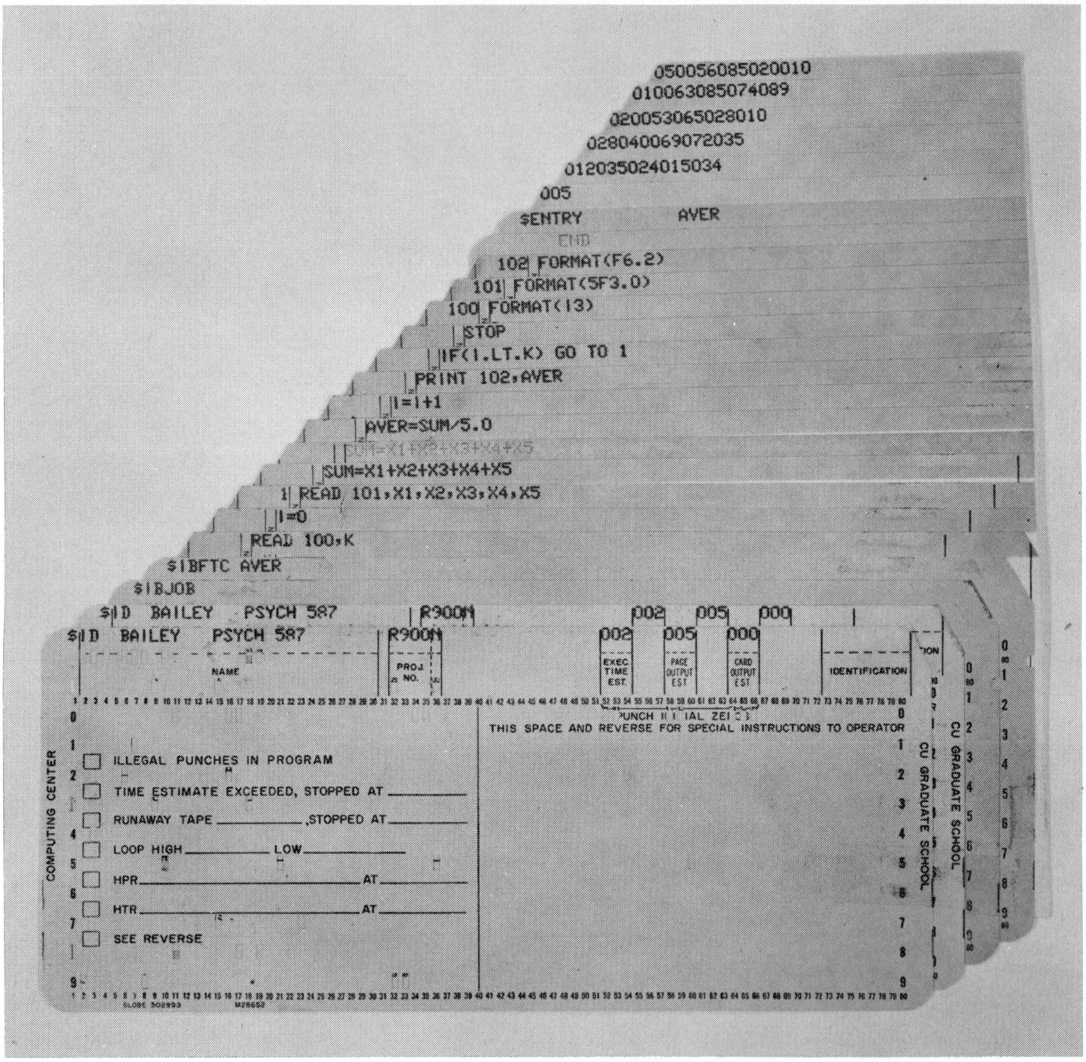

Figure II.2 Illustration of a card deck submitted for compilation and execution.

CHAPTER 3 SUGGESTED COMPUTER PROJECTS

The beginning student of computing often approaches the subject with a very specific problem in mind. This approach is both desirable and undesirable. It is an advantage that the beginner is motivated by some specific problem. However, this motivation may cause blindness to the generality of the programming language and impatience with principles of computing not relevant to his immediate problem. This chapter is intended to alert the beginner to many problems, other than his own perhaps, that will help rationalize the specific details of the language. An understanding of the projects will facilitate an understanding of the language since they involve most of the features of Fortran IV. The projects are not intended to be an exhaustive representation of behavioral science computer applications but rather to suggest a broad range of such applications.

The focal point in a project is always the problem involved, not the computer or computer language. Unlike the desk calculator, the computer has often seduced otherwise rational scientists into computing purely for the sake of computing. This is an insidious trap and is more difficult to avoid than one might think. The computer is a fascinating device that extends the programmer's logical and clerical capacity to the point that it becomes fun to develop programs even though they may have no extrinsic value. There is nothing wrong with having fun—indeed, unless science were enjoyable as well as potentially useful it would be a dreary pursuit. However, the enjoyment one obtains from computing need not be useless. The greatest pleasure in computing is a combination of the fun of computing and the usefulness of the finished computer project.

All of the projects suggested in this chapter can be challenging and rewarding to the beginning programmer. They are also illustrative in that the programming required is the kind that the behavioral scientist is likely to need in his research endeavors.

The student is encouraged to select two or three of the projects and begin now to conceptualize a computing scheme that would do the work or solve the problem. Select projects that are interesting to you, but choose diverse projects. Then, as you progress through this book you will have specific and concrete applications to consider with the various elements of the Fortran language as they are introduced. By attempting to find a use for each of the concepts and procedures of Fortran in your projects, the language will become less a formal set of concepts and will take on more practical significance.

In designing a program do not attempt to generalize to bigger problems, more variables, more sets of data, more cases, etc., in any way. Stick to the specific problem proposed and the suggested data. Otherwise, you may find yourself in difficulty. The beginning programmer may be trapped into attempting a program of such size that he may never finish.

Complete listings and sample outputs of four of the projects are given in Appendix C. Along with these completed projects are program descriptions including the sort of write-up useful in communicating with other users of your program. In some instances, programs written for one purpose are quite general and might be useful to other people. In order for the program to be used by others, several things in addition to the program must be provided. The purpose and general goals attained in the program must be described in detail. The specific calculational formulas and the logic of the computation must be indicated clearly. Limitations and options built into the program must be indicated. Instructions regarding the preparation of data cards must be spelled out in detail. The output from the program (printed information, cards punched, etc.) must be described along with any interpretative aids necessary to decipher the output numbers and symbols.

If the program is to be exported fairly generally, the sort of documentation that will be required by the importer (user) of the program will depend on the use to which he will put the program, and on his skill in computing. In general, there are two extreme kinds of users: (1) a person with no knowledge of programming but a desire to use the program and facilities whereby he can punch cards; and (2) a person with a basic knowledge of Fortran IV programming and a desire to understand the working of the program and perhaps a desired to modify it to his specialized needs. The first type of user needs to know only briefly what the program does and how he should punch cards, etc., in order to use it. The second type of importer will want to know how the program was put together, the meaning of its cryptic notation, the placement and duties of loops and decision points, etc. Program documentation must serve both kinds of users.

Even if the program you write is exported only to local colleagues (or even if you will use it only occasionally) a complete documentation will prove useful. The programmer who returns to use a program of his own after several months, during which time he has not used the program, will find it somewhat dim in his memory. A careful documentation when the program is fresh in the mind of the programmer will save time, energy, and frustration at a later date.

Eighteen projects are suggested. An attempt has been made to order the projects in accordance with their difficulty, either of conception or of execution. The ordering is by no means uniformly consistent with any single criterion of difficulty. Several of the projects lower on the list might be suggestive of interesting applications using the computer as a simulator or symbol manipulator, topics which are discussed in later chapters.

1. Learning scores
2. Automated social psychologist
3. Automatic diagnosis
4. Scoring on several measurements
5. Rating scale data cards
6. Data plotter, frequency function
7. Data plotter, scatter plot
8. Sampling distribution of $\overline{X}$
9. Sampling distribution of miscellaneous statistics
10. Quantitative genetics
11. Random sampler
12. Noisy signal generator
13. Randomization test for correlations
14. Queuing at supermarket check-out stand
15. Election prediction
16. Nerve network simulation
17. Music composer
18. Contagion model for rumor propagation

PROJECT 1. LEARNING SCORES

Imagine an experiment where 10 subjects are observed in a learning task. For each subject, six values are of interest: (1) the total number of correct responses during the experiment, (2) the total number of responses required to meet the learning criterion of four consecutive correct responses, (3) the number of incorrect responses made before the first correct response, (4) the number of incorrect responses made after the first correct response, (5) the total number of correct responses between the first correct response (including the first) and the last incorrect response, and (6) the total number of runs of two consecutive correct responses.

The data collected for a subject are strings of checks (✓) and crosses (×), the ✓'s meaning a correct response and the ×'s meaning incorrect responses. The experiment is terminated when a subject has reached criterion. Data for the 10 imaginary subjects are given in Table III.1.

Write a program to find the six scores for each of the 10 subjects. Then find the mean and variance for each of the six scores in the sample of ten subjects. Print suitable headings, titles, column and row headings, etc., as well as the statistics calculated.

Do the program as a main program and a subroutine. First check out a main program to find the six variables from the raw data. Then check out a subroutine to calculate and print the statistics.

Hint: Let ✓ be a 0, × be a 1, and a blank be 9 (this last is not necessary but for some ways of doing the program it is useful).

PROJECT 2. AUTOMATED SOCIAL PSYCHOLOGIST

Some social psychologists spend a good deal of time at a counting card sorter determining the frequency of certain events that have been recorded on punch cards. For example, in an attitude survey the value given to an attitude item by subjects might be punched in a given column of a card. The counting sorter sorts the cards into separate pockets, each pocket receiving cards with a particular value punched in the specified column. The counting sorter keeps a cumulative record (count) of the number of cards that are sorted into each pocket. If the psychologist wanted to break the cards down even more finely, he could sort the cards from a given pocket a second time using a different column indicating another attitude. Thus all of the cards containing a 3 in column 2 might be sorted out to determine the frequency with which these cards had 0, 1, 2, . . . in column 5. By resorting all of the card decks separated in the first sorting, the joint frequencies

Table III.1

Data for Project 1 in the Form of an Experimental Record Sheet

	Trial 1	2	3	4	5	6	7	8	9	10	11	12
Subject 1	X	X	✓	X	✓	✓	X	X	✓	✓	✓	✓
Subject 2	X	X	X	✓	✓	X	✓	✓	✓	✓		
Subject 3	X	X	X	X	✓	✓	✓	✓				
Subject 4	✓	✓	✓	✓								
Subject 5	X	X	✓	✓	✓	✓						
Subject 6	X	✓	X	✓	X	✓	✓	✓	✓			
Subject 7	X	X	X	X	✓	✓	✓	X	✓	✓	✓	✓
Subject 8	X	✓	✓	✓	✓							
Subject 9	X	X	✓	X	✓	X	✓	✓	✓	✓		
Subject 10	X	X	X	X	✓	X	✓	X	✓	✓	✓	✓

of the characteristics represented in the two columns can be determined.

Imagine a survey of attitudes regarding sexual behavior. The psychologist (or sociologist, or anthropologist) interviews ten college students, recording the following information: name, college class, sex, and their response ("strongly agree," "agree," "don't agree or disagree," "disagree," and "strongly disagree") to the statement "Americans have lost their sense of morality in sexual conduct."

Several items might be of interest in such a survey, for example, the frequencies and relative frequencies of responders in the one-way classification (in this case, sex, college class, and attitude expressed). In addition, the breakdowns of responders according to attitude by sex, attitude by college class, and attitude by sex by college class can be determined.

Write a program that will provide the frequencies and relative frequencies for the three one-way classifications, the three two-way classifications and the single three-way classification. Provide a print-out of the frequencies and relative frequencies together with appropriate headings, titles and comments.

Use the following protocols as sample data:

1. L.S.D. Trip, freshman, male, strongly agree.
2. Merry Muffitt Tuffit, senior, female, strongly agree.
3. Olive Erl, sophomore, female, don't agree or disagree.
4. Patty Y. R. Cake, freshman, female, agree.
5. F. S. M. Cal, freshman, female, strongly disagree.
6. Count Von Toothree, senior, male, disagree.
7. B.M.O.C. Burton, sophomore, male, strongly disagree.
8. L.M.O.C. Fisher, senior, male, strongly agree.
9. Elizabeth T. Campus, senior, female, strongly disagree.
10. Inry Iggins, freshman, male, agree.

Hint: Code each part of each protocol and write the program to deal with the codes: there are three "variables," the first with four "values," etc.; to sort, compare subjects for equality of the values on variables or pairs of values, etc.

PROJECT 3. AUTOMATIC DIAGNOSIS

In recent years some clinical psychologists have proposed so-called "pattern" rules for using several scores on a test to arrive at a diagnosis. As an example, imagine four scores X_1, X_2, X_3, and X_4 and five diagnostic categories: The Sarbin Syndrome, the Meehl Complex, Fisher's F, Normal Deviation, and Symbol Shock. Experts in the field of diagnosis for these nosological classes give the following rules:

Sarbin Syndrome. If $X_1 > 14$, $X_2 < 10$, $X_3 = 1$, and $X_4 < 10$, or if $6 \leq X_i < 14$ for $i = 1, \ldots, 4$, then Sarbin's Syndrome is present. Otherwise Sarbin's Syndrome is not present, unless all scores are in excess of 15 in which instance the case is not classifiable with respect to the syndrome.

The Meehl Complex. If X_1 is greater than 10, Rule I applies, otherwise Rule II applies. *Rule I:* If $X_1 + 3X_2 - 4X_3 + X_4$ is greater than X_1, then the Meehl Complex is present; otherwise it is not. *Rule II:* If $(X_1 + X_2)/(X_3 + X_4)$ is 1.0 or greater, then the Meehl Complex is present; otherwise it is not.

Fisher's F. If $1 - (X_1^2 + X_2^2)/(X_3^2 + X_4^2)$ is positive then Fisher's F is a significant factor in the patient's disease. If it is negative the patient is not troubled by Fisher's F. If it is zero the patient is unclassifiable.

Normal Deviation. If $\frac{1}{4}(X_1 + X_2 + X_3 + X_4) > 10$ apply Rule I; otherwise apply Rule II. *Rule I:* If $\frac{1}{4}(3X_1 + 3X_2 + 3X_3 + 3X_4) > 30$ then Normal Deviation is present; otherwise it is not. *Rule II:* If $\frac{1}{4}(5X_1 + 5X_2 + 5X_3 + 5X_4) \leq 50$ then Normal Deviation is present; otherwise it is not.

Symbol Shock. Let $A = X_1[X_1 - (X_2 - X_3)] - X_4$, and let $B = X_1^2 - X_4 - X_1X_2 + X_1X_3$. If $A \neq B$, then the patient has

Symbol Shock; otherwise the patient does not have Symbol Shock.

Write a program to determine the diagnosis for each of a number of patients, recognizing that a patient can fall into more than one diagnostic category. Print the name of a patient and the pertinent diagnostic information. Keep records as to how many patients fall into each diagnostic category. Keep records regarding the pair-wise incidence of the diagnoses. Use the data of Table III.2 to test your program.

Hint. Do not launch blindly into a computer program. Make a careful analysis of the apparent problem to determine if it is really a problem. Does the "problem" make sense? Could the "problem" be solved by a little analysis without the computer?

PROJECT 4. SCORING ON SEVERAL MEASUREMENTS

Measuring some quantitative characteristic of behavior is often fraught with error. One way of reducing the relative importance of error is to devise several operationally independent ways of assessing the characteristic. If these different assessments are not influenced in the same way by the same sources of measurement error, then averages of the assessments for a given subject will tend to have less error, since errors will tend to cancel out (unless of course they are biased, i.e., preponderantly in the same direction due to the measuring instruments).

Write a program to find an "average score" for each of N subjects from 5 separate measurements. Let the score desired for the ith subject be X_i and the component scores be Y_{i1}, Y_{i2}, Y_{i3}, Y_{i4}, and Y_{i5}. For more generality we calculate the X_i scores in such a way that the contributions of the Y_j are all equal in terms of variance. To do this, calculate for Y_j, $j = 1, \ldots, 5$,

$$S_j^2 = \frac{N \sum_{i=1}^{N} Y_{ij}^2 - \left(\sum_{i=1}^{N} Y_{ij} \right)^2}{N^2}$$

and

$$\overline{Y}_j = \frac{1}{N} \sum_{i=1}^{N} Y_{ij}$$

Then calculate

$$A = \frac{\overline{Y}_1}{S_1} + \frac{\overline{Y}_2}{S_2} + \cdots + \frac{\overline{Y}_5}{S_5}$$

Table III.2

Example Data for Project 3

Patient	X_1	X_2	X_3	X_4
T. Test	02	11	11	17
R. Correlation	05	13	02	20
A. Variance	10	12	08	01
P. Level	16	06	20	05
F. Statistic	10	10	10	10
U. Set	20	16	19	20
B. Regression	12	8	9	13
R. Z. Transform	5	10	10	5
S. Deviation	09	16	11	16

Then let

$$X_i = \frac{1}{S_1} Y_{i1} + \cdots + \frac{1}{S_5} Y_{i5} - A$$

X_i is the sum of standardized observations.

Now, to rescale X more sensibly, give it a mean of 50 and a standard deviation of 10 by adding

$$X_i^* = 10 \left(\frac{X_i - \overline{X}}{S_x} \right) + 50$$

where

$$S_x^2 = \frac{N \sum_{i=1}^{N} X_i^2 - \left(\sum_{i=1}^{N} X_i \right)^2}{N^2}$$

$$\overline{X} = \frac{1}{N} \sum_{i=1}^{N} X_i$$

Use the data given in Table III.3 to check out your program.

Note: The sequence of calculations indicated above involves a number of unnecessary divisions. Division takes a long time to execute compared with addition and subtraction. Also, division generally involves the risk of round-off error that affects all subsequent calculations. To avoid these problems, reanalyze the algebra of the project to improve the speed and accuracy of the calculation.

Table III.3

Example Data for Project 4

Subject	Y_1	Y_2	Y_3	Y_4	Y_5
1	20	17	15	20	19
2	4	9	3	6	2
3	10	10	10	13	9
4	6	7	8	5	4
5	12	13	11	14	12
6	2	1	3	2	4
7	9	8	7	10	9
8	17	16	19	19	20
9	15	14	16	14	20

PROJECT 5. RATING SCALE DATA CARDS

Frequently it is necessary to prepare raw data for input to an already available program. Much of this preparation or preliminary analysis can be done by the computer. The output from such a preanalysis program is usually in the form of punched cards that can be used as an input to the already available program.

Consider the situation where N individuals describe a set of K objects (i.e., cars, girls, colors, sounds, etc.). The descriptions are in the form of ratings of the objects on a set of M descriptive scales. If K girls are described, each of the subjects rates each girl on an M item scale as shown in Figure III.1.

Each of the intervals on the scale can be assigned a numerical value from 1–9 representing how each one of the N subjects rated that particular object (girl) on the scale defined by the pair of objectives. The data can be visualized three-dimensionally, as illustrated in Figure III.2.

Assume that the program to be used in the data analysis must work with two-way arrays of data. Write a program that collapses the 3-dimensional array into 2 dimensions by averaging over subjects. That is, the resultant array should be $K \times M$, as shown in Figure III.3, where each entry represents the mean rating over N subjects. While you are averaging, find the standard deviation of each column as well.

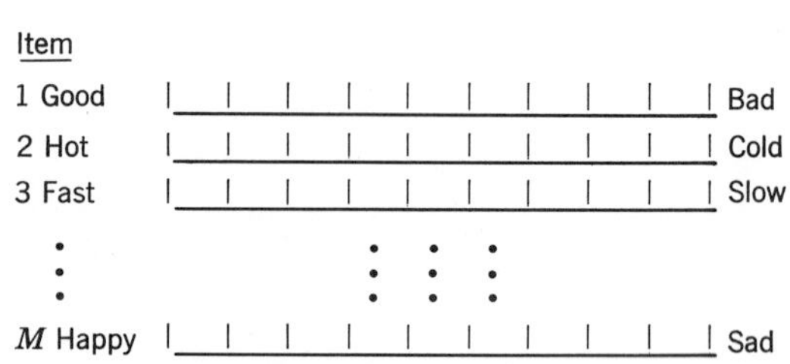

Figure III.1 Illustration of rating scale in Project 5.

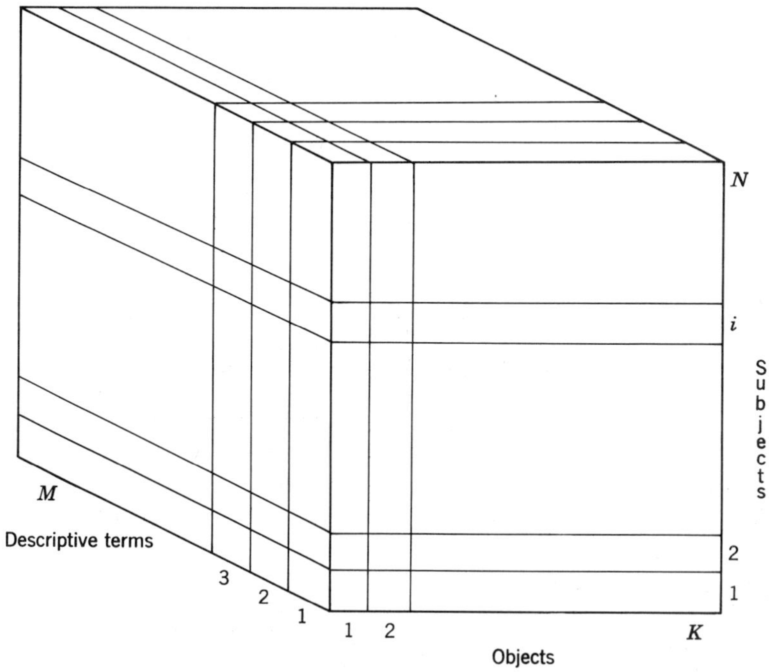

Figure III.2 Schematic representation of a three-dimensional data array.

Print out the matrix of means along with the matrix of standard deviations. Label the rows and columns. Also punch the matrix of means by rows onto cards for use in another program. Columns 73–80 of the punched cards should contain information identifying the row of the matrix and, if more than one card is needed per row, the part of the row. Use the data of Table III.4 to test your program. Note that $N = 3$, $M = 4$, $K = 5$.

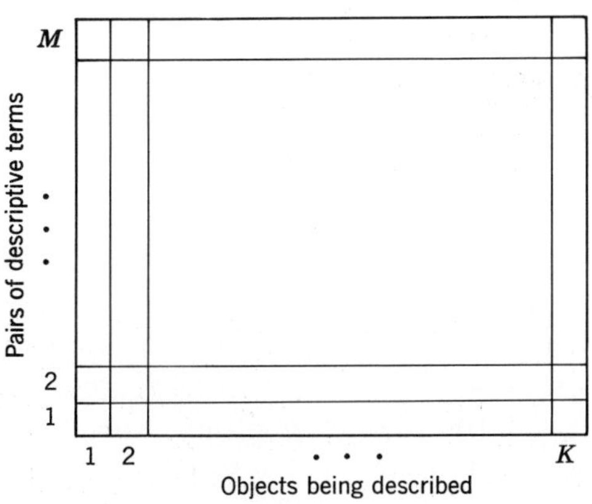

Figure III.3 Schematic representation of the two-dimensional array.

PROJECT 6. DATA PLOTTER, FREQUENCY FUNCTION

The frequency function of a set of observed values is often used to describe experimental data. Where there are many sets of data this clerical job is very time consuming and tedious. The computer can perform the job flawlessly and correctly.

Taking the simplest case of N observations, find the frequency of each of the values. Assume that the values are integers ranging from 00 to 20. Let the printed page be the graph, the columns representing the values (spaced out appropriately) and the rows representing the frequencies (zero frequency at the bottom, the largest observed frequency at the top of the page). Make a column of X's represent the frequency of each of the values. Print the relevant headings, titles and comments. A page on the printer will have 120 to 136 columns and from

Table III.4

Example Data for Project 5

Subject 1

Descriptions	1	2	3	4	5
1	8	5	9	3	8
2	2	5	1	3	8
3	7	7	8	2	1
4	1	3	1	1	5

Objects described

Subject 2

Descriptions	1	2	3	4	5
1	2	6	6	1	2
2	1	7	6	6	3
3	5	1	1	8	1
4	6	4	1	4	5

Objects described

Subject 3

Descriptions	1	2	3	4	5
1	2	6	6	1	2
2	1	7	6	6	3
3	5	1	1	8	1
4	6	4	1	4	5

Objects described

55 to 65 rows depending on the computing system. Use the numbers of Table III.5 as trial data.

PROJECT 7. DATA PLOTTER, SCATTER PLOT

The correlation of jointly observed variables is a central concept in behavioral science theory and research. A traditional measure of correlation is based on a linear model. In order visually to determine the linearity of the relationship of the observed values, the values may be plotted in a scatter plot. Each pair of values (X and Y), a subject at a time, is represented as a point in a plane. The scatter of these representations should be fairly linear if the usual calculation of correlation is to be a good description of the degree of relationship.

This "scatter plotting" can be done by the computer. Let the printed page be the graph, rows representing Y values and columns representing X values. Assume that the values are limited to integers between 01 and 20 inclusive, and write a program to plot the frequencies of the 400 possible pairs of values: (01, 01), (01, 02), ..., (20, 20). Scale (by spacing) the rows and columns appropriately. Print headings, titles, and comments with the scatter plot. Pairs of values with zero frequencies should be left blank. Use a numeral to indicate how many pairs fall at a given point. Use the data given in Table III.6 to test the program.

PROJECT 8. SAMPLING DISTRIBUTION OF $\overline{X}$

Imagine that we do not know the central limit theorem. That is, we do not know that when large samples are drawn from a random variable with a value set of, say $0 \leq x \leq 1$ where $f(x) = 1$ for all values (i.e., uniform distribution), the distribution of $\overline{X}$ from the samples is approximately normal. We want to inspect the sampling distribution of $\overline{X}$ with $N = 1, N = 4, N = 30$. This means that for $N = 1$ we make one observation and calculate

$$\overline{X} = X/1$$

Repeating this 100 times gives 100 means, i.e.,

$$\overline{X}_1, \overline{X}_2, \ldots, \overline{X}_{100}$$

each $\overline{X}$ based on $N = 1$ observations. The distribution of $\overline{X}$ can be displayed by plotting the relative frequencies of values for $\overline{X}$ for class intervals in the range of the random variable. Let the intervals be .1 in length. Then

$$I_1 = \{x \mid 0 \leq x < .1\}$$
$$I_2 = \{x \mid .1 \leq x < .2\}$$
$$\vdots$$
$$I_{10} = \{x \mid .9 \leq x \leq 1.0\}$$

Table III.5

Example Data for Project 6

00	19	19	18	07	17	10	00
03	20	20	19	08	18	11	05
04	03	03	20	09	18	12	06
05	04	04	03	17	19	15	07
06	05	05	05	18	07	16	08
07	06	06	06	19	07	17	09
08	07	07	07	20	03	18	16
09	08	08	09	10	04	19	17
10	09	09	11	19	05	17	18
11	10	10	15	08	06	18	19
12	11	11	19	07	07	19	20
13	12	12	17	06	08	17	03
15	13	13	18	05	09	18	04
16	15	15	20	20	09	19	07
17	16	16	03	19	08	15	09
18	17	17	05	17	07	16	11
06	18	18	06	19	06	17	13

Table III.6

Example Data for Project 7

X	Y	X	Y	X	Y	X	Y	X	Y
05	06	03	04	07	07	15	18	03	02
09	05	04	01	08	06	19	19	04	03
13	20	05	03	09	09	17	15	09	09
20	20	06	06	10	12	18	20	10	10
03	02	07	05	11	10	20	19	11	09
07	03	08	08	12	14	03	01	12	14
11	10	09	07	13	16	05	01	13	15
19	19	10	10	15	14	06	02	15	16
07	07	11	13	07	01	17	20	16	15
13	07	12	13	03	03	18	20	17	19
04	19	07	05	04	05	19	16	18	20
18	20	08	05	05	01	17	15	19	20
19	19	09	08	06	01	18	18	20	20
11	08	17	19	07	01	19	19	05	03
03	20	18	20	08	02	15	12	06	05
17	18	19	19	09	03	16	19	13	12
18	17	20	19	09	07	17	15	15	15
09	13	10	10	08	09	18	17	16	16
20	03	19	07	07	04	19	19	17	19
16	16	18	04	06	07	05	05	18	17
18	19	07	02	10	12	06	04	19	20
19	17	06	06	11	10	07	03	20	19
19	16	05	02	12	14	08	06	03	01
08	06	20	20	15	19	09	12	04	05
17	19	19	20	16	19	16	12	05	01
18	20	17	20	17	17	17	17	06	04
						18	20	07	06

Find relative frequencies

$$f(I_1),\ f(I_2),\ \ldots,\ f(I_{10})$$

by calculating for the jth interval, i.e., for I_j,

$$f(I_j) = \frac{\text{Number of times } \overline{X}\text{'s fall in } I_j}{100}$$

Print, with appropriate headings, descriptions, etc., these ten relative frequencies. Next, $N = 4$ values are selected for each of the samples. These are, say X_1, X_2, X_3, and X_4. Then $\overline{X} = \frac{1}{4}(X_1 + X_2 + X_3 + X_4)$. The 100 sample means, each determined by this method, are

$$\overline{X}_1,\ \overline{X}_2,\quad \overline{X}_{100}$$

Find the relative frequencies with which these values fall in the intervals $I_1, \ldots, I_{10}$.

Do the same again but let $N = 30$.

Hint: The pseudorandom number generator with the Fortran coding below gives values of X with the limits $0.0 \leq x \leq 1.0$ with theoretically equal probabilities. Going through this sequence N times produces N observed values of X from a uniform distribution. An initial value of RAN must be supplied by the programmer or by input. The value of RAN should be some 5 digit odd number

```
RAN = 23. *RAN
  I = RAN/100001.
  F = I
RAN = RAN − 100001. *F
  X = RAN/100000.
```

Going through the statements N times is essentially equivalent to observing a uniformly distributed random variable on the unit interval $(0, 1)$. An extensive discussion of pseudorandom number generation is presented in Chapter 11.

A larger number of samples than 100 may be required to get a very smooth curve of relative frequencies.

PROJECT 9. SAMPLING DISTRIBUTION OF MISCELLANEOUS STATISTICS

Do the same program as indicated for Project 8 with the exception of the sample statistic employed. Let N be some value greater than 1 for the smallest sample. Evaluate the frequency function of the sampling distribution of one of the following:

Median
Mode
Range
Mean absolute deviation
Variance
Standard deviation

$$t = \frac{\overline{X} - .5}{\sqrt{S/(N - 1)}}$$

$$Z = \frac{\overline{X} - .5}{\sqrt{1/12N}}$$

PROJECT 10. QUANTITATIVE GENETICS

The normal random variable is derivable as a sum of many random variables. In particular it can be seen to be a model of behavioral variation where the behavior is determined by many genetic factors obeying simple laws.

Assume that k gene pairs completely determine some quantitative behavior property X. Each gene in a pair carries a "value." The value of the gene pair is given by the sum of the values of the genes in the pair. The genotypic value of the behavior property for a given organism will be equal to the sum of the k gene pair values.

Assume $k = 2$ gene pairs are involved where g_1 and g_2 are the genes from one parent and G_1 and G_2 are the genes from the other parent. Let each of these four genes have four values, say one or another of the values, 0, .1, .2, or .3. This gives an array of possible genes values

Parent a Gene 1	*Parent a Gene 2*	*Parent A Gene 1*	*Parent A Gene 2*
$g_{1,1} = 0$	$g_{2,1} = 0$	$G_{1,1} = 0$	$G_{2,1} = 0$
$g_{1,2} = .1$	$g_{2,2} = .1$	$G_{1,2} = .1$	$G_{2,2} = .1$
$g_{1,3} = .2$	$g_{2,3} = .2$	$G_{1,3} = .2$	$G_{2,3} = .2$
$g_{1,4} = .3$	$g_{2,4} = .3$	$G_{1,4} = .3$	$G_{2,4} = .3$

A given individual is found by some combination

$$\{[g_{1,j}, G_{1,k}], [g_{2,j}, G_{2,k}]\}$$

Assuming X is the behavior function and the genes act additively we have

$$X = g_{1,j} + G_{1,k} + g_{2,j} + G_{2,k}$$

There are 4^4 ways of forming genetically distinct individuals. Many of these genetically distinct individuals are identical with respect to the quantitative property X, which has a value set 0, .1, .2, .3, …, 1.2.

Construct a program that will calculate the probability distribution of X where *two* pairs of genes are involved as above. Do the same for *three* pairs of genes. Print the genotypic values with appropriate titles, headings and comments.

Hint: If k pairs of genes are involved, each gene having one of four values, there are $4^{2k} = 16^k$ separate genetic combinations. Hence for one pair of genes, 16 combinations are possible; for two pairs 256 combinations; for three pairs, 4096 combinations. The first 16 pairs are easy to find. The set of 256 2-gene pair combinations are formed from the set of 16 1-gene pair combinations by completing the middle part of the tree, shown in Figure III.4. Extending the tree to 3-gene pair combinations is also indicated.

PROJECT 11. RANDOM SAMPLER

Workers in a number of the behavioral sciences find it useful to draw a random sample from a specified population. The sociologist may sample from the precincts of a census tract to determine the political opinions of the region. An anthropologist may sample from the members of a primitive society to develop interviews. The economist may sample from firms in a city in order to determine the economic condition of the city.

In most sampling situations the population is defined by a limited number of identifiable individuals (firms, people, precincts, etc.). The number of individuals to be sampled is determined on the basis of statistical consideration and specific individuals are selected by a random process. In one special case the random process involves giving each individual in the population the same chance of being selected as any other individual. One way of doing this is to assign each individual a number. If there are M individuals in the population the integers 1, 2, ..., M are obtained (from a table of random numbers, or from a pseudo-

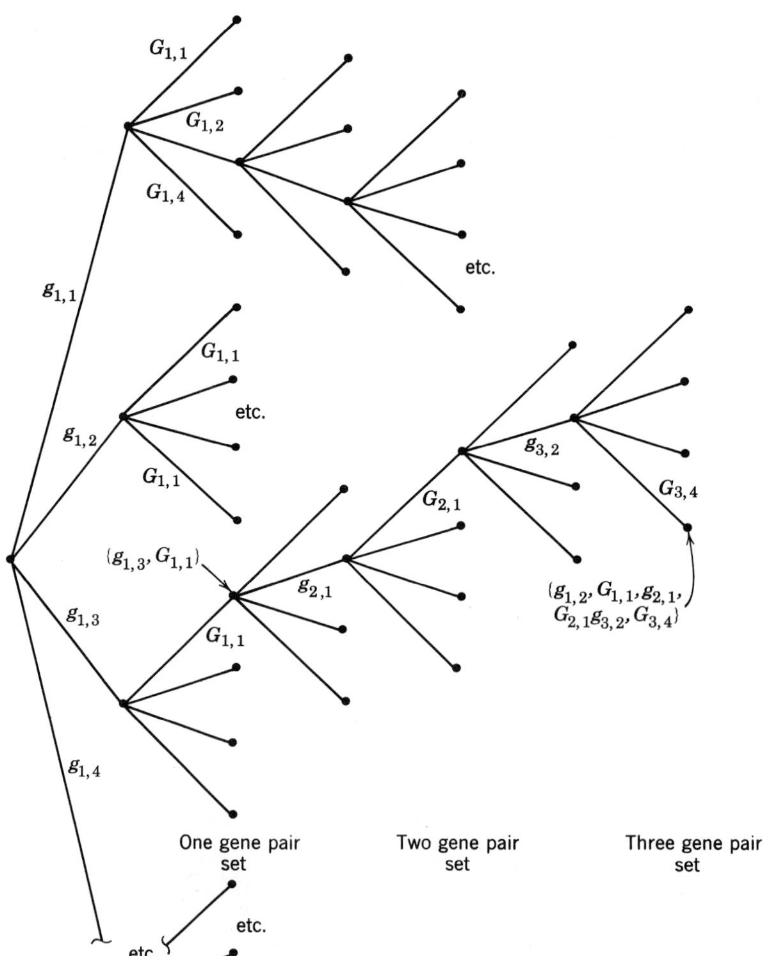

Figure III.4 Tree diagram representing genetic combinations.

random number generator in a digital computer). The random numbers are selected in such a way that all of the integers 1, 2, ..., M have equal likelihood of being selected. The individuals to whom the obtained random numbers have been assigned compose the sample.

Imagine that there are 40 business firms in a given district, and that we want to select ten of them for study. Write a computer program that will select, on an equal probability basis, ten of the forty firms. Check the program by imbedding it in another program to repeat the selection one hundred times so that you can determine the relative frequency of each firm being chosen. If the population sampling probability is uniform, the relative frequencies over the one hundred sample selections will be approximately equal for each of the forty firms. Invent names for these firms and use the names in the output of your program.

Hint: Using the pseudorandom number generator of Project 8, obtain a value X with equal probability between zero and one. The integers between 1 and 40 inclusively are given by

```
I = (40. * X) + 1.
```

where X is the value returned from the generator. If the names of the firms are stored in any array with an index I, the element in the array containing the name of a selected firm may be referred to directly with the random number generated.

PROJECT 12. NOISY SIGNAL GENERATOR

In several fields of behavioral science the concepts of signal detection and signal discrimination play important roles. An information channel (e.g., a telemetry channel) is used to transmit information from one point to the other. This information is composed of a sequence of signals with specified properties at the point of initiation. In the process of transmission a certain amount of "noise" is introduced into the sequence of signals. At all times there is "noise" in the channel and the task of the receiver is to determine whether or not there was a signal transmitted at a given moment of interrogation of the channel. Two actual states may exist: the channel is carrying only noise, or the channel is carrying noise and a signal. In the standard psychological experiment regarding detection and recognition of signals the channel is repeatedly interrogated by the subject. On each interrogation, the subject indicates whether there was a signal present or not. A signal is generally defined as a fixed value (e.g., a tone at a given intensity level in a background of noise). The noise, however, is random (varying as a random variable from interrogation to interrogation).

The classical mathematical theory of signal detection generally assumes that the noise component of a channel transmission is normally distributed. Hence, at a given interrogation the transmission is represented as a value from a normally distributed random variable if only the noise is present. If a signal is present the transmission is represented as a value of a normally distributed random variable plus the constant representing the signal. In order to execute experiments on human signal detection, the experimenter needs to have a series of transmissions. To define such a series, it is convenient to generate random numbers that are normally distributed and to add the signal value to a given random number. The signal value is added to the random number on a probabilistic basis. Imagine that the distribution of the noise is unit normal, i.e., with an expectation of 0. and a variance of 1.0, and that the signal has a value of 1.24. Imagine also that the probability of transmission of a signal (i.e., that a transmission is both signal and noise) is .40 (i.e., over the long run 40 percent of the interrogations will correspond to transmissions of signals).

Invent a program to provide the experimenter with a list of interrogation values, including noise and signal with the signal occurring with probability .40. Print out the sequence of transmission values, the corresponding noise values, and an indication of the presence or absence of the signal. Label the data output in an appropriate fashion. As a check on the distribution of the noise for the sample of transmission values determine the frequency function of the noise values and print out this frequency function.

Hint: A generator of normally distributed random numbers may be constructed in the following way. Write two random number generator programs like that illustrated in Project 8, start each with a different value of RAN (must be odd and not too different from the value assigned in Project 8). Call the first number X1 and the second number X2. Using these values, two random numbers V1 and V2 are generated by the following Fortran statements.

```
V1 = (- 2.0 * LOG(X1))**0.5 * COS(6.283 * X2)
V2 = (- 2.0 * LOG(X1))**0.5 * SIN(6.283 * X2)
```

The variables V1 and V2 will be normally distributed with expectation 0.0 and standard deviation 1.0. For a distribution with expectation E and standard deviation S, the random numbers X3 and X4 are given by

```
X3 = E + S*V1
X4 = E + S*V2
```

PROJECT 13. RANDOMIZATION TEST FOR CORRELATION

The classical standard statistical tests for relationship are dependent on the assumption of a joint normal distribution of the correlated variables. Imagine that a researcher wants to determine if the relationship between two jointly observed variables is statistically significant but that he cannot support the notion that the variables are jointly normal. The researcher might argue in the following way. The relationship of basic interest is the degree to which the relative magnitudes of the two variables are in agreement in both variables. Therefore, the rank values can be substituted for the observed values. A convenient measure of the difference between two observations on each subject is the square of the difference in the ranks. The sum of these squared differences over all subjects is a measure of the relationship of the two variables—small sums for high positive relationships, moderate sums for negligible relationships, and large sums for high negative relationships.

Calculating this measure of relationship does not give a measure of the significance probability of the sample. If the relationship were nil and the sample values were paired on a completely random basis (equal probability of all pairings of rank values) the observed sample measure would be surpassed or equalled by a certain proportion of the random pairings. If we could easily calculate the proportion, it could be used as a measure of the significance probability of the observed sample. The proportion can be calculated easily when the sample size is small, but when sample size is large the calculation becomes impractical even with a digital computer. However, an approximation is quite simple. Imagine that the ranks of the first variable are fixed but that the ranks of the second variable can be assigned in any order at all. This assignment could be done many times, each time choosing the assignments at random so that for each rearrangement the pairs of rank values had the same likelihood. The proportion of times the artificial assignments of ranks produced a larger measure of relationship than the observed measure could be taken as a measure of the significance of the observed measure.

Write a program to assign the numbers 1, 2, ..., N to N locations in such a way that each unassigned number has the same chance of being assigned next. Calculate the sum of squares of the differences of the location numbers and the numbers assigned to the locations. Repeat this process M times (say 500 times), keeping track of the sums of squares for each repetition. The frequency distribution of the M sums of squares will approximate the sampling distribution of the sample sum of squares for M observed samples of jointly distributed unrelated random variables.

Compare the sum of squares of the rank differences in data of your own choosing and the computer generated sums of squares of rank differences. Choose a moderate sample size (N) for your problem (30 to 40 observations).

Hint: In order to assure that each of the N locations are filled with a unique number, and to keep from having to select the last few numbers out of all N possibilities, continually decrease the set of numbers from which the selection is made and continually modify the scaling factor of the random number generator. (If there are N-2 numbers already assigned, the probability of selecting, by way of the random number generator, one of the two remaining values is $2/N$, which could be a very small probability, implying a very long run of attempts before selecting one of the remaining numbers). If there are k numbers left to be assigned, generate a random number between 1 and k. Keep the numbers still unassigned in the first k locations of an array and use the random number (between 1 and k) as the index to the location of the number assigned.

PROJECT 14. QUEUING AT SUPERMARKET CHECK-OUT STAND

The Big chain of supermarkets wishes to know how many stands to install in its new branch store. In order to evaluate this question the Big marketing expert requests a computer program that will indicate how many people will turn away from the service of the store for each of the practical numbers of stands. In order to do this he must know how many people in each check-out line an incoming customer will tolerate before the customer turns on his heels and leaves the Big supermarket, heading for Super supermarket. The expert must also estimate how long it will take to service a customer once he is being serviced at the stand and how long a customer is in the store before he enters a check-out line.

The probability that a customer will arrive at the store in a given interval of time is p. Only one customer arrives in a given interval of time. Once a customer arrives he will enter the store if there are no more than three other customers in line to be serviced at the stand. If there is more than one stand the customer will enter the store if any stand has fewer than three customers waiting. The number of customers in the store but not in the queues of the stands does not influence the behavior of the potential customer. The time a customer will spend in the store before entering a check-out stand queue is a random variable having an exponential distribution with expectation equal to 5 time intervals. The time it takes to service a customer at the check-out stand is a random variable distributed exponentially with an expectation equal to the time the customer spends in the store prior to entering the queue. A customer will always enter the shortest queue or if several are equally short he will enter the first he comes to. If any stand is empty (no customer being serviced, no queue), it is chosen in preference to a busy stand. Customers do not change queues. All stands are attended at all times.

Two parameters in this problem are permitted to take on different values. The first has to do with the location of the new market. The second has to do with the number of stands the market will have. The location of the market will determine the frequency with which customers will attempt to enter the market. If the market is in a place highly accessible to a large population, the probability p that a customer will attempt to enter the market in a given time interval will be close to 1.0. On the other hand if the market is not easily accessible to a large population of potential customers the probability p will be small. The number, k, of check-out stands in the market is determined at the option of the marketing expert. Each stand costs a given amount of money to maintain. Hence, the number of stands should be limited by the amount of business that will pass through the stands. The profit from X customers per unit of time, on the average, is sufficient to cover the cost of operating a stand. Hence, if more than X customers per unit of time, on the average, are lost because of the length of queues at the stands then an additional stand (or more) is called for.

Write a computer program that will evaluate the number of customers lost over a period of 500 units of time for a selection of values p and k. The resulting table of X (number of customers divided by 500) as a function of p and k permits the marketing expert to evaluate the number of stands required to serve as many customers as possible with no more than a profitable number of check-out stands.

Hint: Let an overall loop, in which all of the details of incoming customers, customers being checked out, customers entering queues, etc. are done, be the unit of time—once through the loop represents one unit of time. Be sure to keep track of all customers at all times.

If X is a value from a uniformly distributed random variable on the unit interval and if E is the expectation of an exponentially distributed random variable, then

```
Y = -E*LOG(X)
```

gives a value from that exponentially distributed variable.

PROJECT 15. ELECTION PREDICTION

A team of sociologists and political scientists is engaged by the Statewide Radio Network to work out a computer program which will analyze the incoming returns in an upcoming election. They are to make predictions on election night, after the polls close, on a continually updated basis, as to who will win the office of governor of the state. The reports of the vote come from the separate precincts of the state at random.

In order to use the sociological and political information the team has, they do not base the prediction on a simple proportion of the votes returned. Rather, the state is subdivided into sociopolitical units. Each precinct is placed into one of these subdivisions. Imagine that there are six classes of precincts. In a given class the precincts should all vote in about the same way if the sociopolitical theory is correct. Hence, if the first reporting precinct in a class of precincts votes 40 percent for candidate A and 60 percent for candidate B, all of the precincts in that class enter the momentary prediction with a 40-60 split of the vote between A and B. On receiving a report from the second precinct in a class, a new prediction is made for that class of precincts. The new prediction is made by determining the proportion of votes for A and B for all of the votes reported in the class of precinct involved. The actual prediction is in terms of the number of votes expected in the entire election. Since this must at first be estimated by the scientific team the estimate should be revised as the voting proceeds. The total number of registered voters in each precinct is recorded and the proportion expected to vote is estimated. The proportion estimated before any vote counts are reported can be replaced with the proportion of voters out of possible voters in precincts reporting. Thus, with each precinct report the proportion of eligible persons actually casting a ballot can be updated to give an updated estimate of the overall number of votes in the election. The prediction at each step of the sequence is based on the updated estimate of the overall number of votes.

For each precinct type, at each step of the sequence, a prediction of the number of votes for A and the number of votes for

B can be generated by calculating the updated proportion of votes cast for A and for B and the updated predictions of votes to be cast in total for the precinct type. The total vote for A and the total vote for B is given by summing these totals for the precinct types.

Write a program that gives a new prediction every time a precinct reports. Provide a way for the program to read the data regarding the original proportion of voters expected to vote, the list of precincts, the class of precinct in which each precinct belongs, and the number of eligible voters in each precinct. Read the precinct results from cards separate from the preliminary data. Select the precincts for reporting one at a time by generating random numbers in order to simulate the random reporting of the precincts.

Devise data of interest as a part of the project. Let the number of precincts in each of the six classes be different and the number of registered voters in each precinct be different. Select "reported" votes to reflect partial (good but not overwhelming) accuracy of the notion that all precincts in a class will vote the same way. Also let the proportion voting of those eligible vary from precinct to precinct.

PROJECT 16. NERVE NETWORK SIMULATION

An exciting game played by many biologically oriented behavioral scientists is that of constructing finite models of neural networks that operate on theoretically interesting principles. The basic method of nerve network simulation is to imagine a storage location in a computer as a neural cell and an associated collection of storage locations as properties of the cell. For each cell there are such properties as the threshold of the cell, the amount of excitation arriving at a given moment, the "names" of cells to which the cell sends excitations when it fires, the names of cells which send to it an excitation when they fire, etc.

As a specific example of such a network imagine a double system of elements that is designed to detect edges of figures in fields of illumination (e.g., such as might be found in the eye). The system consists of a 50 by 50 rectangular grid of elements in interacting pairs. The pairs are stacked with connections directly between the upper and lower elements in the pair and between the upper element in a pair and all lower elements in the adjacent pairs. Looking at a cross section of the grid, we would see a picture similar to that of Figure III.5*a*. A given upper member sends connectors to the lower members in the surrounding grid. From above, the connections from the upper level to the lower level would appear to be a three by three array of elements with connectors going from the central upper element to the lower outside elements as shown in Figure III.5*b*.

If a stimulus intensity at one of the upper level elements is great enough, the element sends an excitatory impulse to the element directly below it in the lower level by way of the direct connector. At the same time the stimulated upper ele-

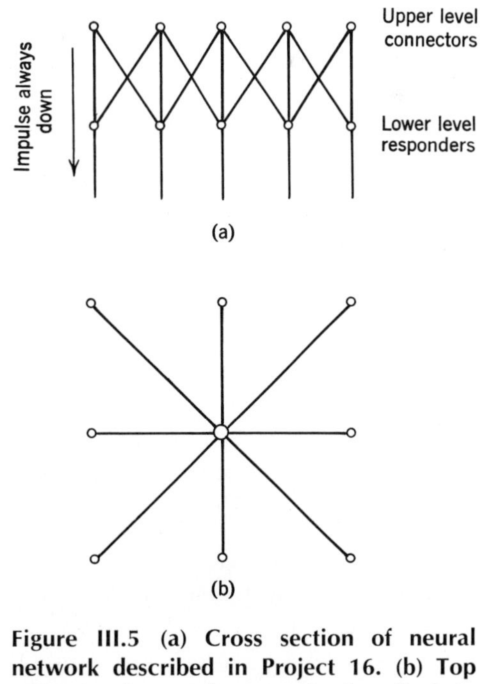

Figure III.5 (a) Cross section of neural network described in Project 16. (b) Top "view" of neural network described in Project 16.

ment sends an inhibitory impulse to all of the adjacent elements in the lower level. The strength of the inhibitory impulse is not enough to prevent reaction from the lower element unless six or more inhibitory impulses are received at the same time. A single excitatory impulse will fire the lower level element unless six or more inhibitory impulses are received at the same time.

Imagine projecting onto the upper surface of this grid a figure on a background. The figure is made by a field of stimulus intensity above the threshold of the upper elements. The neural model, if it works, should respond with activity of the responder fibres along the contour formed by the edge of the figure on the background.

Write a computer program that simulates this system. Use a 50 by 50 array of zeros and ones to represent the stimulus intensity on the 50 by 50 grid of upper elements. A zero represents a background intensity and a one represents a figure intensity. Write the program so that any arbitrary figure-background can be input to the model. Output the contour defined by the activation of the responder fibres. Test the "contour accuity" of the model with some well chosen test patterns.

PROJECT 17. MUSIC COMPOSER

A number of attempts have been made to use the digital computer to "compose" music. A number of schemes have been employed, some of them quite complex. Actual composers, e.g., Bach, have been emulated by composing music according to principles taken from the composer's own music and building these principles into a computer program. Where the principles leave room for choice among musical elements the programs use a random device to make the choice.

A relatively simple scheme for composition involves the generation of random numbers to select notes. Just any sequence of random numbers does not suffice—the notes are screened by a set of rules governing the "style" of the composition. For example, some rules might be concerned with the intervals between two successive notes. Other rules might impose constraints on the length of the sequence of notes, etc.

Write a program to generate sequences or phrases of eight notes each, subject to the rules given below. Generate random digits between 1 and 15 inclusive (integers), allowing a range of two octaves on the musical scale. In the key of C, for example, the numbers would correspond to notes in the following manner:

Number	*Note*
1	C (octave below middle C)
2	D
3	E
4	F
5	G
6	A
7	B
8	C (middle C)
9	D
10	E
11	F
12	G
13	A
14	B
15	C (octave above middle C)

Generate sequences of eight notes subject to the following constraints:

1. The first note of the sequence must be 8 (middle C).
2. The last note must be either an 8, a 1, or a 15, thus ending the phrase on the same note as it was begun, with the possibility of an octave difference.
3. The seventh note must be either a 5 or a 12. This requirement will give a rudimentary cadence to end the phrase.
4. The remaining notes in the phrase must not be in uniformly ascending or descending order. For example, the phrase 8, 9, 10, 11, 12, 13, 14, 15 is not allowed. However, any particular pair of notes may be adjacent, within the rules given below.
5. The same note cannot appear more than three times in sequence.

6. The distance between two adjacent notes cannot be greater than an octave—that is the difference between two adjacent notes must be less than 8.

A number of variations and elaborations of this project are possible. New rules can be added or existing rules removed. The phrase length can be extended, perhaps 16 is the best longer length. Additional notes may be used. The scale may be expanded to include another octave or chromatics (half steps between the scale notes). Rhythmic variation may be introduced. A simple way of introducing rhythmic variation is to let two numbers stand for each note, one number representing the scale note and the other number representing duration (say a number between 1 and 4). A set of rules may be developed for duration as well as for scale (e.g, the first and last notes must be of duration 4, the next to last of duration 2, etc.).

PROJECT 18. CONTAGION MODEL FOR RUMOR PROPAGATION

The propagation of rumors and the spread of contagious infection appear to have a good deal in common. A contagious disease is spread by contact between individuals in a population. The type of contact required may be specific to the particular disease and the likelihood of infection will be a function of the properties of the person coming into contact with the infected person. Other properties will influence the spread of the disease, e.g., the size of the population, the length of the incubation period for the disease, and the activity of the infected persons in the population. Imagine that the disease is a rumor and that the spread or propagation of rumors follows laws similar to those of disease propagation.

Write a program to serve as a model of the propagation of rumors along the lines of the disease propagation process just described. Establish a population of N individuals, one of whom initiates a rumor by passing it on to K_1 individuals. Each of the K_1 individuals passes the rumor to K_2 individuals who in turn pass it to K_3 individuals, and so on for P cycles, the last cycle of which the K_P individuals carrying the rumor pass it to K_{P+1} individuals in the population. When an individual comes in contact with a rumor-carrying person he is either infected or not. Whether or not the contacted person is infected is of no importance to the rumor carrier, the contacted person is still one of the K individuals to whom the rumor was passed. Whether or not the contacted person is infected is a function of a parameter value assigned to that person: a random number (uniform distribution) in the range of (0,1) is generated at the time of contact and if the number is larger than the parameter the person is infected. Once a person is infected, i.e., becomes a rumor carrier, he can forget the rumor before infecting his alloted K other individuals. The forgetting parameter is a personal characteristic of each of the persons in the population. After becoming a carrier, a person forgets or does not forget the rumor depending on a random number, uniform distribution on (0,1), generated after the infection. If the number is larger than a parameter value associated with the person, the person forgets the rumor. If an infected person does not forget he will transmit the rumor with a given probability to each of the persons he contacts. This last procedure operates in the following way: each person in the population has a parameter indicating how many persons he is likely to contact and a probability that he will transmit the rumor (when he is a carrier) to the person contacted. The actual number of persons to whom a carrier will transmit the rumor is determined by generating a random number from a binomial distribution with the probability of transmission serving as the probability of success and the number of persons contacted as the number of trials. Once the number of individuals to whom the rumor will be transmitted is determined, the specific individuals are selected at random (equal probabilities) from the population and the rumor is transmitted to each of them.

The parameters that are defined for each individual in the population are (1) a resistance parameter, indicating the probability that the individual will be infected with the rumor on transmission to him from a carrier; (2) a forgetting parameter, indicating the probability that the infected individual will forget the rumor before he transmits it to others in the population; (3) an activity parameter, indicating how many persons the carrier is likely to meet; and (4) a transmission parameter, the probability that the carrier will transmit the rumor to a person contacted.

The parameters defined for each individual in the population will depend on the population, the circumstances of the rumor, and other circumstances not explicitly represented in the model. The program should be written so that the parameters can be read from data cards or so that the parameters can be generated by the program. If they are generated by the program they might be somewhat like the following: (1) resistance parameter, a random variable X within the range (0,1) with a density function specified by a straight line function having a value of 2 at $X = 0$, and a value of 0 at $X = 1$; (2) forgetting parameter, a random variable with a uniform distribution with range (.25,.5); (3) activity parameter, a random variable with an integer value-set ranging over (1, $N/20$) and an approximately normal distribution over that range with an expectation equal to

$$(N/20 - 1)/2$$

and a standard deviation equal to one fifth the magnitude of the expectation; (4) transmission parameter, a random variable uniformly distributed on the range (p,q) where p and q are input to the program, $p \geq 0$ and $q \leq 1.0$.

The rumor is substantiated if it reaches the person starting it. The rumor is enhanced in credibility by 1 degree for each time an infected person hears it after the first time.

The program should keep track of the number of persons infected at each of the P cycles and the number of persons for whom the rumor has degree 1 of credibility (hearing it twice), degree 2 of credibility (hearing it three times), ..., degree P-1 (hearing it on each cycle). Assume that a reinfection operates just like an initial infection and that the reinfected person transmits the rumor under control of the same parameters as in the first infection, etc. Keep track of the substantiation of the rumor, i.e., the cycle numbers on which the originator of the rumor hears it from other members of the population. Run the program with other assortments of parameter values.

PART II

FORTRAN IV PROGRAMMING

CHAPTER 4 FORTRAN IV: PRELIMINARY TO FORTRAN

Fortran is a language for writing digital computer programs. As such, it has a vocabulary and a syntax, and, in some sense, semantics. In a manner similar to natural languages, Fortran permits the expression of a wide variety of concepts. The concepts for which Fortran was designed are the concepts of mathematical and arithmetic analysis. However, many other concepts can be expressed in the language, although perhaps with less elegance and simplicity than we might wish. The abstract nature of mathematics and arithmetic permit an interpretation of numerical results as the nonnumerical results of symbolic manipulations.

Fortran has evolved to the present language, Fortran IV, over a number of years involving several convolutions of change and compromise. The features of the current language are the result of a history of use and change in the language. Some of the features of the language are archaic, retained because of inertia, while others are conventions built into the language without a clear practical purpose. As is true with natural languages, the user of Fortran takes what is there, for better or worse, makes the best use of it that he can, and attempts to find ways to make clear and efficient use of the language to express his concepts. Often the expressions will involve circumlocutions and approximations because the language is not expressly designed for the purpose to which it is being put. However, we have found Fortran to be a flexible and useful tool for expressing complicated nonnumerical and nonmathematical ideas that have some importance in behavioral science. Fortran is superb as a language for expressing statistical and data analysis concepts. Fortran is adaptable and capable in expressing concepts concerning behavioral theory and behavioral process.

Fortran is not the "native" or "natural" language of the digital computer. Rather, Fortran is a language that can be translated into a language that can be followed step-by-step by a digital computer. All computers have their own "machine language" comprised of instructions that the computer can execute. Machine language instructions vary from machine to machine. However, most modern digital computers have been programmed to translate Fortran into machine language. Such a program is called a compiler, specifically a Fortran compiler (there are other languages and compilers). When a Fortran program is punched onto cards it can be treated as data for the Fortran compiler, i.e., read by the compiler and translated into machine instructions. When the Fortran program is compiled into machine instructions it can be executed by the computer—it has become a set of machine instructions to be executed by the computer.

This entire second section of the book is devoted to a presentation of the vocabulary and syntax of the Fortran language. In the context of this presentation a good deal of the semantic content of statements in the Fortran language is developed and discussed. Examples are used to illustrate some of the semantic content and use of the vocabulary and syntax in the expression of the semantic content.

When a Fortran program is written, several steps are usually followed. The first step is a detailed consideration of the problem to be solved, the concept to be expressed, and a determination of correct and efficient computation procedures implied by that problem. Second, the program is designed. This step usually involves an outline or chart of the steps that the computer is to go through in solving the problem. This outline is sometimes called a "flow chart" because it is usually a chart indicating how the program is to flow to completion. The third step is composing the program, generally called coding the program—the translation of the flow chart into statements in the Fortran language. The fourth step is compilation or translation of the program into machine instructions by the Fortran compiler. The fifth step is "debugging" the program, i.e., correcting errors made by the programmer, both syntax and logical errors.

The Fortran compiler is difficult to communicate with. The compiler interprets each statement literally, including errors, and the programmer is forced into being very precise; the slightest coding error must be eliminated. The compiler aids in the early stages of checking the program by indicating the occurrence of certain kinds of errors, usually in the vocabulary and syntax. However, before a program is completely debugged, its computational accuracy must be checked. Does the program do what it should? Are the answers within the tolerable range of accuracy? If the program is designed to work with data provided by the user, a desirable practice is to submit illustrative data (with known results) to be analyzed in testing the program. The analysis should be inspected for accuracy at several stages in the computation, not only at the final result. The computer will execute a syntactically correct program even if the program does not do the job for which it was designed.

FLOW CHARTING

A variety of notational conventions have been proposed for flow charting. The material presented in this book does not require detailed flow charting. Therefore, we have chosen a simple and easily followed set of symbols. The symbols are consistent with the American Standards Association standards for flow-chart notation (see Communications of the Association for Computing Machinery, 1963, *6*, 601–604). After the reader has gained some experience in writing programs, it may be to his advantage to consult the ASA standards and adopt the more complete standard system of flow charting.

A flow chart is a collection of symbols connected by lines to indicate the operation of the program. The symbols indicate certain kinds of operations or computer instructions. Some of the symbols will be defined here, others are introduced as they are needed.

A rectangular box indicates an arithmetic operation. Thus, if at a certain point in the program, it is desired to add A to B, the operation would appear on the flow chart as

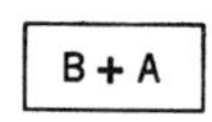

The symbol used to designate an input operation, such as reading a card has the appearance of a card. For example, the operation of reading a card that was to contain a number called M would be symbolized as

A diamond-shaped symbol indicates a point in the program from which there may be more than one way of proceeding depending upon whether the "question" asked inside the diamond is true or false; or whether some quantity is greater than, less than, or equal to zero. If alternative computations are to be made depending upon the relationship between I and N, the choice is indicated on the flow chart in one of the two forms shown.

The choice of the form depends upon the logic of the program.

A symbol looking like a torn-off piece of output paper is used to indicate printed output. To indicate the printing of results, A, B, and C, the symbol would be

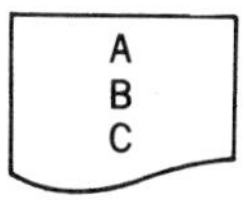

Finally, the end of a program is symbolized by an oval containing the word STOP.

With this much symbolic notation in hand, we can look at an example of a program written in Fortran. In doing so, we illustrate the first three steps in programming—analysis, design, and coding.

AN EXAMPLE FORTRAN PROGRAM

To illustrate the development of a Fortran program from the very beginning, we take a comparatively simple computational problem—the correlation coefficient for two jointly observed variables, *X* and *Y*.

The problem to be solved is simple. An experiment has led to the observation of variables *X* and *Y* for a group of *N* subjects. The question is whether the variables are correlated in the sample of observations. The data assume the following general form:

Subject	X	Y
1	15	25
2	9	18
·	·	·
·	·	·
·	·	·
i	X_i	Y_i
·	·	·
·	·	·
·	·	·
N	16	19

Each of *N* subjects has a score on each of the two variables.

A number of computational formulas

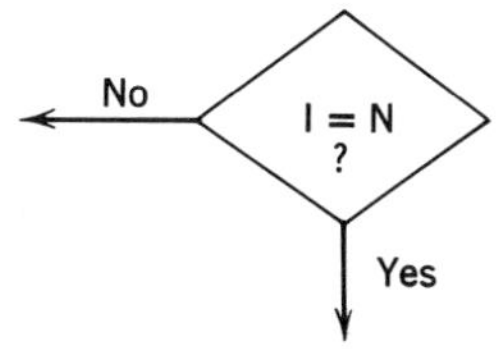

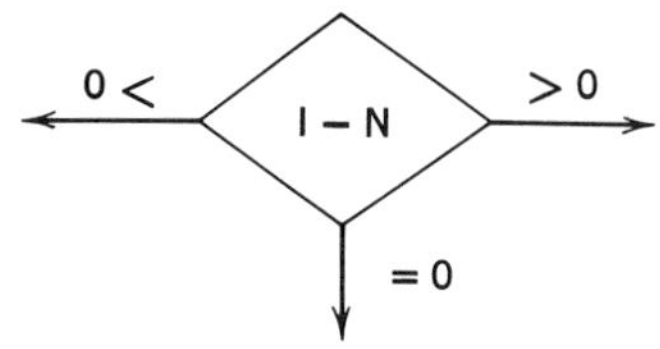

for the correlation coefficient are well known to behavioral scientists. The most familiar calculational form is

$$r = \frac{N\Sigma XY - (\Sigma X)(\Sigma Y)}{\sqrt{[N\Sigma X^2 - (\Sigma X)^2]\,[N\Sigma Y^2 - (\Sigma Y)^2]}}$$

which is adequate for use on a desk calculator. However, we cannot always use the computer like a calculator. Although a routine may be very satisfactory in *hand* calculation, it may lead to error in computer analysis. One source of error is the manner in which the magnitude of the difference of two very large numbers is obtained in the computer. The computer, under certain circumstances can cause the difference to have fewer significant digits than might be needed. For example, if the values $N\Sigma XY$ and (ΣX) (ΣY) are very nearly the same and very large, then the difference between the two values will be in the rightmost digits of the numbers. If the values involved are large enough, the difference might be represented in only a very gross manner (e.g., the value 119563 may be represented by 119500). The reason for this will become apparent later.

Considering how numbers are represented leads to the suggestion that the program should be constructed along some other lines. There is less danger in misrepresenting the difference of relatively small numbers and hence there is a distinct advantage to work with the formula

$$r = \frac{\Sigma(X - \overline{X})(Y - \overline{Y})}{\sqrt{\Sigma(X - \overline{X})^2 \, \Sigma(Y - \overline{Y})^2}}$$

Before the summations in this formula can be made, the mean values for the variables X and Y must be obtained. Therefore, the calculation itself is in two steps, the first to obtain the means of the variables X and Y, and the second to obtain the sums of deviations from the means, etc.

Before developing a flow chart, a few other questions must be considered. First, what are the data needed in order to complete the calculation? In this problem the answer is quite simple—the number of pairs of observations and the pairs of observations themselves. Second, how shall the data be read into the computer? Perhaps the simplest way of doing this is to let each observational unit occupy a separate card and to read the data "subjectwise." Other ways can be devised without any inherent difficulty or without involving any inherent disadvantage, e.g., all of the X values on one set of cards, value after value, and all of the Y values on another set of cards. The "subjectwise" representation of the data for the correlation problem permits a simple approach to the reading of the data in the program. The specification of how the data are to be arranged is the responsibility of the programmer. We must provide some mechanism whereby the program is informed of the number of subjects (i.e., the number of cards to be read). If the program is to be used only once for a specific set of data, the number of subjects can be defined directly in the program itself. However, if the program is to be used with different sets of data where N might vary from data set to data set, the program can be written to read N first and then proceed to read the N pairs of values. Finally, the plan of the program should include considerations of the desired output. In our example we will print the value of N and the two means as well as the correlation coefficient calculated.

Some notational characteristics of Fortran IV must be introduced before proceeding with the flow charting and coding of the program. Because the keypunch cannot represent subscripts or superscripts, arithmetic and logical operations in Fortran are written in a straight line notation, character after character without regard to vertical displacement. For example, in ordinary algebraic notation the score of subject 5 on the X variable would be designated X_5, or in general, for the ith subject X_i. In Fortran notation these designations are X(5) and X(I) respectively. Furthermore, all operations like addition, squaring, multiplying, etc., are represented by specific symbols. In ordinary algebraic notation the square of the number X may be designated by X^2. Since we are restricted to straight line representation, the vertical location of the 2 in X^2 cannot be used to imply the operation of squaring. Fortran uses the arbitrary convention of a double asterisk, **, as the symbol for "raise to some power" with the power specified after the **, e.g., X**2 stands for X^2. Ordinary algebraic notation permits certain implicit operations, as in multiplication of two terms, e.g., $(X - A)(Y - B)$ is taken to mean the product of the two values defined inside the parentheses. Fortran requires explicit representation of all operations, e.g., multiplication is indicated by a single asterisk and the product of the deviation terms is expressed (X − A)*(Y − B). Finally, the equal sign, =, has a different meaning in Fortran. The contents of locations named by the left-hand portion of a statement with = in it are replaced by the value (or the result of the operation) indicated on the right side of the =. For example, the statement I = 1 means to replace the present value of I with the value 1. The statement I = I + 1, which is not correct in algebra, means to replace the current value of I with that value plus 1.

We are now ready to proceed to develop a flow chart of the problem. Although the design of the program may be clear with respect to the input and output and all of the calculational steps, the organization of these aspects becomes more specific and clear with formal flow charting. The finished flow chart of the correlation program is shown in Figure IV.1.

The first step in the program is to determine the number of observations involved in a particular use of the program, i.e., read the value of N. Next, some variables are set to zero. There follows the first loop of the program, the loop to read the X and Y values and to find the sums of observations of X and of Y. The counter of the loop, I, is set to 1 before the first cycle through the loop. The means are calculated when the read loop has completed N turns. The second loop of the program begins with a reinitialization of the index I (another index, e.g., J, K, ICOUNT, etc. could have been used). The loop is executed N times and then the correlation is calculated from the sums found by execution of the loop. Finally, four values, N, XBAR, YBAR, and COR are printed. The sums, along with the raw data, could have been printed as well.

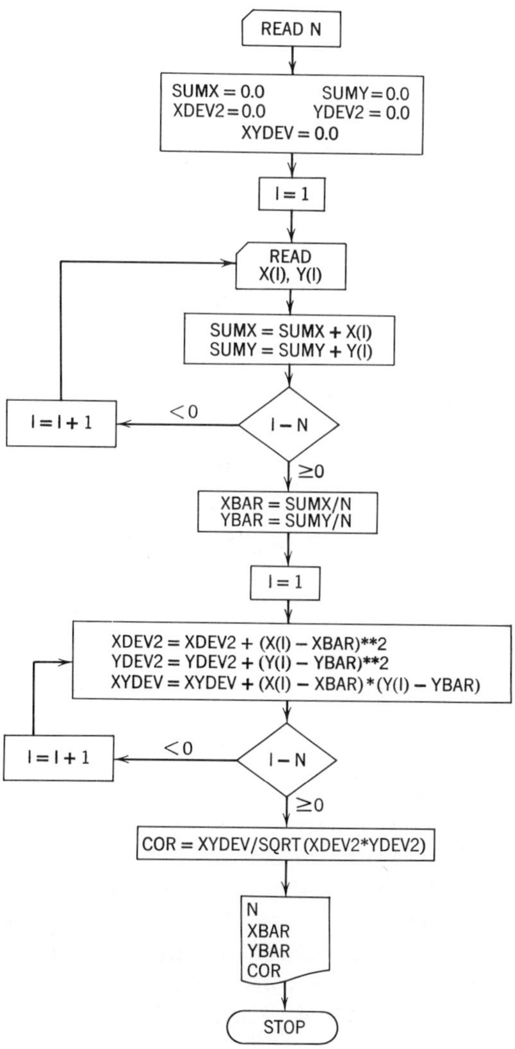

Figure IV.1 Flow chart for simple correlation program, CORDEM.

A program corresponding to this flow chart is listed in Figure IV.2. The construction of this program is described here without going into the details. The various statements will become clear as we proceed to develop the language. Cards (program lines) containing a C in the first column are taken simply as comments by the programmer in the Fortran source program—they do not appear in the compiled (machine language) program. The first actual program statement specifies information needed by the program to set aside storage locations for the N observations on X and Y. After reading the value of N (using the information in statement number 1 to specify the form in which N is to appear on a data card) an equivalent form of the value N is stored as XN. N and XN are the same value but they are represented internally in the computer in different modes. For some purposes N is used and for others, XN. This distinction is explained in detail in the next chapter.

KINDS OF FORTRAN IV STATEMENTS

The example program illustrates five of the six basic varieties of statements in the Fortran programming language: arithmetic, control, declaration, input/output, and function or subprogram. The example does not include a "logical" operation statement. These six types of statements make up the subject matter of the six chapters to follow—the heart of the Fortran programming language. The

```
CCORDEM
CCORDEM         EXAMPLE PROGRAM                                              001
C      COMMENTS ARE ALWAYS USEFUL **** SEQUENCE NUMBERS ON                   002
C               IN COLUMNS 73-80 ARE ALSO USEFUL IN KEEPING                  003
C               THE PROGRAM DECK IN ORDER AND IN IDENTIFYING                 004
C               SPECIFIC STATEMENTS IN THE DECK ****                         005
C               CARDS WITH A C IN COLUMN 1 ARE TAKEN SIMPLY                  006
C               AS COMMENTS IN THE FORTRAN SOURCE PROGRAM --                 007
C               THE DO NOT APPEAR IN THE OBJECT PROGRAM.                     008
C                                                                            009
C               STATEMENT NUMBERS ARE IN COLUMNS 1-5                         010
      DIMENSION X(500),Y(500)                                                011
CFIRST FIND OUT HOW BIG THE SAMPLE IS AND FLOAT N                            013
      READ(5,1)N                                                             014
    1 FORMAT(I3)                                                             015
      XN=N                                                                   012
CNOW SET SOME VARIABLES TO ZERO                                              016
      SUMX=0.0                                                               017
      SUMY=0.0                                                               018
      XDEV2=0.0                                                              019
      YDEV2=0.0                                                              020
      XYDEV=0.0                                                              021
CLOOP THROUGH SUMMING X AND Y, READING ON THE WAY,                           022
      I=1                                                                    023
  100 READ(5,2)X(I),Y(I)                                                     024
    2 FORMAT(2F6.3)                                                          025
      SUMX=SUMX+X(I)                                                         026
      SUMY=SUMY+Y(I)                                                         027
      IF(I-N)3,4,4                                                           028
    3 I=I+1                                                                  029
      GO TO 100                                                              030
CTHE IF STATEMENT JUST ABOVE CAUSES STATEMENT 3 TO BE                        031
C     EXECUTED IF I-N IS LESS THAN ZERO AND STATEMENT                        032
C     4 TO BE CALCULATED IF I-N IS ZERO OR GREATER                           033
    4 XBAR=SUMX/XN                                                           033
      YBAR=SUMY/XN                                                           034
CNOW WE WILL LOOP THROUGH THE SUMS OF SQUARED DEVIATIONS                     035
C     AND PRODUCTS OF DEVIATIONS--AND FIND COR                               036
      I=1                                                                    037
  444 XDEV2=XDEV2+(X(I)-XBAR)**2                                             038
      YDEV2=YDEV2+(Y(I)-YBAR)**2                                             039
      XYDEV=XYDEV+(X(I)-XBAR)*(Y(I)-YBAR)                                    040
      IF(I-N)5,6,6                                                           041
    5 I=I+1                                                                  042
      GO TO 444                                                              043
    6 COR=XYDEV/SQRT(XDEV2*YDEV2)                                            044
CSEVERAL MATHEMATICAL EVALUATIONS LIKE THE SQUARE                            045
C     ROOT OF A VALUE, AS IN SQRT(VALUE), CAN BE                             046
C     DONE BY SO CALLED FUNCTION STATEMENTS.                                 047
CNOW TO PRINT THE DESIRED RESULTS                                            048
      STOP                                                                   051
      END                                                                    052
```

Figure IV.2 Program listing for CORDEM.

order of these chapters, and the order of presentation within each of the chapters is designed to facilitate the student's rapid entry into the practical aspects of actually writing programs and working with them to check them out.

Arithmetic Statements. Arithmetic statements are expressions involving operations of the usual arithmetic sort; add, subtract, multiply, divide, and exponentiate. Arithmetic statements cause computations to be carried out and values to be stored at specified locations when the compiled program is executed. For example, the statement I = 1 in the correlation program of this chapter causes the value 1 to be stored at the location in primary storage called I by the compiled program. Likewise, the statement

SUMX = SUMX + X(I)

causes the computer to add SUMX and

X(I) and to store the sum in the location called SUMX. The Fortran programmer does not need to be concerned about what the location is or how it is named by the compiler.

Control Statement. Control statements govern the flow of execution of the program in the computer. Normally, the program executes one statement after another in a linear fashion. One of the simplest of control statements is the GO TO statement which directs the program to execute the statement with the number specified in the GO TO statement rather than the next statement. For example,

GO TO 4

causes the statement numbered 4 in the Fortran program to be executed following the GO TO. More subtle and complex control statements extend the programmer's control over the behavior of the computer (the programmer "controls" the computer at the time he writes the program). For example, the statement

IF(I−N) 3, 4, 4

in the correlation program example provides for alternative courses of action by the computer. The programmer determines what the alternative states of the difference I − N mean to the calculation and writes the control statement to accord with this meaning.

Declaration Statement. Declarations generally do not cause any action to take place in the execution of a program. Rather, they convey information to the compiler regarding the structure of the program, of the data, and of certain parts of the program (such as constants). For example, the statement

DIMENSION X(500)

causes 500 locations to be set aside and named X(1), X(2), . . ., X(500).

Input and Output Statements. The transfer of information into the machine and out of the machine are performed by input and output (I/O) statements. The statement

READ 3, N

causes the computer to read a card containing the value of a variable called N in the program. The value is stored by the READ in location N. Similarly,

PRINT 4, N, XBAR, YBAR, COR

causes the values from the named locations to be printed on paper as output from the program. Two chapters in this section of the book are devoted to I/O statements and operations. Perhaps this is testament to the difficulty of the subject. The complexity is somewhat alleviated by taking the topic in two doses. The first dose is simple and straightforward. The second dose is much more palatable after having had the first dose and the other material between the two chapters.

Function or Subprogram. It is not precisely correct to call functions or subprograms a type of Fortran statement. However, functions and subprograms are ways of using collections of Fortran statements as though they were simple Fortran statements with properties chosen at the convenience of the user. These statements (or programming segments) permit the programmer to break his program up into smaller segments or call upon already available subprograms. For example, the following part of a Fortran statement causes the computer to calculate the square root of the quantity X:

SQRT(X)

A Fortran statement involving the SQRT statement is "replaced" in the compiled program by code designed to calculate the square root. This replacement is done by the compiler and the actual code is of no concern to the programmer. A number of so-called functions are a part of the Fortran language. In addition, the programmer can define his own functions and break up his program in any way that he wishes, within very broad rules.

Logical Statement. Logical statements

are similar to arithmetic statements in that they operate on the values of variables and constants with named locations. The basic difference is that the operations result in one of two possible states, "true" or "false." Imagine that two variables A and B are logical variables, having states of true or false only. An example of a logical statement is the operation .AND. applied to A and B:

(A.AND.B)

This is true only if both A and B are true. Mixtures of logical operations and control statements are provided in Fortran as logical control statements. These are especially useful in nonnumerical operations and in making decisions in a computer program.

KEYPUNCHING FORTRAN STATEMENTS

Fortran statements are punched into standard 80-column cards, each card representing one Fortran statement. The characters that are recognized by the Fortran compiler are the letters A through Z (generally printed in upper case), the 10 digits 0 through 9, and a number of special characters: . , ( ) + − * / = $. Figure I.2 shows all of the allowable characters, together with the patterns of punched holes that represent them. No other characters are allowed, and the use of any other combination of punches in a column will lead to an error indication from the compiler. A blank, no punches in a column, is also a permitted "character" although blanks are ignored under certain circumstances.

Fortran statements may be punched in columns 7–72 of the program cards. Columns 73–80 are used by the programmer for identification. The first five columns are reserved for statement numbers. Any Fortran statement may be given a statement number. Usually, however, only those statements referred to by other statements are assigned statement numbers. Column 6 on a program card is used to indicate continuation of a Fortran statement from the previous card. If a Fortran statement is too long for one card, it may be continued on additional cards (the number of continuation cards permitted differs from machine to machine). If column 6 contains a nonzero punch, the information on that card is interpreted as a continuation of the card before. The Fortran statement itself may begin anywhere in columns 7–72. Spaces in the statement are ignored everywhere except in FORMAT and DATA statements. Figure I.6 shows Fortran cards punched with Fortran statements.

The comment card is a useful device in Fortran programming. These cards may be punched from columns 1 through 80 but *must* contain a C in column 1. When a C is punched in column 1, the contents of the card appear when the Fortran compiler prints out the card-by-card listing of the Fortran program. Comment cards have no other effect. The number of comment cards is, therefore, of no concern in the magnitude of the compiled program. However, the number of notes that can be "attached" permanently to the program listing by way of the comment cards is unlimited. These notes become a valuable aid in keeping track of the development of a program throughout the debugging stage, and in noting the work performed by each segment of the program.

Virtually all of the programs presented in this book are named—e.g., CORDEM, AVER. While this is not always necessary, it is advisable. In the first place, it allows easy reference to a particular program. Second, the executive systems used at some installations require that each program deck be given a "deck name" or a program name. The reader should consult a programming advisor at his computer installation regarding the rules for program and deck names. All program names used in this book will consist of from one to six letters or numbers, the first of which will always be a letter.

The last statement in a Fortran program must be

END

This statement informs the Fortran compiler that it has encountered the physical end of the program. The

STOP

statement marks the logical end of the program. It frequently appears just before the END statement but may appear elsewhere in the program.

An essential definition in digital computing is that of a card field. A field is simply a collection of adjacent columns on a punch card. A field may be of any size from 1 to 80 columns in width. A field may not extend from one card to another. For example, the definition of a 10-column field beginning in column 75 is not allowed, since to complete the field another card is required.

Several kinds of fields have already been defined in discussing the card format for Fortran statements. The letter C appearing in the first column of a Fortran card defines the remaining 79 columns of that card as a comment field, and comment fields are ignored by the Fortran compiler. The standard Fortran program card, like those illustrated in Figure I.6, is divided into four fields. Columns 1 through 5 form a five-column statement number field. Column 6 is a one-column continuation field. The 66-column field made up of columns 7 through 72 is for the actual Fortran statement, and the final field, columns 73–80 is the identification or card number field. This assignment of fields on a Fortran statement card is absolute—the programmer is not free to change it except by placing a C in column 1, which of course defines the entire remainder of the card as a comment field.

When data cards are being considered, on the other hand, the programmer is free to assign fields to data cards. Figure IV.3 illustrates a typical data card containing four numbers. The first value, 10.168, is punched in a 6-column field. The next value, 19, occupies a two-column field, and the third, -.37, appears in a 4-column field. The next field, columns 13–15, is a blank field—that is, it contains no data whatsoever. Nonetheless, it is regarded as a field. The final data value is located in a one-column field in column 16. The remainder of the card, columns 17–80, is regarded as a blank field.

Although the placement of data in fields and the assignment of fields to columns is more or less arbitrary, the Fortran program must contain precise infor-

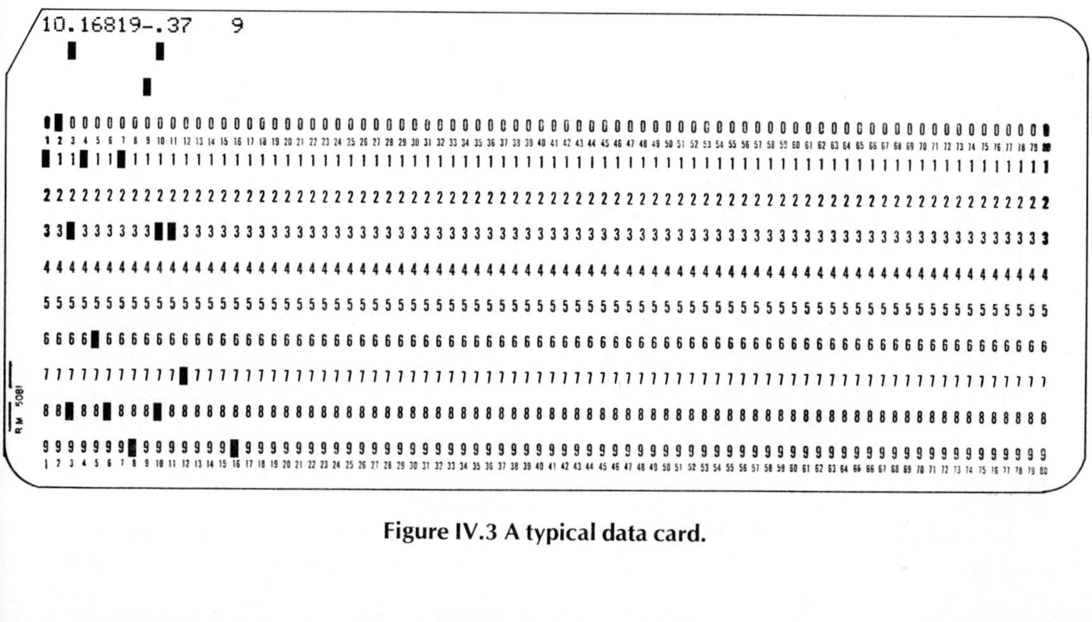

Figure IV.3 A typical data card.

mation about the nature of each field on a card to be read, and what is to be done with the numerical value found in that field. The specification of fields occupies a considerable portion of Chapters 5 and 9, the two I/O chapters.

PROGRAM CHECKING (DEBUGGING)

It is rare for an experienced programmer to write a program without making an error of some sort. It is true that experienced programmers make fewer errors, and probably more sophisticated errors, but they do make mistakes with regularity. Since errors are an ever-present hazard in programming, it is appropriate here that some space be devoted to them.

Errors made in programming fall largely into two categories, syntax and logic. A syntax error is made when a program statement does not obey the rules of the language. For example, omitting a comma where the compiler expects to find one is a syntax error. Such errors are usually simple to locate and simple to correct. In fact, the compiler often provides considerable assistance in locating syntax errors.

A logical error occurs when the programmer instructs the computer to do the wrong thing. When the computer executes a program, it follows the program exactly. A logical error may stem from errors in conceptualizing the problem, in organizing the program or in coding the program.

Detecting Errors. Of the two kinds of error, syntax errors are usually the easiest to locate. Most compilers detect syntax errors and print appropriate comments. The offending Fortran statement is usually printed, along with an error message. For example, the following statement, a faulty FORMAT statement and the corresponding diagnostic might be

```
99 FORMAT 16)
THERE IS NO LEFT PARENTHESIS
AFTER THE WORD FORMAT.
```

When corrected, the FORMAT statement would be

```
99 FORMAT (16)
```

Likewise, the statement

```
DO 100, I = 1, 10
```

might produce the diagnostic message

```
THIS STATEMENT CONTAINS AN
UNNECESSARY PUNCTUATION MARK.
```

When correctly written, the program statement should be

```
DO 100 I = 1, 10
```

Logical errors are often difficult to locate. When located, this correction usually involves more extensive modification to the program. Some kinds of logical errors (and some syntax errors) are discovered when the program refuses to run, or "aborts" by some kind of system termination. Other kinds of logical errors permit the program to run, but produce incorrect answers.

Perfecting a Program. As a first step in perfecting a program, the programmer must face the fact that there *will* be errors, and that they will be programmer errors. The beginning programmer should avoid falling into the trap of assuming the errors detected are due to a machine failure. If a program fails to execute properly, it is almost *never* due to a machine failure. Such failures are rare and should be regarded as the possible cause of program failure only on the advice of the advanced programmers in the computing center.

The programmer should have some plan that he can follow in perfecting his program. This should start in planning the program and in building the flow chart. The flow chart and program plan must accurately reflect the intentions of the programmer. It is usually worthwhile to "play computer" by following the flow chart yourself, using some sample data. In this way, many logical errors can be corrected before the Fortran program is written.

In a program of considerable complexity or length (i.e., longer than about 100

Fortran statements), the programmer should consider writing the program in segments. In Chapter 10 the techniques of segmenting (subroutines and functions) are discussed in detail. For the time being, the reader should be aware that programs can be written as collections of discrete packages called subroutines. Each subroutine can be checked out individually, thus saving effort. Checking parts of a program separately does not guarantee that the complete program will operate correctly when the parts are put together, but it is a convenient technique.

Logical errors are of two general types. One of these is the result of an incorrect design of the program. The other kind of logical error results from violating rules of computer usage, e.g., calculations producing numbers that are too large or too small and reading numbers incorrectly. Logical errors usually become evident when the program is executed and incorrect answers are produced. Logical errors generally can be located by working through the program and making a logical analysis of its operation.

In the next several chapters, debugging and checking programs are discussed in more detail. In particular, when Fortran statements are presented, the common kinds of syntax errors that are made in writing these statements are pointed out with illustrative error messages. Three Fortran compilers are used as sources of error messages—the IBM System 360 Disk and Tape Monitor System, the Control Data 6000 Series Monitor System, and the UNIVAC 1107 Fortran Monitor System. No attempt is made to list all possible kinds of errors nor to list all error messages. Methods of using the computer as an aid in discovering the nature and location of logical errors are introduced at several places in the following chapters.

EXERCISES

As a review and self-test, the student is advised to answer the following questions and work the following problems and check his answers by referring back to the appropriate sections of the chapter.

1. From the list below, pick the appropriate kind of operation symbolized by each of the flow chart symbols shown.

Operations

Choice point
Output
Input
Arithmetic
End of program

Symbols

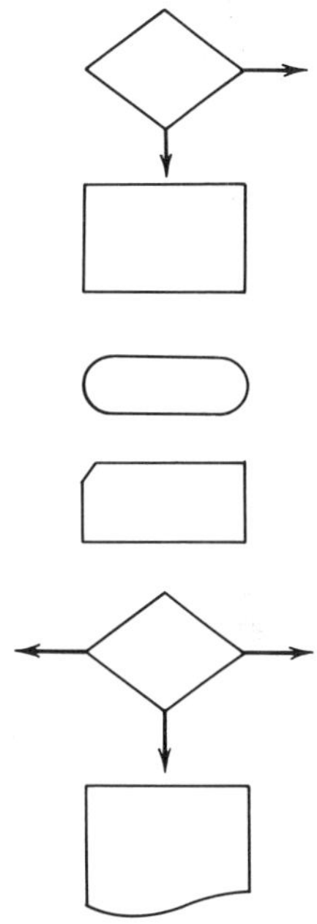

2. In light of the considerations in the text regarding the differences in magnitude of large numbers, which of the following two formulas for the standard deviation is *least likely* to give erroneous answers on the computer?

$$s = \frac{\Sigma X^2}{N} - \bar{X}^2$$

$$s = \frac{\Sigma\,(X - \bar{X})^2}{N^2}$$

3. Each of the following Fortran cards is incorrectly "punched." Indicate why, and correct the card where possible.

(a)
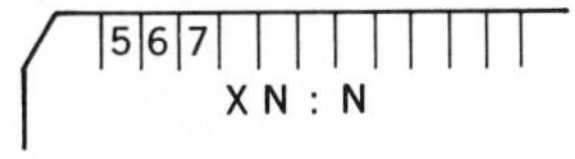

(b)
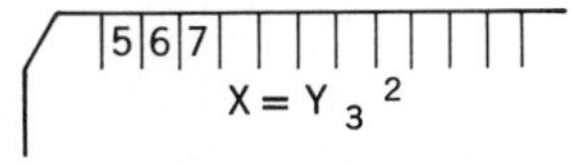

(c)
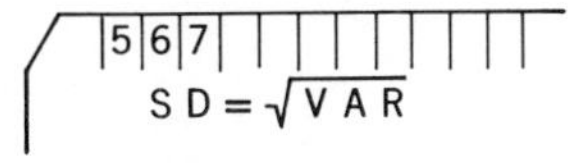

(d)

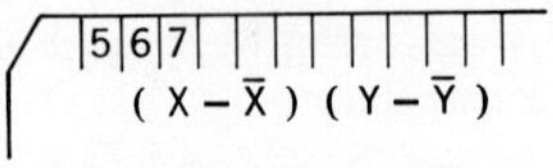

(e)

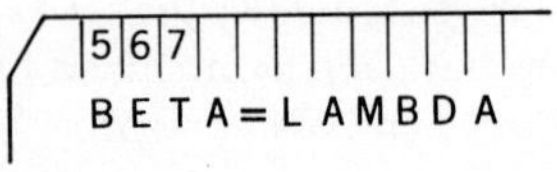

4. Define the following terms
   (a) Fortran
   (b) Compiler
   (c) Flow chart
   (d) Field
   (e) Syntax error
5. What are the Fortran characters?
6. What are the Fortran program card fields (name them and indicate the columns)?

CHAPTER 5 FORTRAN IV: FUNDAMENTAL EXPRESSIONS AND OPERATIONS

In this chapter the technical substance of Fortran IV is developed to the extent that the reader can write a wide variety of Fortran programs. To allow the student to practice what he has learned, two programs are given. The student can write arithmetic operations and incorporate them into the provided program, which accomplishes all of the input/output operations.

Several basic concepts of data analysis or logical manipulation are introduced and discussed in this chapter. Of fundamental importance is the notion that a computer program is focused on numbers even though the numbers may stand for strictly nonquantitative sorts of things. Therefore, the character of the numbers occupies a good portion of our attention in this chapter. Although the computer and programs directing the operation of the computer are innocent of the "meaning" of the numbers, this limitation does not extend to the programmer. The program always deals with numbers but the meaning and logical interpretation of those numbers is completely at the command of the programmer.

Programs are usually written to be fairly general, i.e., the numbers with which the program is concerned are seldom included in the program. Rather, symbolic expressions and notations are substituted for the numbers. A program to do data analysis or logical operations can be written before specific data or problems are encountered. The actual numbers are input when the program is executed or are calculated during the execution of the program.

Once we define numbers and symbols standing for numbers, the next topic is the relationships that these numbers and symbols have to one another. In general, there are two kinds of relationships, arithmetic and logical. This chapter is devoted primarily to arithmetic relationships. Some discussion of logical relationships is useful here but a full scale discussion is delayed to a later chapter.

Also in this chapter we introduce the notion of collections of numbers in arrays. Particularly relevant is the notion of subscripted variables, in which the numbers are arranged in lists or arrays; the position of a particular number is designated by a numerical index.

One of the most powerful features of Fortran is a statement that permits the programmer repetitively to apply arithmetic and logical operations. This statement, the DO statement, defines a loop whereby an operation or set of operations is applied successively to elements of an array without requiring the programmer to keep track of the indices and the termination criterion of the loop.

Finally, this chapter introduces a special arithmetic function, the square root of a number, that is useful in manipulation of data. This function is only one of many functions defined in the Fortran language. It is so useful, however, that it is introduced here.

NUMBERS

In terms of the Fortran applications discussed in this book, there are two fundamental classes of numbers. The two kinds of numbers are differentiated by the way the computer represents them. In the first class, each number is represented by a string of zeros and ones in binary fashion. Numbers in this class are called fixed point or INTEGER numbers because the "decimal point" is always assumed to be at the far right of the string of digits. The second class of numbers is represented by two parts, one part indicating the significant digits and the other indicating the order of magnitude of the number (e.g., 11.0 and 11000.0 have the same significant digits but their magnitudes differ by a factor of 10^3). The part that indicates the order of magnitude may be changed without a change in the significant digits, a change that corresponds to moving the decimal point. Because the decimal point can be changed in this second type of number without changing the digits represented, numbers of this type are called "floating point" numbers. Floating point numbers are designated REAL numbers in Fortran, although this is not technically consistent with mathematical usage.

A less precise distinction, but one that may be more comfortable to deal with, is the division of numbers into those that are whole and those that have fractional parts. Fixed point or INTEGER numbers are always numbers that have no fractional parts. Floating point or REAL numbers always have a fractional part even though it may be zero. In terms of the distinction in Fortran the two types of numbers REAL and INTEGER are illustrated by

INTEGER	*REAL*
4	142.578
24000	.123456
131547	−19.00000
−16	11000.00
1012	.003333
14	.1400

In the integer representation of a number, all the digits are represented directly, even the three zeros of the 24000, while in the floating point, only the leftmost digits are represented. For example, the value 11000.00 can be represented by the digits 11 multiplied by 1000. In scientific notation this is

$$.11 \times 10^5$$

In the computer, REAL numbers are represented by two values; the fraction (the significant digits, assuming that the decimal point is to the left of the most significant digit) and the exponent (the 5 in 10^5 above, indicating the location of the demical point). Therefore, the computer (floating point) representations of the REAL numbers in the list above are:

Number	*REAL Representation*
142.578	$.1425 \times 10^3$
.123456	$.1234 \times 10^0$
−19.00000	$-.1900 \times 10^2$
.003333	$.3333 \times 10^{-2}$
14.	$.1400 \times 10^2$

These illustrations depend on the assumption that the computer stores only four decimal digits in the fraction part of a REAL number. Ordinarily, more digits are stored and the accuracy of floating point numbers exceeds that suggested by these examples (e.g., 7 decimal digits on the IBM 360, 8 on the UNIVAC 1108, and 11 on the Burroughs B5500). However, it is something that we must be wary of. When magnitudes representing two quantities differ only by digits in the rightmost part, the floating point representations of the magnitudes may not provide the information accurately to evaluate the difference of the magnitudes. For example, suppose that the computer is to determine the difference between the magnitudes 1872639.1 and 1872015.5. Assume that the computer can store only four significant digits. The computer representations of the two magnitudes would be

$$.1872 \times 10^7$$
$$.1872 \times 10^7$$

indicating no difference between the magnitudes, when actually there is a difference of 623.6. This is, of course, the reason why the correlation program in Chapter 4 was written the way it was.

Although the objects with which a program deals are numbers, both REAL and INTEGER, these numbers may mean anything that the programmer wishes. Of course the conventions used by the programmer must be sensible or the result will not be sensible.

The most straightforward interpretation of the numbers is in terms of magnitudes or quantities of some attribute, such as length, number of trials to criterion, or judged intensity of a light source. Such numbers have direct physical or operational meaning and the results of operations performed on them can be interpreted in terms of the physical and operational meaning. On the other hand, the numbers may be taken to imply relative magnitudes. For example, the number 9 may mean only that the object to which the 9 is associated is 9th in order of magnitude with respect to some property. The numbers themselves do not directly represent the quantity but only some relative aspect of it. Still more removed from magnitudes or quantities is the use of numbers to indicate the classification of an object within some classification scheme. For example, the fifty states of the United States might be represented in a coding by the numbers 501, 502, ..., 550, each distinct state corresponding to a distinct number. Thus, in the operation of a program the state of birth of a subject in a sociological study might be represented by a code number. Finally, a number might be used to indicate a dichotomy, the existence or nonexistence of some condition, etc. Imagine that the presence or absence of a given diagnostic sign depended on whether the number of indicators on a test surpassed 45. All patients scoring higher on the test than 45 show the diagnostic sign, all patients scoring 45 or lower are free of the sign.

The use of numbers for nonnumerical purposes requires only the trick of setting up a code and then encoding and decoding in order to manipulate and interpret the nonnumerical meanings of the numbers. For example, in the second project suggested in Chapter 3 the social psychologist begins with selecting certain codes with which to indicate the characteristics of the interviewed subjects and the responses that they make. By comparing the magnitudes of the code numbers, the psychologist may sort each subject into the appropriate category. By comparing the coded categories with a code key in the program (built into the program by the programmer or read by the program as data), the output of the sorting program can be in terms of the decoded (meaningful) categories instead of the codes used.

NAMED QUANTITIES

When a Fortran program is written, most of the quantities to be dealt with by the program are represented by symbols, i.e., the quantities are given names. These symbols are the names of the locations in which the numbers will be stored as the program is executed. Quantities represented in this fashion are called "variables" even when the number assigned to the named location may be a fixed value throughout the execution of the program. The variable name and the value of the variable are distinct. The variable name is given by the symbol. The value of the variable is given by the contents of the location associated with the name.

CONSTANTS

The distinction between a variable and a constant helps to clarify the meaning of the terms variable and constant. A constant in a Fortran program is spelled out directly as a number in the coding, with or without a decimal point depending on whether the constant is REAL or INTEGER. Thus, if the number .3345 is written into a Fortran statement according to the appropriate rules, the number .3345 is said to be a constant. In other words, if a numerical constant is involved in a Fortran calculation, that numerical constant may be represented in the Fortran statement in "clear code" by indicating the number itself. Constants are of two kinds, INTEGER and REAL:

INTEGER Constants	*REAL Constants*
16	.11111
−3245	.0009
100	−1.
12345	0.
0	12345.

The only difference in the two kinds of constants is the presence of the decimal point and fractional digits in REAL constants and the absence of these in INTEGER constants.

Note that constants are never written with the comma separating groups of three digits. Common practice in writing a number, such as 12345, calls for a comma between the 2 and the 3—12,345. The comma is dropped completely in Fortran; it is not permitted.

The magnitudes permitted for constants depend on the specific computer. For example, in the IBM 7094 the greatest integer constant is 11 digits while in the CDC 6000 series computers 18 digit integer constants are permitted. Real valued constants generally have 6 to 11 significant digits depending on the computer. Overall magnitudes vary widely among computers, the smaller ranges being about 10^{-38} to 10^{38} and the larger ranges being about 10^{-294} to 10^{322}. Zero is represented on all machines. Both positive and negative magnitudes are defined. A constant falling outside the range of the computer will usually lead to a diagnostic message from the compiler.

VARIABLES

Variables are denoted by names that may take on a variety of forms. In general, a variable name is denoted by a string of up to six letters and numerals the first of which must be a letter. None of the special characters in the Fortran character set (i.e., .,()*/=$+−) may be used in a variable name. The first letter of the name of a variable is used to designate whether the variable is INTEGER or REAL. Variable names beginning with the letters I, J, K, L, M, and N are INTEGER variables. All other variable names (i.e., beginning with other letters) indicate REAL variables. The first-letter designation of the type of variable can be overridden by a type declaration, which is discussed in the chapter on declarations. Examples of names of variables of both types are:

REAL variables	*INTEGER variables*
X	M
X1	N
CULT	I
TRIAL	J
A235	ITRIAL
VARIAN	K235
XMEAN	MEANX

Although single character names are simpler to write and to work with from a clerical point of view, multiple character names have the advantage of suggesting meanings. The variable names TRAIT, FREQ, GENO, LOCI, and TYPE are suggestive of the meaning of the variables used in the project on quantitative genetics. The variable names XSUM, YSUM, XMEAN, and YMEAN are useful to remember which sum, mean, etc., is being dealt with in a correlation program. The mnemonic property of the variable names is a valuable aid in debugging the program—between debugging runs of a program, many of the details might be forgotten were it not for suggestive naming of variables and comments in the program.

The numbers represented by variable names have the same size limitations as have constants. When, during execution of the program, a number attains a value greater than that allowed, a condition known as "overflow" exists, and the execution of the program is usually terminated by the executive system. An "underflow" is a similar condition, except that it results from a number becoming too small. Both overflows and underflows are error conditions in nearly all computers and fall into the category of logical errors that are detected during execution of the program.

RELATIONSHIPS AMONG VARIABLES

One of the general purposes of writing a computer program is to manipulate (analyze) numbers in an arithmetic fashion. In order to carry out these manipulations, the numbers must be brought into relationship with one another. Fortran defines a set of possible relationships between numbers, and a set of rules pertaining to the operation of the relationships. This and the next three sections of this chapter deal with these relationships and the rules regarding their use in a Fortran program.

The arithmetic relationships defined in Fortran are the common ones, although the symbols denoting them are, in two cases, different. Recall that everything must be expressed explicitly in Fortran statements because of the straight line keypunch representation of the components of a statement. The cues of spatial location, and notational symbols like the square root sign, are replaced by other notations.

There are five operations relations or arithmetic defined in Fortran:

Operation	*Fortran Symbol*
Addition	+
Subtraction	−
Multiplication	*
Division	/
Exponentiation	**

The values of two variables are added together when their names are related by a plus sign. For example, the values of variables A and B are added when A + B appears in a Fortran statement. Likewise, when the values of two variables are related by the minus symbol (−), the value on the right is subtracted from the value on the left.

The operation of multiplication, designated by the asterisk (*) results in the product of two numbers. If A and B are in the relationship expressed by A * B in a Fortran statement, the values with the names A and B are multiplied. Likewise for the operation of division and the operation symbol /. If A and B are related by A/B, the value of A is divided by the value of B. Finally, exponentiation of A by B is expressed as A**B and corresponds to the operation of finding the Bth power of A: A^B.

A detailed description of logical relationships is made in Chapter 8. However, at the end of this chapter we introduce a Fortran statement that permits using the relative magnitude of two numbers to branch in three possible ways. Two numbers bear a relationship of relative magnitude to each other; the numbers can be equal in magnitude, the first number larger than the second, or the first smaller than the second. Often, in making decisions in a computer program, the magnitude of an index, or a cummulated value, etc., is used to determine when an alternate course of action will be initiated. Several times in the earlier chapters, examples involved testing the difference between two numbers. For example, if the index I is equal to N in the loop, the loop may be terminated and the next successive operation executed.

REPLACEMENT STATEMENTS

In ordinary algebraic and arithmetic notation the equal sign, =, means that the quantities (or logical expressions) represented on either side of the sign are equivalent, equal, or have the same value. The meaning of the = sign in Fortran has altogether a different meaning. It means that the value of the variable or constant on the right of the = sign replaces the value of the variable on the left side of the = sign. The left-hand member in a replacement statement must be a single variable while the right-hand member may be either a variable, a constant, or several variables and constants related to one another by arithmetic operations. Logical relationships may also be involved in replacement statements but these follow different rules and are discussed in Chapter 8.

The use of the = sign as a symbol for replacement frequently causes novice programmers difficulty. The replacement symbol, =, must not be confused with the algebraic meaning of the symbol. The replacement symbol strictly means that the value of the variable, constant, etc., on the right-hand side takes the place of the value of the variable on the left-hand side. This use permits writing meaningful Fortran statements that would be meaningless if interpreted as algebraic notation. For example, when the value of an indicator or index I is to be incremented by one, the Fortran statement would be

```
I = I + 1
```

meaning that the value I is replaced by the value of I plus one. Before the execution of the statement, imagine that I has a value of 435. After the statement is executed the value of I is given by 435 + 1 or 436.

The operation of replacement has a characteristic that can be of value to the programmer but may also cause problems. If a replacement statement is written to replace the value of an INTEGER variable by the value of a REAL variable or constant (i.e., in the form INTEGER = REAL) the fractional part of the REAL variable or constant is lost. The REAL variable is said to be "truncated." Truncation is due to the different internal representation of INTEGER and REAL variables and constants. There literally is no way of representing the fractional part of a REAL variable or constant in the INTEGER word. Rather than rounding the REAL value to the nearest INTEGER value and then replacing the value of the INTEGER variable in the statement, the fractional parts simply are lost. Other combinations of REAL and INTEGER variables and constants in a replacement statement do not involve a change in the value of the variable or constant on the right side.

Imagine several variables and constants: I, R, V, N, G, 4.0045, 3, 4444., .99999. The values of the variables are:

Variable	*Value*	*Type*
I	0	Integer
R	16.32	Real
V	−0.	Real
N	456	Integer
G	0.	Real

There are four types of replacement statements to consider: REAL replacing REAL, REAL replacing INTEGER, INTEGER replacing INTEGER, and INTEGER replacing REAL. The examples in Table V.1 show the values of the variable on the left side of the replacement statement, after the execution of the statement.

Replacing an INTEGER value by the value of a REAL variable, i.e., the truncated REAL value becomes the value of the INTEGER variable (INTEGER = REAL), is called "truncating" or "fixing" a REAL number. On the other hand, when the value of an INTEGER variable replaces the value of a REAL variable (REAL = INTEGER), the operation is referred to as "floating" an INTEGER because of the "floating point" designation of REAL variables.

EXPRESSIONS

In the last section it was indicated that the right-hand side of a replacement statement could be made up of several variables and constants related to one another by arithmetic operations. Such a combination of variables and constants in arithmetic relationship to one another is called an expression. This section deals with the rules of forming expressions and the properties of replacement statements involving expressions.

The first rule that must be observed is that the left side of a replacement statement must always be a single variable regardless of the nature of the right side of the replacement. The right-hand side of the replacement statement may be any variable, constant, or expression allow-

Table V.1

Examples of the Results of Replacement Statements Involving REAL and INTEGER Variables and Constants

Statement	Value of left hand variable after execution
REAL replacing REAL	
V = R	16.32
R = G	0.0
V = .99999	.99999
R = .99999	.99999
REAL replacing INTEGER	
I = R	16
N = G	0
I = 4.0045	4
I = .99999	0
N = 4444.	4444
INTEGER replacing INTEGER	
I = I	0
I = N	456
I = 3	3
INTEGER replacing REAL	
V = I	0.
R = N	456.
G = 3	3.

able under the rules of Fortran. The general form of a replacement statement may now be stated. Let V be a variable, and E an expression made up of variables and constants in permissible arithmetic relationships. A replacement statement has the general form

$$V=E$$

All of the variables and constants in an expression must be of the same type, REAL or INTEGER. This restriction is due to the internal storage form of the two types of numbers. Perhaps the best way of dealing with this restriction is to think of an expression as a REAL or an INTEGER expression. In a REAL expression all of the variables and constants must be REAL. In an INTEGER expression all variables and constants must be INTEGER. An exception to the rules is in the operation of exponentiation in which the exponent of a REAL variable or constant may be an INTEGER variable or constant. An expression that includes components that are INTEGER and components that are REAL is called a mixed expression (sometimes referred to as "mixed mode" or "mixed type" expressions). The reader is urged to be careful in using the decimal point in REAL constants when they do not have a fractional part. Omission of the decimal point in REAL constants like 1., 4., etc., is a common programming error. Some implementations of Fortran allow mixed expressions. They should not be written without consulting a local programming advisor. If the Fortran compiler does not allow mixed expressions, they are treated as syntax errors and usually are diagnosed by the compiler. If mixed expressions are allowed, they usually are evaluated as if all elements were REAL, although Fortran implementations vary in this regard.

In order clearly to understand the operation of truncation in the replacement statement where the right member is an expression the programmer should remember that the expression is first evaluated, i.e., the value of the expression determined, and then the replacement takes place. The expression is evaluated in its own mode before replacement. If the left-hand variable is an INTEGER variable, only the whole part of the expression is involved in the replacement, i.e., the expression is evaluated and the value truncated at the time of replacement. Truncation within INTEGER expressions is encountered when the INTEGER expression involves division. If the expression I/K is executed when I has a value 16 and K has a value 5, the expression 16/5 has a value 3. The replacement statement

```
XINT = I/K
```

results in the value 3 replacing the value in the location named XINT, even though the left-hand variable is a REAL variable.

Evaluation of Fortran expressions is governed by rules different than those of ordinary arithmetic and algebra. The evaluation of an expression is the same as "plugging in" the values of the variables and constants in the expression and performing the operations that relate these values. However, the order of computation is dependent on the conventions of the Fortran compiler. The sequence of adds, subtracts, multiplies, exponentiations, etc., is established in the machine language program by arbitrary rules built into the compiler. These rules for evaluation of Fortran statements can lead to nonsense calculations if they are not considered in writing the statements.

Fortran sequencing rules are defined in terms of parentheses in the expressions, priorities assigned according to the location of operations in the expressions (left to right), and priorities assigned to different operations. Only one operation is performed at a time.

The use of parentheses in expressions is essentially the same as that in standard algebraic notation and arithmetic. A part of an expression enclosed in parentheses is considered to be a separate subexpression and is evaluated as a unit. The number of parentheses used in unlimited except that they must be in matched pairs—for each opening parenthesis, there must be a closing parenthesis. The implicit expression of multiplication, as in (Y−A)(X−B), is not permitted. All operations must be stated explicitly, i.e., for the example (Y−A)*(X−B).

Parentheses may be imbedded within other parentheses without practical limitations. The most deeply imbedded parentheses are evaluated first. Nonoverlapping parentheses at the same stage of evaluation are evaluated from left to right. For example, in the above expression, the value of (Y−A) is calculated first, then the value of (X−B), and finally the product of the two values is obtained. In an expression like FN * (X + (Y−A)), the innermost subexpression, Y−A, is evaluated first, that value added to X, and finally the sum multiplied by FN.

Each variable or constant in an expression must be separated from (or related to) each other by an operation symbol. Thus, if the constant 4.0321 and the variable VARIAB are to be multiplied they must be separated by the multiplication symbol: 4.0321 * VARIAB. If two variables appear in a statement without being related by an operation indicator one or another of two things will happen. If the variable names have a total of fewer than six characters the two names will be combined by the compiler into an unintended variable name (the compiler will generally indicate this by printing the diagnostic message that the "variable" is not referred to elsewhere in the program). On the other hand, if the combined names involve more than six characters the compiler will indicate that the name is too long.

Operation symbols in Fortran expressions must not appear without intervening variable names, constant values, or parentheses. Thus, adding the negative of a variable cannot be expressed as a +−VARIAB but must take the form

+(−VARIAB)

In addition to the evaluation of parenthetic components as separate entities, other rules of order of evaluation of expressions are defined. Excepting where parentheses indicate a different order, the operations take place from left to right in the statement, with all operations of a given priority being performed all the way across the expressions before the next priority operations are performed. The order of priorities are:

Operation	*Priority*
** exponentiation	First (highest)
* and / multiplication and division	Second
+ and − addition and subtraction	Third

Imagine an expression without parentheses, such as

X − XBAR * Y − YBAR/Y − YBAR ** 2 * X − XBAR ** 2

The evaluation of the expression would proceed with the squaring of XBAR and YBAR to give the following expressions, where brackets are used to indicate completed evaluations:

X − XBAR * Y − YBAR/Y − {YBAR ** 2} * X − {XBAR ** 2}

Next the operations of multiplication and division are performed from left to right to give:

X − {XBAR * Y} − {YBAR/Y} − {{YBAR ** 2} * X} − {XBAR ** 2}

The final stage of evaluation is the subtraction of the four bracketed components from X. Imagine that XBAR is the symbol for $\overline{X}$, and similarly YBAR for $\overline{Y}$, and that the equation we wish to evaluate is

$$\frac{(X - \overline{X})(Y - \overline{Y})}{(Y - \overline{Y})^2 (X - \overline{X})^2}$$

The Fortran expression is evaluated in such a way that the arithmetic equivalent to the value given by the Fortran program would be

$$X - (\overline{X} \times Y) - \frac{\overline{Y}}{Y} - (\overline{Y}^2 \times X) - \overline{X}^2$$

The expression we want to evalute and the expression evaluated have no resemblance. In order to check the correctness of a Fortran expression a programmer should follow through on the sort of parenthesizing just illustrated. When a misapplication of an operation is found, the addition of parentheses is called for. A rule that will save grief and undiscovered error is to use parentheses whenever there is any doubt about the correctness of a Fortran expression without them.

An additional example will help make clear the necessity of careful planning and thought in writing a Fortran expression. It is often convenient to work arithmetically with INTEGER variables and constants. The fact that division of two INTEGER variables results in truncation of the quotient can cause numerical differences in the answer depending on the order of calculation. Imagine that the sample size of an experiment is calculated by a program. The formula for sample size in the experiment depends on the hypotheses, the risk acceptable for the two types of error, the number of experimental conditions, etc. Suppose that the algebra gives N as

$$N = \frac{i \times j}{k}$$

The values of i, j, and k are determined by the experimenter. Imagine the values are $i = 19$, $j = 4$, and $k = 5$ from which $N = 15.2$. Three Fortran statements appear to be algebraically sound:

```
N = (I*J)/K
N = (I/K)*J
N = (J/K)*I
```

The parentheses in all three of these expressions could have been left off because of the left to right order of evaluation and the equal priority for / and *. In spite of their mathematical equivalence, the three expressions give quite different answers:

	(I*J)/K	(I/K)*J	(J/K)*I
Value after first step	76 (19 times 4)	3 (truncated from 19/5)	0 (truncated from 4/5)
Value after second step (final answer)	15 (truncated from 76/5)	12 (3 times 4)	0 (0 times 19)

This last example is likely to frighten behavioral scientists more than is necessary. The example is contrived to illustrate the difficulties that can be encountered if careful thought is not applied to a calculation before venturing into a computer program. With awareness of the characteristics of a computer and the implications of those characteristics for numerical calculation, the programmer can avoid or correct for potential error.

A PRACTICE PROGRAM, YOU DO

In order to permit the beginning programmer to write programs from the very first a practice program is developed here. The program is called YOU DO. This practice program permits use of all of the arithmetic introduced so far. Fortran expressions can be evaluated by submitting the practice program with the expressions inserted into the program, and allowing YOU DO to handle all input and output.

The practice program reads values for 8 REAL variables and values for 8 INTEGER variables. The names of these variables are X1, X2, ..., X8 and I1, I2, ..., I8. In addition, the program prints the values of three REAL variables (V1, V2, and V3) and three INTEGER variables (IV1, IV2, and IV3). The only replacement statements built into the program set the output variables to zero.

The rules for using the program are as follows. Statements must be inserted between program statements number 100 and 1000 (i.e., replacing cards with sequence numbers 13 and 14). These statements may be any arithmetic replacement statements the programmer wishes, using any constants or variables the programmer wants to use. Input data are variables X1, X2, ..., X8 and I1, I2, ..., I8. The only restriction is that the programmer finally write replacement statements with the output variables V1, V2, V3, IV1, IV2, and IV3 on the left side of the replacement symbol. Any output variables not used can be ignored and the output values for those variables will be zero. The expressions written by the programmer must be in terms of the input variables or in terms of variables and constants defined by replacement statements involving the input variables.

The flow chart of the practice program YOU DO, is shown in Figure V.1. The programming to be written is indicated by a large operations box. The program is listed in Figure V.2.

The input and output of YOU DO are rigidly specified in order to simplify the use of the program. The values of the input variables are punched with the understanding that they occupy successive ten-column fields on a card. All of the REAL values are on the first data card and all of the INTEGER values are on the second data card. For the REAL values the decimal point is punched. If it is not punched, the program will insert a decimal between the sixth and seventh columns in each field. For the INTEGER values, the numerical value is punched all the way to the right of the ten-column field. Figure V.3 illustrates the general layout of the data cards and an example of values punched in cards.

The output gives all three REAL values printed on one line with appropriate labels and all three INTEGER values on another line with appropriate labels.

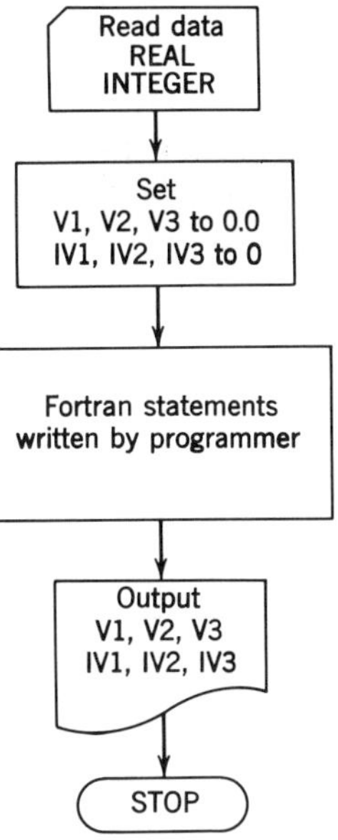

Figure V.1 Flow chart for practice program YOU DO.

Three illustrative sets of Fortran coding for YOU DO are shown in Figure V.4. The three sets of statements are explained in the comment cards in the programming. Several problems that can be solved by writing Fortran statements for YOU DO are presented at the end of the

```
CYOU DO
CA PRACTICE PROGRAM -- FOR PRACTICE WRITING FORTRAN EXPRESSIONS
      READ(5,1)X1,X2,X3,X4,X5,X6,X7,X8
    1 FORMAT(8F10.4)
      READ(5,2)I1,I2,I3,I4,I5,I6,I7,I8
    2 FORMAT(8I10)
      V1=0.0
      V2=0.0
      V3=0.0
      IV1=0
      IV2=0
  100 IV3=0
CINSERT HERE ANY STATEMENTS YOU WISH IN ORDER TO FIND                  13
C     NEW VALUES FOR SOME OR ALL V1,V2,V1,IV1,IV2,AND IV3              14
 1000 WRITE(6,3)V1,V2,V3
    3 FORMAT(1H1,20X,2HV1,18X,2HV2,18X,2HV3,//,15X,3(F10.5,10X))
      WRITE(6,4)IV1,IV2,IV3
    4 FORMAT(///,19X,3HIV1,17X,3HIV2,17X,3HIV3,//,12X,3(I10,10X))
      STOP
      END
```

Figure V.2 Program listing for the practice program YOU DO.

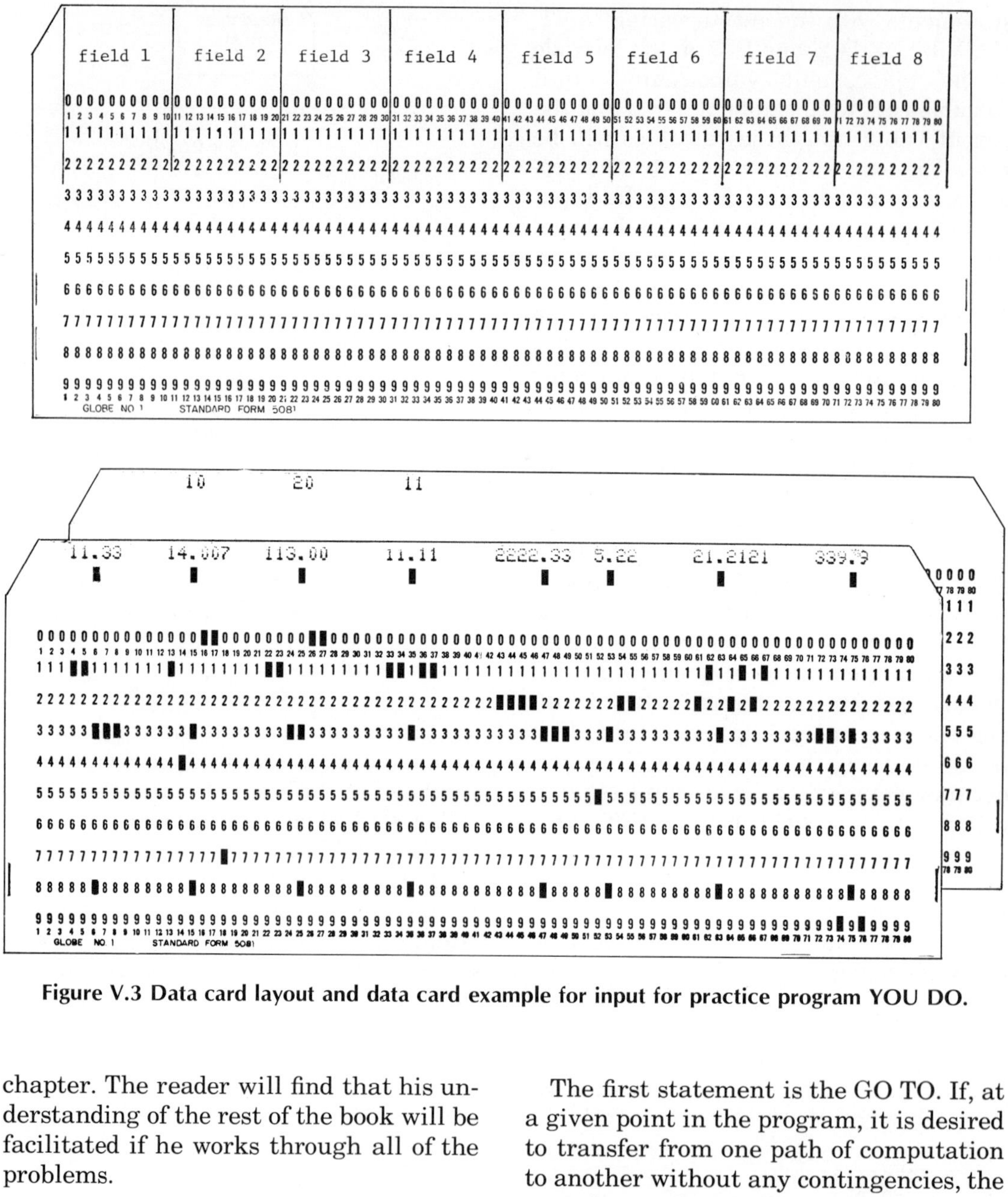

Figure V.3 Data card layout and data card example for input for practice program YOU DO.

chapter. The reader will find that his understanding of the rest of the book will be facilitated if he works through all of the problems.

THE GO TO AND IF CONTROL STATEMENTS

Fortran contains a number of statements that cause execution of the program to depart from the serial order of the program statements. These statements are called control statements. Although a separate chapter is devoted to control statements in Fortran, two control statements are so useful in elementary programming that they are introduced at this point.

The first statement is the GO TO. If, at a given point in the program, it is desired to transfer from one path of computation to another without any contingencies, the transfer can be implemented by the GO TO statement. If the statement number of the statement to which control should pass is n, the GO TO is written

```
GO TO n
```

The actual value of n is always used since it refers directly to a statement number and not a variable.

The IF control statement permits a three-way branching in a program, de-

```
CYOU DO STATEMENTS TO FIND THE MEAN OF THE X VARIABLES
      SUM=X1+X2+X3+X4+X5+X6+X7+X8
      XMEAN=SUM/8.
      V1=XMEAN


C YOU DO STATEMENTS TO FIND OUT THE EFFECT OF ORDER
C     OF OPERATIONS IN FORTRAN EXPRESSIONS
      V1=X1*X2/X3
      V2=X1/X3*X2
      V3=X2/X3*X1
      IV1=I1*I2/I3
      IV2=I1/I3*I2
      IV3=I2/I3*I1


C YOU DO STATEMENTS TO SUPRESS THE WHOLE PART OF REAL
C     NUMBERS. INPUT OF X1,X2,AND X3 WITH DIGITS ON BOTH
C     SIDES OF THE DECIMAL POINT
      KX1=X1
      KX2=X2
      KX3=X3
C X1,X2,X3 ARE NOW TRUNCATED IN KX1,KX2,KX3. NOW FLOAT
C     KX1,KX2,KX3
      FKX1=KX1
      FKX2=KX2
      FKX3=KX3
C NOW SUBTRACT THE FLOATED TRUNCATED VALUES FROM THE
C     VALUES OF X1,X2,X3. FKX1,FKX2,FKX3 ARE THE WHOLE
C     NUMBER PARTS OF X1,X2,X3. THE DIFFERENCES WILL BE
C     THE FRACTIONAL PARTS.
      V1=X1-FKX1
      V2=X2-FKX2
      V3=X3-FKX3
C FIX PROGRAM TO PRINT THE WHOLE NUMBER PARTS OF X1,X2,X3
      IV1=KX1
      IV2=KX2
      IV3=KX3
```

Figure V.4 Illustrative Fortran statements for YOU DO.

pendent on the value of a variable or expression. The general form of the IF is

IF(E) n_1, n_2, n_3

where E is a variable or an arithmetic expression in INTEGER or REAL mode, and n_1, n_2, and n_3 are statement numbers. The execution of the statement causes a transfer to statement n_1 if E is negative (less than zero), to n_2 if E is equal to zero, and to n_3 if E is positive (greater than zero). Assuming A = 5.2, B = 10.9, and C = .5 the statement

IF(B*C − A) 10, 20, 15

would cause a transfer to statement 15 since the expression B*C−A is positive.

The flow charting of the IF statement makes use of the diamond-shaped symbol introduced in Chapter 4. The statement written above would appear in a flow chart as

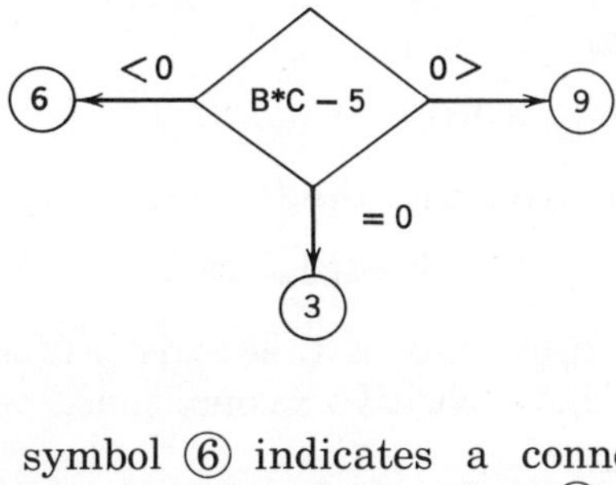

The symbol ⑥ indicates a connection elsewhere in the chart. Thus ⑥ might refer the reader of the flow chart to another portion of the same chart which might have the appearance:

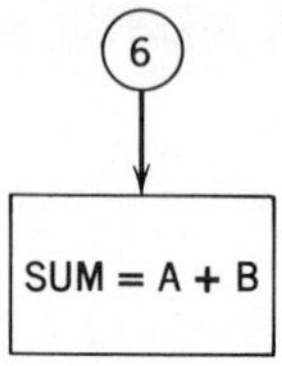

This, of course, implies that the operation SUM = A + B is to be executed if the quantity B*C−A is negative.

The GO TO statement is so simple that few errors are made in using it. The most frequent error is omission of the statement number referred to in the GO TO. That is, the statement GO TO 99 might be written, but the number 99 does not appear in any statement in the program. This kind of syntax error usually is detected by the compiler, which prints an error message.

Two kinds of errors are made frequently in connection with the arithmetic IF statement. One of these is a syntax error like that described for the GO TO statement—omission of one or more of the statement numbers mentioned in the IF. A similar error is the omission of one of the statement numbers in the IF statement itself. For example, the statement

```
IF(X−10.5) 99, 100
```

is in error because it refers only to two statements.

A certain kind of logical error is easily made with the IF statement. This occurs when the sense of the IF is reversed. In an earlier example an IF statement was correctly written as

```
IF(B*C−A) 10, 20, 15
```

It is easy to write the IF incorrectly as

```
IF(B*C−A) 10, 15, 20
```

which interchanges the transfers for the zero and positive conditions. Also, writing

```
IF(A−B*C) 15, 20, 10
```

causes an error by reversing the transfers to 10 and 15. Such errors are not detected by the compiler because the statements are syntactically correct. Such logical errors usually have the effect of giving unexpected and incorrect results when the program is executed.

SUBSCRIPTED VARIABLES

When the correlation program CORDEM was introduced in Chapter 4, the idea of a subscripted variable was mentioned without developing any of the details. In this section the nature of subscripted variables or arrays is discussed more fully. The concept of subscripted variables is one of the most valuable tools a programmer has. With the use of subscripting, the programmer is able to write general and powerful programs with comparative ease.

Consider the following common statistical problem. An experimenter has observed 20 subjects in a study and obtained a value on a variable X for each of them. It is possible to give each of the 20 observed values a symbolic name such as X for the value for the first subject, Y for the value for the second subject, Z for the value for the third subject, etc. A more satisfactory way of dealing with the array of 20 numbers in the abstract is to designate the name of the variable and append a subscript to indicate the subject, for example X_1, X_2, ..., X_{20}. In this way the specific observation is referenced by an indication of the variable name and the number of the subscript. In the abstract, the observation is referenced by the variable name, X, and a name for the typical subscript, such as i. Thus, the observation for the ith subject has the name X_i. The specific subject is indicated by specifying the value of i for that subject and the specific value is indicated by specifying the value of X for the subject. The complete pairing of the X value and symbolic name is shown in Table V.2.

Common algebraic notation permits reference to the entire array of values X_1, X_2, ..., X_{20} in a simple and convenient manner. For example, the sum of the 20

Table V.2

Illustration of a subscripted array

Subject	X	Symbolic Designation
1	25	X_1
2	15	X_2
3	4	X_3
.	.	.
.	.	.
.	.	.
i	31	X_i
.	.	.
.	.	.
.	.	.
20	19	X_{20}

values, $X_1 + X_2 + \ldots + X_{20}$, is designated by the summation notation

$$\sum_{i=1}^{20} X_i$$

Fortran conventions permit a similar type of representation of arrays and operations on the values in the arrays. Due to the straightline representation of characters, expressions, and the like in Fortran, the subscript in X_i cannot be identified by vertical location. Rather, the variable X is declared to be a subscripted variable early in the Fortran program and then when a specific X_i is referred to, it is referred to by writing X(I), the (I) taking the place of the subscript i. The array of numbers $X_1, X_2, \ldots, X_{20}$ is referred to by the symbols X(1), X(2), ..., X(20) in the Fortran convention.

Earlier it was indicated that the names of variables are composed of up to six letters or numerals but that the special characters (including the parentheses) were not permitted in the names. We must now expand our understanding of names for variables. Under certain conditions, a variable name may be made to stand for an entire collection of locations in the computer. Hence, X may be made to stand for all of the twenty locations containing the values observed for the twenty subjects in the example. The specific location being referenced in a Fortran statement is indicated by appending to the variable name a parenthesis containing the relative location number. Thus, if the 14th location in the array contains a value of interest, it is referenced by writing X(14) in the statement. The parenthetic part of the subscripted reference to X is not counted as a part of the name of the variable, although once the variable is declared in the program to be subscripted the parenthetic part must always be present in a reference to the variable. Hence, X23456(3249) is the 3249th element in the array X23456. The value of the subscript in a reference to a subscripted variable is limited to positive integers greater than zero, 1, 2, 3, ... The upper limit on the subscript varies with computers but the practical limit is fixed by the size of the array, which is limited by the size of primary memory storage.

Using subscripted variables in the way that nonsubscripted variables are used does not offer any advantages. For example, nothing is gained if the sum of the twenty observed values of X is formed by the expression

```
SUMX = X(1) + X(2) + ... + X(20)
```

Even less attractive is

```
SUMX = 0.0
SUMX = SUMX + X(1)
SUMX = SUMX + X(2)
  . . .
  . . .
  . . .
SUMX = SUMX + X(20)
```

Both of these are correct but wasteful of time and effort.

Iterative operations like summation may be performed more efficiently by referring to the subscripts of an array variable in symbolic form. Thus, instead of referring to X(14), for example, the programmer refers to X(I) with I set equal to 14. By manipulating the value of

I in one Fortran statement, another Fortran statement can refer to the Ith element in the array. A few Fortran statements can take the place of a long string of statements. The summation problem above can be solved by adding successive values in the X array to a partial sum, say SUMX. If the index I is initialized at 1 and increased by 1 every time the successive values of X are added to the partial sum, the program needs only one expression like the 20 expressions above:

```
SUMX = SUMX + X(I)
```

If the array has 500 elements (i.e., 500 observations, $X_1, \ldots, X_{500}$) the savings are even more obvious.

The summation is done by repeating the addition statement. This is done in a loop that depends on the arithmetic IF. Once the variable SUMX is initialized at zero (to clear out any nonzero quantity that might have been stored in the location named by SUMX) the index, I, is started at 1 and then the statement

```
SUMX = SUMX + X(I)
```

is executed. The value of I is increased by 1 and the accumulation statement is re-executed, and so on until I surpasses twenty. Testing I against twenty in an arithmetic IF statement permits the programmer to repeat the accumulation statement or to go on to another statement in the program. This process is executed by the following Fortran statements:

```
     SUMX = 0.0
     I = 1
   5 SUMX = SUMX + X(I)
     I = I + 1
     IF(I - 20) 5, 5, 10
  10 XMEAN = SUMX/20.0
```

In this example the number of elements in the array is presumed to be fixed at 20. However, it is convenient to let the number of elements in the array be a variable rather than a constant. The value of the variable is read, or computed by the program from data read into the computer. For example, we might wish to find the value of

$$\sum_{i=1}^{N} X_i$$

where N can vary from one application of the program to the next. This is accomplished by reading the value of N as a datum, and using that value to terminate the addition loop. The above program segment is rewritten as

```
     SUMX = 0.0
     I = 1
   5 SUMX = SUMX + X(I)
     I = I + 1
     IF(I - N) 5, 5, 10
  10 FN = N
     XMEAN = SUMX/FN
```

Three changes are made in the coding. First, the termination of the loop (the IF statement) is contingent on N. Second, the divisor in calculating the mean is N, rather than 20.0. Third, since N is INTEGER, it is necessary to float N with the statement FN = N to avoid writing a mixed expression.

In order to make use of subscripted variables, certain information must be conveyed to the Fortran compiler. Two items must be provided: an indication that the variable is subscripted, and the number of storage locations to be set aside for the array (that is, the number of values to be stored in the array—the largest subscript value). If 50 values are stored as the subscripted variable X, the names of the values are X(1), X(2), ..., X(50), and these names refer to the first, second, ..., fiftieth locations in the array X. To convey this information to the compiler, a declarative statement is made at the beginning of the program. The general nature of declarative statements and allocation of computer storage for subscripted variables is discussed in Chapter 7. For the present it suffices to deal with the simplest case. If the variable with the name XNAME is subscripted in a Fortran program, and if the largest anticipated subscript is 400 then the Fortran statement

DIMENSION XNAME(400)

must appear before any reference is made to the variable XNAME.

The DIMENSION statement may be used to convey information about more than one array variable. In CORDEM, for example, the statement

DIMENSION X(100), Y(100)

indicates to the compiler that both X and Y are subscripted variables, each involving up to 100 separate locations. The subscripts used in connection with the variables X and Y may not exceed 100 in this example.

The maximum number of elements in an array, as specified in the DIMENSION statement, need not be involved in any specific application of the program. In the summation program above the number of elements involved in the summation was 20. If the X variable had been dimensioned by

DIMENSION X(500)

the calculation would have involved only the first 20 of the potential 500 locations in which values of X are stored. The remaining 480 locations are allocated but not used. In general, a program using arrays will obtain as input data the actual number of elements in a subscripted variable (array) that is used. For example, the sample size, N, in the summation example might be punched on a card and read into the computer by the program before executing the summation loop. The coding for an elementary averaging program AVER2 dealing with a subscripted variable X is shown in Figure V.5. This program uses no programming knowledge not already developed, excepting the input and output.

The instructions necessary to use AVER2 are simple. The first card in the data deck has the number of observations to be averaged in the first five columns. Hence, if there are 10 observations the first five columns are punched 00010 or more simply 10 in columns 4 and 5. The data are punched on the following cards, eight observations per card entered in eight 10-column fields with the decimal presumed to be three digits from the right or else the decimal is punched explicitly somewhere else in the ten columns. If the observed value is negative the minus sign is punched before any of the digits of the value. If there are more observed values than will fit on a single card, the excess values are punched on additional cards beginning in column 1 of each card. An example data card deck is shown in Figure V.6.

```
CAVER2
CAVER2 ELEMENTARY AVERAGING PROGRAM USING ONE                          AVER 201
C      SUBSCRIPED VARIABLE WITH UP TO 10,000 VALUES                    AVER 202
C                                                                      AVER 203
       DIMENSION X(10000)                                              AVER 204
       READ(5,30)N                                                     AVER 205
    30 FORMAT(I5)                                                      AVER 206
       READ(5,31)(X(I),I=1,N)                                          AVER 207
    31 FORMAT(8F10.3)                                                  AVER 208
       SUMX=0.0                                                        AVER 209
       I=1                                                             AVER 210
    10 SUMX=SUMX+X(I)                                                  AVER 211
       I=I+1                                                           AVER 212
       IF(I-N)10,10,20                                                 AVER 213
    20 FN=N                                                            AVER 214
       XMEAN=SUMX/FN                                                   AVER 215
       WRITE(6,40)XMEAN                                                AVER 216
    40 FORMAT(1H1,7HMEAN = ,F10.4)                                     AVER 217
       STOP                                                            AVER 218
       END                                                             AVER 219
```

Figure V.5 Listing of an elementary averaging program, AVER2.

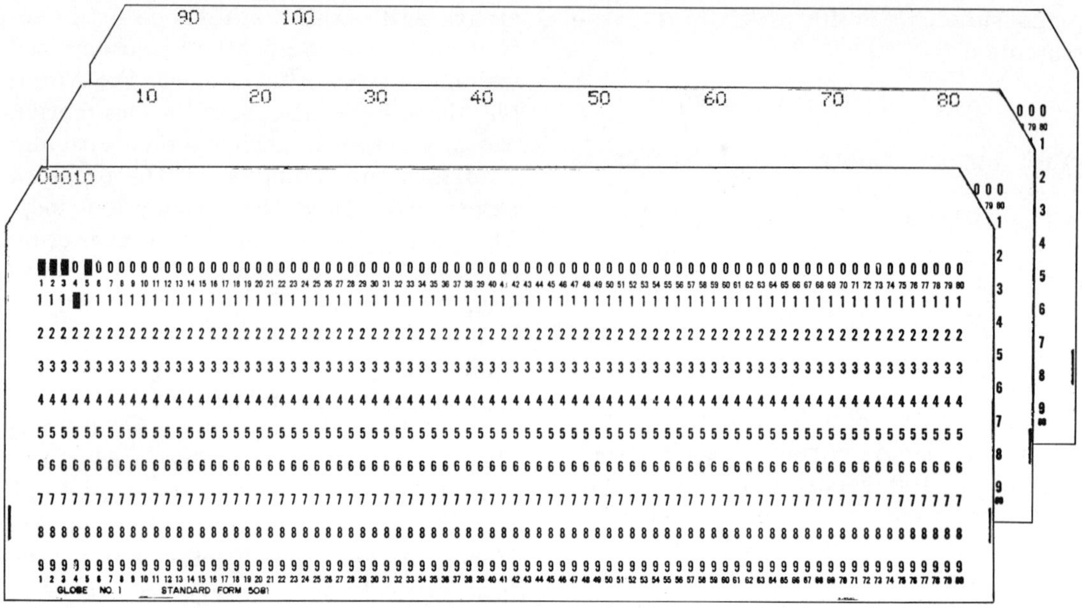

Figure V.6 Data deck for input to AVER2.

The kinds of errors that can be made in dealing with subscripted variables are numerous. The errors usually fall into two broad categories—those concerned with the DIMENSION statement, and those concerned with the use of subscripts.

If the DIMENSION statement is unrecognizable by the Fortran compiler, a large number of error messages can be produced. For example, if the word DIMENSION is misspelled, the entire statement is ignored by many Fortran compilers. As a result, any variable declared in the erroneous DIMENSION statement will not be recognized as a subscripted variable. The Fortran compiler will, in such a case, usually print an error message every place in the program that a subscripted variable is used, since the compiler has not been informed that the variable is to be subscripted. This single error, which is usually simple to correct, can produce a large number of error messages. Other frequent errors in DIMENSION statements are punctuation errors—commas are required between the names of the variables if more than one variable is being defined in a single DIMENSION statement.

Some Fortran compilers require that DIMENSION statements precede the first appearance of a subscripted variable in the program; in other compilers it is immaterial where the DIMENSION statement appears. When a variable has been declared in a DIMENSION statement, it must be used always with a subscript.

In using subscripted variables, the value of the subscript must not exceed the value given in the DIMENSION statement. Consider, for example, the case where the variable Y is dimensioned by

```
      DIMENSION Y(50)
```

and the following statements appear in the program

```
      SUM = 0.0
      I = 1
   30 SUM = SUM + Y(I)
      IF(I - 100) 10, 10, 20
   10 I = I + 1
      GO TO 30
   20 YBAR = SUM/100.
```

The subscript value is allowed to exceed the maximum value as defined in the DIMENSION statement. It is not difficult to make this kind of error. The most accurate statement about the execution of the program is to say that the results are unpredictable. In some computer systems an indication of the error and its cause is printed; in other systems the error may go undetected. Other kinds of errors are possible with subscripts—a discussion of these appears in Chapter 7.

AUTOMATIC LOOPING, THE DO STATEMENT

Whenever a series of operations are to be repeated a number of times with a changing index, coding similar to that in the summation part of AVER2 is adequate to the job. However, a very powerful and simple Fortran statement, the DO, permits writing loops with a good deal more programming simplicity. The DO statement is used to establish and to monitor the execution of a loop. The statement has the form

DO n $i = k_1, k_2$

where n is a statement number, i is the index modified in the loop, k_1 is the first value of the index and k_2 is the terminating value of the index. The DO causes all Fortran statements between the DO and the statement numbered n to be executed regardless of whether they involve the index i or not. The number of times that the loop is repeated depends on the initial value of the index, k_1, and the final value of the index, k_2. If k_1 is 1 and k_2 is 20 the loop is repeated 20 times with i taking on values, 1, 2, ..., 20 for the successive repetitions. If the initial value, k_1, is 10 and k_2 is 20 the loop is repeated 11 times with i taking on values 10, 11, 12, ..., 20 for the successive repetitions.

The coding to find the sum of the X values for I from 1 to N in the program AVER2 can be replaced by a DO statement. The statements on cards with identification numbers AVER2 10 through AVER2 13 are replaced by

```
   DO 10 I = 1, N
10 SUMX = SUMX + X(I)
```

These two statements result in the sum of the X's with I from 1 through N being stored in the location of the variable named SUMX.

On a flow chart, the DO statement is represented as an operation symbol with three compartments:

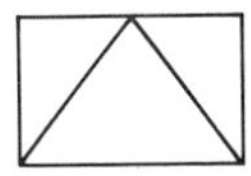

Each compartment contains a parameter pertinent to the looping variable. The general form of the DO given above would appear on the flow chart as

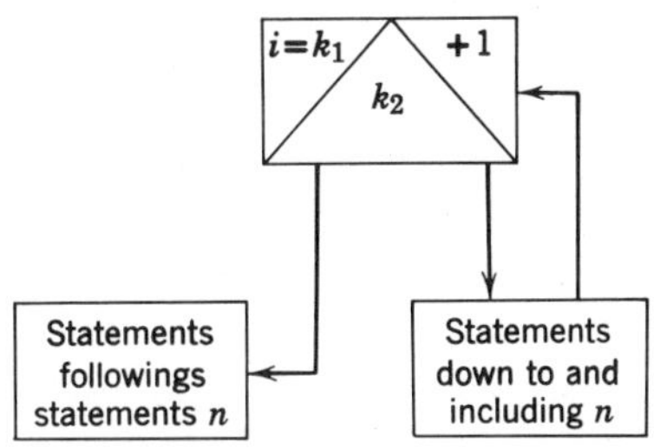

The addition loop just above is charted as

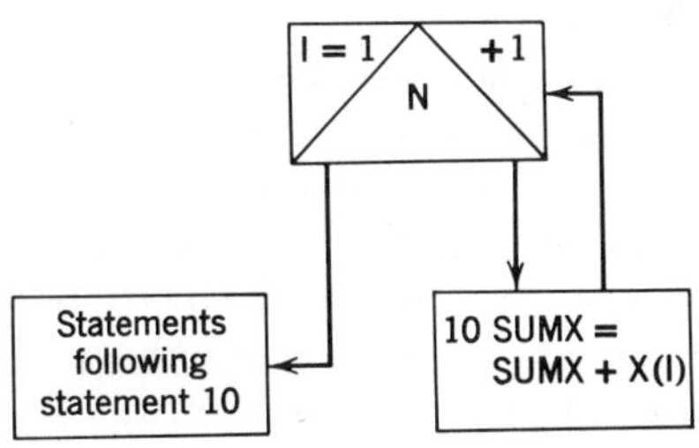

The upper-left compartment of the symbol defines the looping variable and its initial value. The upper-right compartment indicates that the variable i is to be increased by 1 each time through the loop. The center compartment sets the termination criterion k_2.

An extremely useful statement frequently used in connection with the DO is the statement having the simple form

CONTINUE

This statement causes no computation to be performed and, in fact, does literally nothing. Its usefulness arises in part from the fact that the statement whose number is mentioned in a DO must not be an IF statement. On the following pages, two program segments are developed in which the last statement in a DO loop should logically be an IF. Since we are not allowed to use the IF in this manner, (see below), the CONTINUE is placed just after the IF and it, not the IF, becomes the last statement in the loop.

Several kinds of errors are often made in connection with DO statements. Most of the errors, however, are made in connection with features of the DO that are not introduced until Chapter 8 and are discussed at that time. For the present, it should be pointed out that when the DO is used together with subscripted variables, it is possible to define the value of k_2 in such a way that the maximum subscript value is exceeded. It is also important to note that k_1 and k_2 must be separated by commas, but that no comma precedes k_1. Also, the n and i are not separated by commas.

ARITHMETIC FUNCTIONS

It is possible to write Fortran programs to evaluate virtually any mathematical formula. This includes such things as the square root of a quantity even though the arithmetic operations that are defined in Fortran do not include a square root operation. In order to take the square root, then, the programmer must find an expression or an algorithm for calculating the square root by using the operations defined in Fortran. A number of mathematical methods for doing this are known. Any of these methods may be expressed as a Fortran program.

A number of functions like square root are provided as special operations in Fortran. The Fortran function for finding square roots is introduced here. A number of other Fortran functions are introduced and discussed in the chapter on subroutines and functions (Chapter 10).

The general form of a Fortran function is the function name and an argument (or arguments) to which the function operation is applied. The argument may be a constant, or an expression involving one or more variables and constants. The general form is

Function name (argument)

The function reference must appear in a replacement statement but it can be part of an expression. For example, in the program CORDEM, the Fortran square root function (SQRT) appeared in

```
COR = XYDEV / SQRT(XDEV2*YDEV2)
```

In this example the square root of the product of the variables XDEV2 and YDEV2 is evaluated before the division. If the argument is an expression, it is evaluated first. The value of the expression is then entered into the function and the function is evaluated. The function value then enters into the expression of which the function reference is a part. The argument may be a simple variable or constant.

PRACTICE PROGRAM U DO 2

The practice program YOU DO enabled the programmer to use all of the arithmetic operations in replacement statements involving eight REAL and eight INTEGER variables. It is possible now to extend the practice program to much more sophisticated programming. The practice program U DO 2 is based on the principle of YOU DO. U DO 2 provides all of the input and output and other statements necessary to handle the data and arithmetic programming. The programmer provides the statements to deal with the input data.

The program U DO 2, listed in Figure V.7, will read as many as 500 REAL values into an array with the name X beginning with X(1) and continuing with X(2), X(3), ..., up to X(N). The programmer does not have to specify N. U DO 2 keeps track of the number of values entered into the array X and sets N to

```
CU DO 2
CU DO 2
C
C A SECOND VERSION OF YOU DO, USING A SUBSCRIPTED VARIABLE X
C AND PERMITTING INPUT OF UP TO 500 VALUES OF FLOATING
C POINT DATA
C
C EACH DATA CARD CONTAINS UP TO 8 DATA VALUES, THE
C FIRST IN COLUMNS 1-10, THE SECOND IN 11-20, ETC. IF NO
C DECIMAL POINT IS PUNCHED, THE PROGRAM INSERTS ONE
C FOLLOWING EACH NUMBER, I.E. AFTER COLUMNS 10, 20, 30, ETC.
C
C THE NUMBER OF DATA VALUES, N, IS DETERMINED BY THE PROGRAM
C
C THE PROGRAM WILL OUTPUT UP TO 50 FLOATING POINT ''ANSWERS''
C THE ANSWERS WILL APPEAR ONE LINE AT A TIME WITH APPROPRIATE
C LABELS
C
C AN ANSWER IS GENERATED BY A REPLACEMENT STATEMENT
C OF THE FORM Y(J)=(EXPRESSION IN TERMS OF X AND CONSTANTS).
C ANSWERS SHOULD BE GENERATED IN THE ORDER Y(1),Y(2),Y(3),....,Y(M)
C THE PROGRAMMER MUST REPLACE M WITH A SPECIFIC VALUE
C INDICATING THE NUMBER OF ANSWERS (E.G.,4 ANSWERS,M=4).
      DIMENSION X(500),Y(50)
      DATA BLANK, M / -99999., 50 /
C
      DO10001 L=1,63
      K=L*8
      I=K-7
      READ(5,10000)(X(J),J=I,K)
10000 FORMAT(8F10.0)
C
      DO 10001 J=I,K
10001 IF(X(J).EQ.BLANK) GO TO 10002
C
10002 N=J-1
C
C     DO 10003 I=1,50
10003 Y(I)=0.0
C
C
C INSERT HERE ANY STATEMENTS YOU WISH IN ORDER
C     TO FIND NEW VALUES FOR SOME OR ALL OF
C     Y(1)...Y(M),WHERE M IS ANY VALUE NOT GREATER
C     THAN 50. YOU SHOULD ASSIGN A VALUE TO M.
C BEGIN OUTPUT OF ARRAY Y.
      WRITE(6,10006)
10006 FORMAT(1H1)
      DO 10004 I=1,M
10004 WRITE(6,10005)I,Y(I)
10005 FORMAT(1H0,7HANSWER ,I2,3H = ,F10.3 )
      STOP
C
      END
```

Figure V.7 Listing of the practice program U DO 2.

the total number entered. In order to do the counting correctly the program requires that the N + 1 field contain −99999. Each data card is to be punched with eight values, each in successive ten-column fields. The first value on a card in columns 1−10, the second in 11−20, etc. If no decimal point is punched the program inserts one at the far right of each field, i.e., after columns 10, 20, 30, etc. If the data are INTEGER numbers they have to be input in REAL number form and then converted to INTEGER by a replacement statement.

An array Y in the program is used to store any answers generated by the program. The answer array is capable of storing up to 50 elements. The number of elements actually stored in the array must be designated by the programmer in a replacement statement with the variable name M on the left of the replacement sign and a constant or expression on the right giving the value of M. The answers must be stored in the first M locations of the array Y as these are the M elements printed out by U DO 2. The answers must be REAL numbers and are printed out with three digits following the decimal point (values less than .001 will be printed as .000).

As an illustration of the use of U DO 2, two examples are worked out here. Both examples calculate three of the variables from Project 1 of Chapter 3. The variables calculated are the number of correct responses, the total number of responses to criterion, and the total number of incorrect responses before the first correct response. The first example deals with only one subject, while the second deals with as many as 16 subjects.

The first U DO 2 program to analyze the three learning variables for one subject is flow charted in Figure V.8. The program listing is given in Figure V.9. The data are coded so that the value 1 indicates a correct trial. A field punched

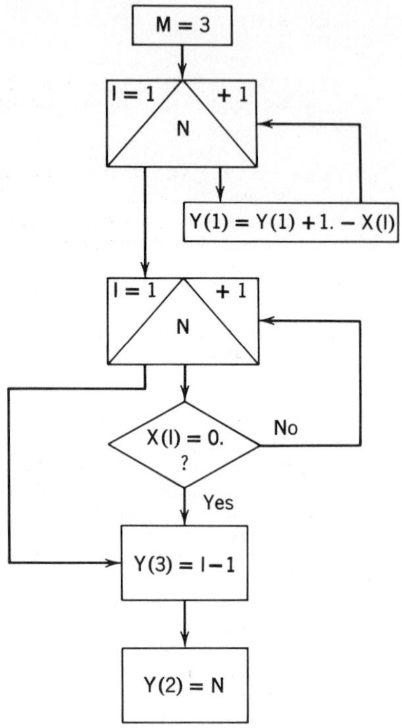

Figure V.8 Flow chart for U DO 2 segment to calculate learning scores for one subject.

```
C U DO 2 ROUTINE FOR SCORING LEARNING DATA.
C
C  USES VARIABLES ONE THROUGH THREE FROM PROJECT NUMBER 1, AND ANALYZES THE
C      DATA FOR ONE SUBJECT.  DATA ARE ENTERED INTO X(1)...X(N), WHERE 1 IS AN
C      ERROR TRIAL AND 0 IS AN ERRORLESS TRIAL.
C      OUTPUT IS AS FOLLOWS--
C      Y(1)=NUMBER OF CORRECT RESPONSES
C      Y(2)=TOTAL NUMBER OF RESPONSES TO CRITERION
C      Y(3)=NUMBER OF INCORRECT RESPONSES BEFORE THE FIRST CORRECT RESPONSE
C
C      FIRST SET THE NUMBER OF OUTPUT VALUES.
C
      M=3
C
      DO 1 I=1,N

    1 Y(1)=Y(1)+1.-X(I)
C THIS ACCUMULATES THE NUMBER OF CORRECT RESPONSES
C
C NOW CYCLE THROUGH X(1)...X(N) UNTIL THE FIRST 0.0 IS
C      ENCOUNTERED. THE INDEX OF THE FIRST X=0.0 IS
C      THE TRIAL NUMBER OF THE FIRST CORRECT RESPONSE
C
      DO 3 I=1,N
      IF(X(I))3,4,3
    3 CONTINUE
    4 Y(3)=I-1
C
C N IS THE NUMBER OF TRIALS TO CRITERION
C
      Y(2)=N
```

Figure V.9 Fortran program segment to calculate learning scores for one subject in U DO 2.

−99999. indicates that criterion has been reached. The program U DO 2 checks the number of data entered, and thereby obtains the total of number of trials—it is simply the number of trials for which data are given to the program.

The three variables to be calculated from the subject's data are output as Y(1) for the number of correct responses, Y(2) for the total number of trials to criterion (N), and Y(3) for the number of incorrect responses before the first correct response. The first calculational step defines the number of values to be output as required by the program. Next, a loop is entered to scan the N scores for the subject, accumulating into the variable Y(1) the number of trials on which a correct response occurred. This loop is programmed as the DO 1 loop. Next, the routine loops through the N values until the first occurrence of X(I)=0.0. When this happens, the program jumps out of the loop with the statement IF(X(I)) 3,4,3 and sets the value of Y(3) to I −1. Since the first correct response occurred on trial I, there are I−1 incorrect answers previously. Finally the value of Y(2) is set to N and U DO 2 outputs the results.

Figure V.10 shows an input data deck for the U DO 2 routine for one subject, along with the computer-produced output.

The program segment to deal with up to 16 subjects is essentially the same as the segment just presented. The flow chart for this program is given in Figure V.11. The procedure is embedded in a larger loop controlled by the index K. The subjects are indicated by the value of

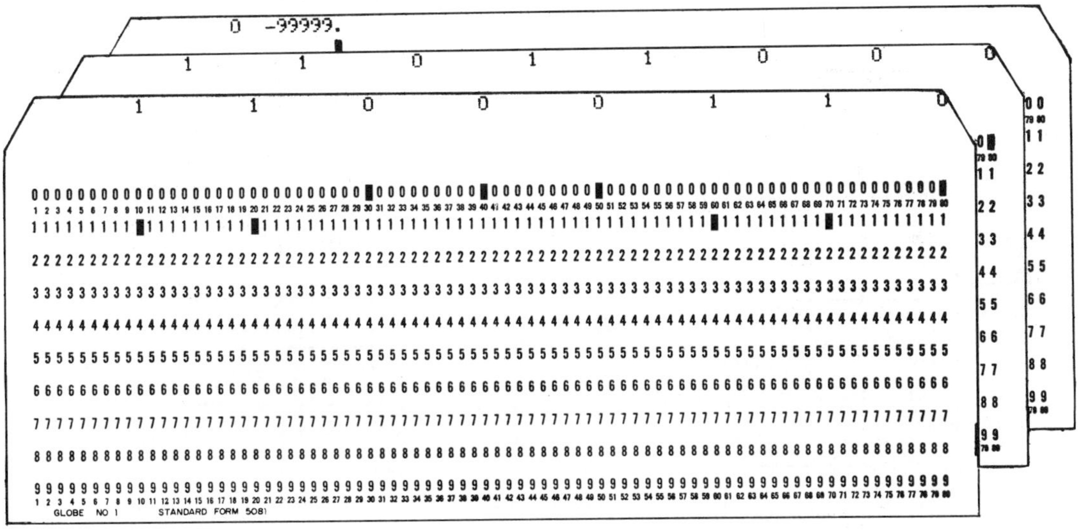


```
ANSWER  1 =      9.000
ANSWER  2 =     17.000
ANSWER  3 =      2.000
```

Figure V.10 Data cards and output from U DO 2 segment.

K. Thus, when K = 1, the first subject is being considered, etc. The comments in the program listing (Figure V.12) describe the data cards. In general, the data are the same as for the single subject program, with the subjects being separated by a data field containing a 9. The output variables are the same as in the single subject program, with a few exceptions. For the first subject, variables Y(1), Y(2), and Y(3) have the same meaning as in the single subject case. The output values for the second subject are placed in Y(4), Y(5), and Y(6). In the single subject analysis, the position in the Y array was indicated by a constant value as a subscript—in this case a variable (I) is used. I is set to one for the first subject, indicating the first variable for that subject is to be placed in Y(I), or Y(1). When the outermost loop (the subject loop) moves to the next subject, the variable I is redefined by the statement I = I + 3, indicating that the first result for the second subject is placed at Y(4). The same procedure, the increase in I by 3, is followed to define the location of the first answer for each successive subject.

Several additional counter variables are used in the program segment. I1 is used to indicate the first value in the data for the subject being considered. It begins with a value of 1, since the data from the first trial is in X(1), that is, in X(I1) where I1 = 1. The variable I2 is determined by the program—it is the subscript of the last data location for the subject. Since the end of a subject's data is indicated by a 9, the program scans (examines) the data array until the first 9 is encountered. The value of I2 is then that subscript minus 1. For example, if a subject required ten trials, the eleventh data value for him would be a 9. The first

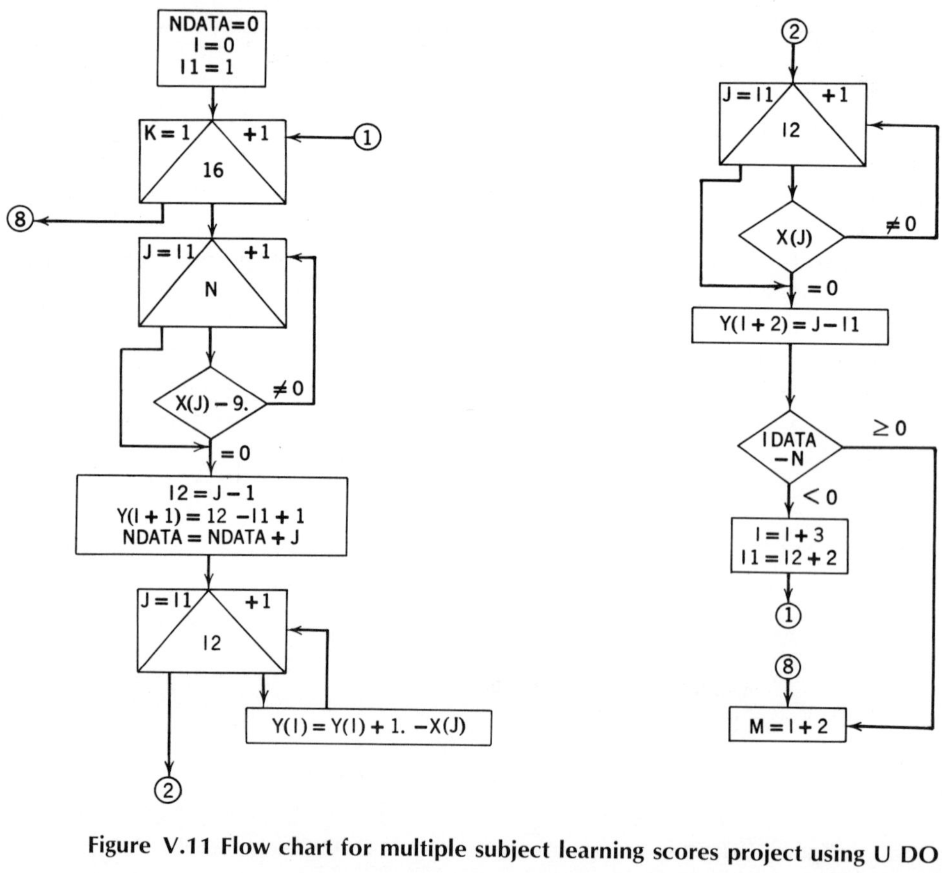

Figure V.11 Flow chart for multiple subject learning scores project using U DO 2.

```
CU DO 2 LEARNING SCORES PROJECT PROGRAMMING TO DEAL
C      WITH K SUBJECTS
C
C THE DATA FOR SUCCESSIVE SUBJECTS ARE SEPARATED BY
C      PUNCHING A 9 IN THE FIRST DATA FIELD FOLLOWING
C      A SUBJECTS DATA. THE NEXT SUBJECTS DATA
C      FOLLOWS IMMEDIATELY. OTHERWISE THE DATA
C      ARE PUNCHED AS IN THE SINGLE SUBJECT PROGRAM
C
C      OUTPUT VARIABLES ARE THE SAME, EXCEPT THAT
C      EACH SUBJECT HAS SCORES ON ALL THREE
C      VARIABLES.
C
C      MAXIMUM NUMBER OF SUBJECTS IS 16 DUE TO
C      LIMITATION ON Y.
C
C LET THE SUBJECT NUMBER BE K, THE FIRST ELEMENT (RESPONSE VALUE) FOR A
C      SUBJECT BE I1 AND THE LAST ELEMENT FOR A SUBJECT BE I2. THE NUMBER
C      OF TRIALS IS GIVEN BY I2-I1+1. LET I KEEP TRACK OF THE ANSWER
C      NUMBER,I OF 1, 2, AND 3 FOR THE FIRST SUBJECT, 4, 5, AND 6
C      FOR THE SECOND SUBJECT, ETC.
       NDATA=0
       I=1
       I1=1
       DO 1 K=1,16
C
C THERE ARE AT MOST 16 SUBJECTS.
C
       DO 3 J=I1,N
       IF(X(J)-9.0)3,4,3
     3 CONTINUE
     4 I2=J-1
       NDATA=NDATA+J
       Y(I+1)=I2-I1+1
C THIS LAST STATEMENT STORES THE NUMBER OF TRIALS TO CRITERION FOR THE K
C      TH SUBJECT (THE SECOND VARIABLE VALUE FOR THE KTH SUBJECT)
C
       DO 5 J=I1,I2
     5 Y(I)=Y(I)+1.0-X(J)
C
C THE LAST STATEMENT ACCUMULATES THE NUMBER OF CORRECT RESPONSES FOR THE
C      KTH SUBJECT INTO THE LOCATION OF THE FIRST ANSWER FOR THAT SUBJECT
C
       DO 6 J=I1,I2
       IF(X(J))6,7,6
     6 CONTINUE
     7 Y(I+2)=J-I1
C
C
C    THE LAST STATEMENT GIVES THE NUMBER OF ERRORS BEFORE THE FIRST
C     CORRECT RESPONSE WITHIN THE KTH SUBJECTS DATA.
C
C
       IF(NDATA-N)9,8,8
C
C I1 IS NOW THE LOCATION NEXT BEYOND THE LOCATION WITH THE 9.0 FOR THE K
C      TH SUBJECT. I1 IS THE FIRST LOCATION FOR THE K+1 SUBJECT.
     9 I1=I2+2
     1 I=I+3
C I NOW IS THE INDEX OF THE FIRST ANSWER OF THE K+1 SUBJECT.
     8 M=I+2
```

Figure V.12 Fortran program segment for multiple subject learning scores project.

subject, for example, might be represented by the values of X as shown by:

X(1) 1.0
X(2) 1.0
.
.
.
X(9) 0.0
X(10) 0.0
X(11) 9.0

In this case, I1 = 1 so that the program examines the X values beginning with X(I1) until a 9 is found. This occurs when the subscript of X is I1. Thus I1 − 1 = 10, the number of trials.

While U DO 2 determines the total number of values read in, N, the number of subjects is not determined and must be found by the program segment being written. Finally, although the logic of the program allows termination, a termination criterion is provided by the variable NDATA, which is a count of the number of values of X processed. When NDATA is equal to N, the program terminates by calculating M, the number of answers output.

The first statements in the program segment initialize the values of NDATA, I, and I1. Next the program enters the subject loop (DO 1 K = 1, 16). This loop is terminated normally when 16 subjects have been processed. If there are fewer than 16 subjects, termination is caused as indicated above, when NDATA = N.

The second loop in the program segment (DO 3 J = I1, N) searches the data for the subject and finds the end—the value 9. When this is located, the program jumps outside the loop (IF(X(J)−9.0) 3,4,3) and calculates I2, the number of trials for that subject, stores the number of trials in the answer position appropriate for that subject (Y(I+1)), and increases the count of the number of data words—NDATA—by J. The next two loops (DO 5 and DO 6) perform identical functions to the comparable loops in the single-subject example—they count the number of correct responses and the number of incorrect responses before the first correct response. Except for the indexing using I1 and I2, these loops are the same as those in the previous program segment.

The statement IF (NDATA − N)9, 8, 8 allows termination of the loop by jumping to the calculation of M when all data have been processed. If all data have not been processed, the two indices I and I1 are prepared for use in dealing with the next subject. Figure V.13 illustrates input to, and output from, the program segment as used in U DO 2.

ILLUSTRATIVE ERROR MESSAGES

Table V.3 lists some common compiler error messages for Fortran statements introduced in this chapter. The notations IBM, CDC, and UNIVAC refer to the three kinds of compilers being illustrated. The CDC compiler produces a two-letter code standing for a message—the message and the code are listed in the table.

EXERCISES

1. State whether each of the following is a valid Fortran constant. If it is, indicate the type of constant. If not, indicate why not.

   (a) 12345.6789   (f) −.00000009
   (b) 99988   (g) .673279826
   (c) 999888777.555   (h) 11111
   (d) +.88975   (i) +00079
   (e) −2345   (j) 98765432

2. Indicate which of the following are valid Fortran variable names. Where the name is invalid, indicate why. If the name is valid, give its type.

   (a) BOY   (i) ALPHA10
   (b) GIRL   (j) AX+3
   (c) 12XB3   (k) QRDT
   (d) 3M667   (l) −XB5C
   (e) ABC3X   (m) GAMMA
   (f) BIGONE   (n) 2BC/X
   (g) X   (o) $ADBC
   (h) XB653

3. Write creative variable names (correctly) to stand for the mean, median, mode, standard deviation, correlation coefficient, variance, first quartile, and second quartile.
4. Write the appropriate Fortran expressions for each of the following mathematical expressions. Check your work by calculating values by hand and in YOU DO.

   (a) $\dfrac{X + Y}{Y + Z}$

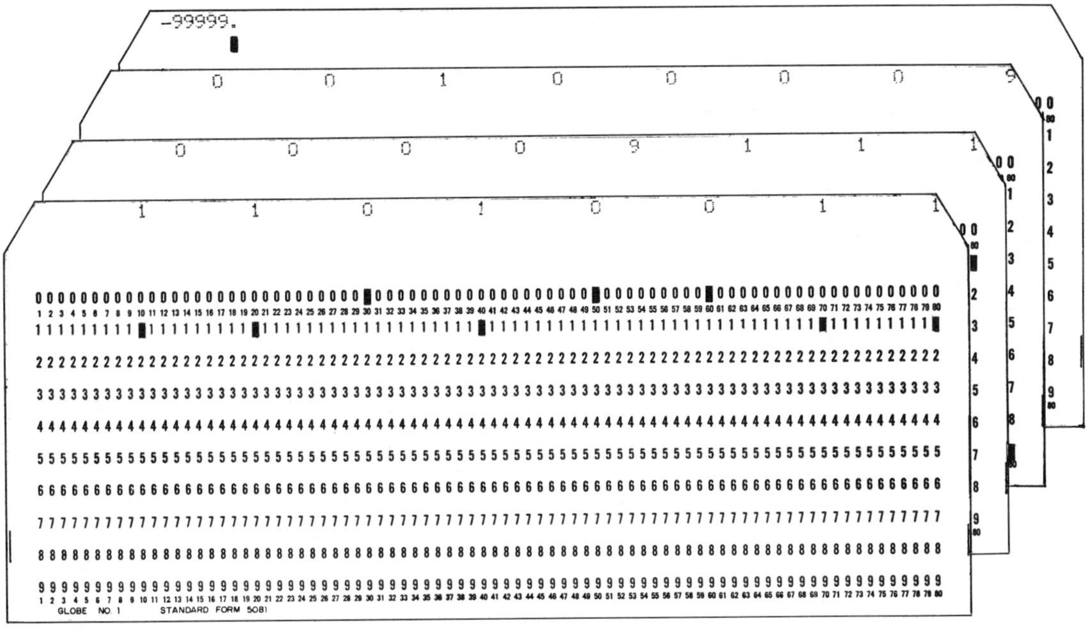


```
ANSWER  1 =      7.000
ANSWER  2 =     12.000
ANSWER  3 =      2.000
ANSWER  4 =      6.000
ANSWER  5 =     10.000
ANSWER  6 =      3.000
```

Figure V.13 Illustrative input cards for U DO 2 for the multiple-subject learning scores project, together with sample output.

(b) $X + \dfrac{X + Y}{Z}$ (e) $\dfrac{A\,(A - 1)\,(A - 2)}{3}$

(c) $\dfrac{X + Y}{Z} + AB$ (f) $\dfrac{(A + C)\,(B - D)}{\sqrt{XAC}}$

(d) $A + \dfrac{B + C}{N/Y}$ (g) $\sqrt{(X^2 + Y^2)^{6.1}}$

5. Correct the errors in the Fortran expressions on the left so that they will correctly represent the mathematical expressions on the right. Check your work by inserting the Fortran statements in YOU DO and applying them to a number of values.

(a) (XY)/Z $\dfrac{xy}{z}$

(b) C+(X(A*X+B)) $ax^2 + bx + c$

(c) 2*AB − 4/3 C ** .5 $\sqrt{2ab - \dfrac{4}{3}c}$

6. Translate the following Fortran expressions into unambiguous algebraic expressions showing the calculation performed according to the Fortran rules of precedence.

(a) A**.2 + B**2 − A *B** 1/2

(b) A + B + C + D/4

Table V.3

Common error messages

Kind of Statement	Message	Cause
arithmetic	PN-parentheses (CDC)	Unpaired parentheses
arithmetic	VC-variable name conflict (CDC)	A variable name is being used incorrectly
arithmetic	XM-expression mode (CDC)	Mixed mode expression
arithmetic or other	DUP. LABEL (IBM)	Same statement number is used more than once
arithmetic	NAME LENGTH (IBM)	A variable name is incorrect for one or more reasons: (1) too many characters (2) two variable names in succession without an operation symbol
arithmetic	SIZE (IBM)	A number, including a statement number is outside the legal range of numbers
arithmetic or other	THERE IS AN ILLEGAL USE OF . . . IN THE LINE BELOW (UNIVAC)	Could be caused by any of several kinds of syntax errors. The characters ... are replaced by the offending symbol(s)
arithmetic or other	A LEFT PARENTHESIS WAS OMITTED (UNIVAC)	Self-explanatory
arithmetic	. . . APPEARS WITH A SUBSCRIPT BUT WAS NOT DIMENSIONED (UNIVAC)	A subscript was used and the compiler did not recognize the corresponding DIMENSION statement
arithmetic	THIS IS AN ILLEGAL ARITHMETIC STATEMENT (UNIVAC)	Any of several syntax errors, perhaps the omission of an = sign
any	UNRESOLVABLE AMBIGUITY CAUSED BY SOURCE LANGUAGE ERROR (UNIVAC)	This is one of the true pearls of wisdom often found in error messages—it is caused by a statement that is so incorrect that the compiler is unable to even detect what the error might be
GO TO or IF	MS-missing statement number (CDC)	References have been made to non-existent statement numbers
DO	UNCLOSED DO LOOP TARGETS (IBM)	A statement number appears in a DO statement that does not appear as a statement number elsewhere
DO or other	A COMMA IS OMITTED FOLLOWING . . . (UNIVAC)	Self-explanatory
any	THIS STATEMENT IS TOO LONG (UNIVAC)	The offending statement exceeds the limit for number of continuation cards

(c) A/4 + B/4 + C/4 + D/4

(d) A − A + B**2 + B − A + B**2

(e) A(1) * A(2) + B(1) * B(2)
− ((A(1) + B(1))/2) * ((A(2) + B(2))/2)

(f) SQRT (A(1) * A(2)
− ((A(1) + B(1)/2)**2))

7. Translate the following algebraic expressions into Fortran expressions. Compare expressions in this exercise with like numbered expressions in the previous exercise.

(a) $A^2 + B^2 - \sqrt{AB}$

(b) $(A + B + C + D)/4$

(c) $(1/4)\,(A + B + C + D)$

(d) $A + B - (A + B)^2$

(e) $A_1 A_2 + B_1 B_2 - \left(\frac{A_1 + B_1}{2}\right)\left(\frac{A_2 + B_2}{2}\right)$

(f) $\sqrt{A_1^{\,2} + B_1^{\,2} - \left(\frac{A_1 + B_1}{2}\right)^2} \times \sqrt{A_2^{\,2} + B_2^{\,2} - \left(\frac{A_2 + B_2}{2}\right)^2}$

8. Define several variables having the values shown below.

Variable	Value	Type
I	1	INTEGER
J	0	INTEGER
K	10	INTEGER
A	0.0	REAL
B	102.1	REAL
C	.5	REAL

Using these values, and the constants given in the expressions, determine the value of the variable on the left of the = in each of the following Fortran statements. That is, determine the value of the variable after the replacement operation is performed.

(a) A = I

(b) A = K**2

(c) J = B / 2.0 * C

(d) I = J

(e) C = I + K

(f) K = (A * B * 155.6)/C – B * C

(g) I = I + 1

(h) K = K + K / 2

(i) A = B ** C

9. Modify the program segment for YOU DO in Figure V.4 to find the standard deviation of the X scores as well as the mean.
10. Write a program segment for YOU DO to find the correlation between the X scores and the I scores. Use the general procedure discussed in Chapter 4. Recall that the I variables are INTEGER and X REAL, so that any arithmetic will have to be done carefully. Develop the flow chart and write and execute the program.
11. The following Fortran statements are to be inserted in U DO 2. Write the flow chart for these, and determine the purpose of the coding. Then punch the statements, insert them in U DO 2, provide the program with some data, and see if your analysis was correct.

```
  Y(1) = X(1)
  DO 1 I = 1, N
  IF (X(I) – Y(1)) 1,1,2
2 Y(1) = X(I)
1 CONTINUE
  M= 1
```

12. Arrange to have N values read by U DO 2. Write an efficient set of statements for U DO 2 to find the largest and smallest values in the array that you have input. Store the largest value as Y(1) and the smallest as Y(2). Begin by a careful analysis of the procedure that you will use. Then develop the flow chart and do the coding. Check your work by running U DO 2.
13. Write a set of statements to insert in U DO 2 to calculate the correlation coefficient between two variables. Have the values of the first variable stored as X(1), ..., X(J) where J is less than or equal to 250. The values of the second variable should be stored as X(J+1), ..., X(N). Place the two means in Y(1) and Y(2), the standard deviation in Y(3) and Y(4), and the correlation coefficient in Y(5).
14. Modify the program written in Exercise 14 to calculate the regression coefficient b_{yx} using the formula

$$b_{yx} = \frac{\Sigma(X - \bar{X})(Y - \bar{Y})}{\Sigma(X - \bar{X})^2}$$

Output b_{yx} as Y(6).

15. The following code is to be inserted in U DO 2. The values of A and I in the program segment are output. Write the flow chart of the program segment and determine what the values of A and I will be when the execution is complete. Punch the coding, insert it in U DO 2 and have it compiled and run. If the values obtained from the computer are different than those you obtained, go back over the coding until you find your error.

```
C
C U DO 2 STATEMENTS FOR EXERCISE V.12.
C    REQUIRES NO INPUT, BUT A DATA CARD CONTAINING
C    -99999. IN COLUMNS 1-7 MUST BE PROVIDED.
C
      I = 10
      A = 10
      I = (I+I)/4
      A = (A*A)/20.
      B = I
      A = A**2 - B**2 + 18.
      IF (A-B) 1, 2, 3
    1 DO 4 J = 1,6
    4 I = A*B/B**J
      GO TO 10
    2 DO 5 J = 1,6
      A = J + 10
    5 I  = I*3 + J*4
      GO TO 10
   3DO 6 J = 1,6
      C = J / 3
    6 A = A + C
   10 Y(1) = A
      F = I
      Y(2) = F
      M = 2
```

CHAPTER 6 FORTRAN IV: BASIC INPUT AND OUTPUT

In the preceding chapter, we assumed that data had already been stored in memory and that numbers resulting from computation could be retrieved from the computer. This chapter deals with the process of placing data in memory and retrieving them. The process is known as input/output (I/O). Only the most elementary I/O operations are presented here, namely, reading numbers from cards and printing numbers on paper. More advanced methods in I/O are discussed in Chapter 9.

The computer rarely is instructed to read cards or print lines directly. As will be recalled from Chapter 1, input to, and output from the computer is usually by means of some kind of peripheral device. Input is most frequently in the form of card images on magnetic tape or disc. In instructing the computer to read data, the program actually specifies the reading of a card image from one of the I/O units attached to the system. Likewise, in printing, the program directs the computer to record the symbolic printed line on an output unit (tape or disc), rather than actually printing it. In most cases, however, the programmer is able to think in terms of actually reading cards and writing lines on a printed page. The fact that the computer is actually reading and writing an output unit is immaterial.

Fortran I/O coding consists of two parts. The first part is an executable statement that causes the computer to read or write. The second part is the FORMAT statement that specifies the exact form that the input or output material is to assume. Thus, the two parts of the I/O code (1) instruct the system to read or print, and (2) indicate the precise form of the I/O.

INPUT FOR YOU DO

The requirements of the input for YOU DO are simple; the program must read eight values called X1, X2, ..., X8 and eight values called I1, I2, ..., I8. Consequently, YOU DO is very simple in its input procedures. When the values are read into the computer they are to be stored in the locations with the proper names. When this is done, the values of the variables are available for computations.

Several things have to be attended to in input. First, the fact that input is required has to be signalled to the computer by a statement in the Fortran program. The place where the input statement appears in the Fortran program will determine when the data will be input as the program is executed. Second, the statement must contain information regarding the general form of the data and its location outside of the computer (on a magnetic tape, on cards in the on-line card reader, on a disc, etc.). This information, appearing in the input statement, becomes a part of the computer program and governs the execution of the program in inputting the data. Third, the program must contain information regarding the way the data are recorded (e.g., punched) in terms of the size of the fields, their numbers, and the types of field. Fourth, the statement must contain information regarding the names of the variables for which the numbers are the values.

The signal for the computer to execute an input operation is given by the compiled machine language coding corresponding to the Fortran instruction READ. The location of the data on an I/O unit in the form of card images and the specific format of the appearance of the data are indicated by the parenthetic information following the READ. In YOU DO the complete read statement is

```
READ(5,1) X1, X2, X3, X4, X5, X6, X7, X8
```

The names of the variables whose values are to be read are listed following the right parenthesis.

The information regarding the way the card is punched is given in a FORMAT statement. The YOU DO input FORMAT statement is

```
1 FORMAT(8F10.4)
```

which indicates that eight numbers are read from one card, each in floating point representation with ten-column fields, and with the decimal appearing four digits from the right.

A similar analysis of the WRITE statements at the end of YOU DO can be made. The difference is that the WRITE statement in YOU DO causes line (printer) images to be placed on the output unit

EXECUTABLE I/O STATEMENTS

The executable statement that causes data to be read from cards has the general form

READ *(i, n) list*

where i is the number of the I/O unit used for input to the computer (usually 5), n is the number of the FORMAT statement describing how the numbers appear on the card, and *list* designates variable names the values of which are to be read. The READ statement accomplishes three things: (1) specifies the I/O unit from which the card image is to be read, (2) specifies the FORMAT statement that describes the appearance of the card to be read, and (3) causes the computer to read the values of the variables named in the list and place those values in memory locations assigned to the variables in the list. For example, the statement

```
READ (5,1) X, Y, Z
```

causes the values for variables X, Y, and Z to be read from a card image on I/O unit number 5. The values are stored in the locations called X, Y, and Z. The FORMAT statement with statement number 1 specifies the exact description of the data on the card.

To print the values of A, B, and C, the statement

```
WRITE (6,2) A, B, C
```

is used. The WRITE statement has the general form

WRITE *(i, n) list*

where i, n, and *list* have the same meanings they have in the READ statement. In the example, the statement causes the values of the variables in the list (A, B, and C) to be written on I/O unit number 6. The usual output unit is number 6. The form in which the data are to appear on the printed page is specified in FORMAT statement number 2.

The elements in an I/O list may consist of single INTEGER or REAL variable names or subscripted elements of INTEGER or REAL arrays. The items in a list are separated by commas, and only variables may appear in a list, constants may not. This is not an exhaustive enumeration of the types of items allowable in a list—the definition of a list is extended later.

The list specifies all of the variables to be transmitted, and the order in which they are transmitted. Thus, in the statement

```
READ (5,1) X,Y,Z
```

variable X is read first, then Y, and finally Z. The order of the numbers on the card must be the same.

REAL and INTEGER variables, subscripted and nonsubscripted, may be intermixed in any order in the list. Thus,

ALPHA, BETA(2), BETA(1), JIM(3), X,Y,Z

is an acceptable list.

THE FORMAT STATEMENT

When data are transmitted from a card to storage, it is necessary to know how the data are assigned in the available 80 columns on the card. If values for the variables X and Y are to be read from a card, the computer must have information as to which columns contain X and which columns contain Y. Likewise, in printing the values of X and Y, the computer must be instructed where the values of X and Y are to be placed on the page. This information is contained in the FORMAT statement specified by the executable I/O statement.

The most simplified general form of the FORMAT statement is

n FORMAT (*a*)

where n is the number of the statement, and a is a string of alphameric information (numbers, letters, and parentheses) describing how the data appear on the card to be read, or how the data are to appear on the printed page. The FORMAT statement does not cause any operations in the execution of the program. It simply contains information necessary to execute the compiled READ or WRITE statement. When the compiler encounters a FORMAT statement it builds into the compiled program the information contained in the statement. Much of this chapter is devoted to the discussion of the alphameric string a.

FIELDS

A card consists of 80 columns. The 80 columns may be divided into fields or subsets of columns, each field consisting of one or more contiguous columns. Each field is a specific type depending upon the nature of the information to be read. Suppose that three numbers are to be read from a card. These numbers are to be values of the variables X, Y, and I where X and Y are REAL and I is an INTEGER variable. Therefore, there must be three fields on the card, two REAL fields and one INTEGER field. Suppose in addition, that the value of X requires 10 columns, Y requires 8 columns, and 6 columns are needed for I; X has three digits after the decimal, Y has five digits after the decimal, and I has no decimal point. The card could be set up as shown in Figure VI.1. The alphameric string a in the FORMAT statement describing this card must contain the following information:

1. The width of each field (e.g., 10 columns).
2. The type of each field (e.g., REAL or INTEGER).
3. The location of the number in each field (i.e., the position of the decimal point in the real fields).
4. The position of each field on the card (e.g., where each field is to be located within the 80 available columns).

The computer also must be informed as to what variable is contained in each field but this is communicated by the list and is not a part of the FORMAT description.

Output may be regarded similarly. If the values for X, Y, and I are to be printed, the fields on the page must be described in the same way. A printed page is somewhat different from punched input in two important ways. First, the page contains 132 columns (136 on some equipment, 120 on other), not 80 as on a card. Second, a printed page generally contains 60 lines (66 under some circumstances). Thus, when specifying output to be printed, the computer must have the following information available:

1. The width of each field.
2. The type of each field.
3. The appearance of the number in the field.

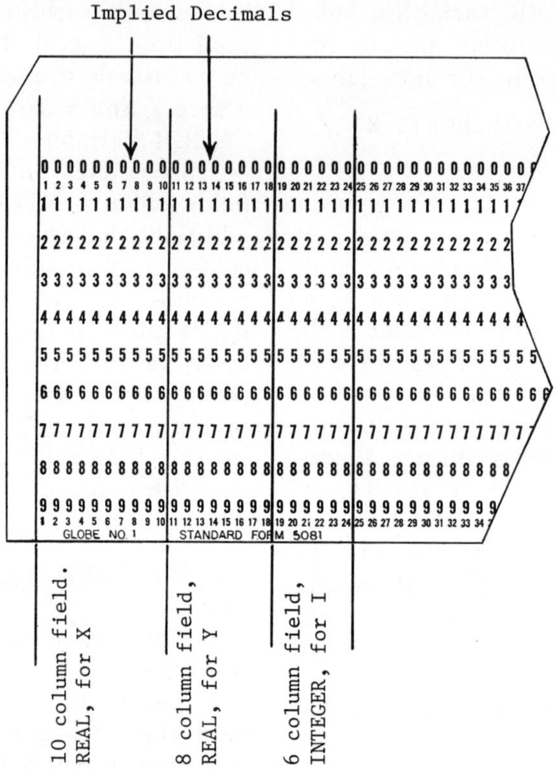

Figure VI.1 Illustration of a data card with three fields.

4. The position of each field (e.g., where each field is to be located within the 132 columns).
5. The line on the page where the field is to appear.

The printed output of the values X, Y, and I might appear as shown in Figure VI.2. Note that all five items of information are needed to specify precisely the appearance of each field on the page.

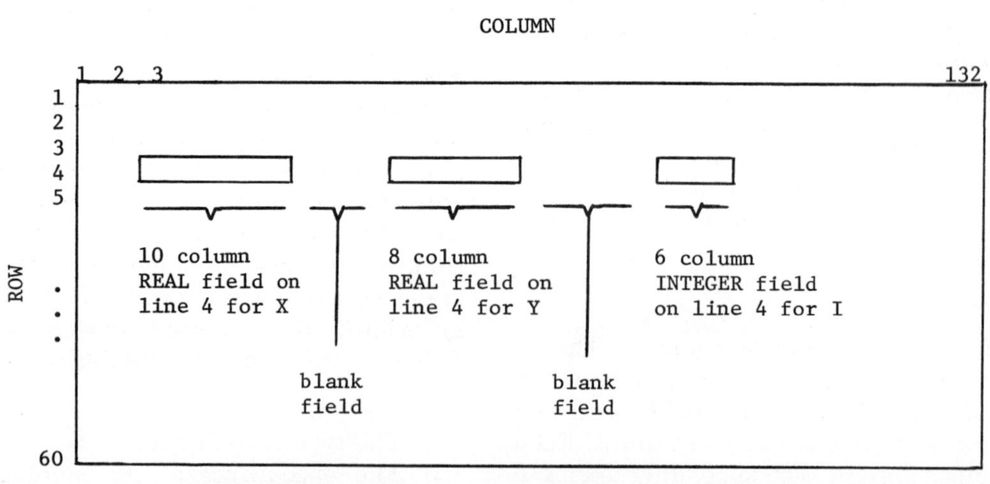

Figure VI.2 Illustration of an output page with three fields.

Numerical Field Description. Types of fields are given code letters to distinguish them from each other. The codes and their meaning are:

Code	*Meaning*
F	REAL
I	INTEGER

An F field description specifies a REAL field containing a floating point number. An I field specifies that the number in that field is an INTEGER. Thus, in a Fortran FORMAT statement, the code letters F and I define the type of the field.

Transmission of data from cards to memory and from memory to paper requires a conversion of the data to the proper form. When data are transmitted they must be converted to binary information. When this transmission is INTEGER the simple conversion to the binary equivalent is possible. However, when the transmission is REAL, the significant digits of the number and the exponent part of the number must be determined separately. On output, the conversion is reversed, resulting in numbers represented in decimal digits. This process is signaled to the computer by the field codes, I and F, for INTEGER conversion and REAL conversion, respectively. The actual procedures in the conversion generally do not concern the user of Fortran. Input or output with the I code is spoken of as I conversion, and input or output with the F code is spoken of as F conversion.

Following the code letter is an INTEGER constant that specifies the number of columns in the field. A specification I5 describes an INTEGER field five columns in width. Likewise, the specification F6 describes a six-column REAL field.

When the number being transmitted is REAL (field description code F), an additional item of information must be provided, namely, the location of the decimal point in the field. Fortran permits reading numbers from cards without the decimal point being punched, but nevertheless having it "understood" as being between certain columns. This information is communicated in the field description by an INTEGER constant that represents the number of columns in the field to the *right* of the decimal point. This constant appears immediately following the constant giving the field width, separated from field width constant by a period. For example, F6.3 describes a 6-column REAL field with three columns following the decimal.

The table below gives the field description codes, the appearance of numbers on cards as described by those codes, and how the number so punched is represented in the computer.

Field code	*Number as punched*	*Number as represented*
I2	23	23
I6	354657	354657
I3	−67	−67
F7.3	+142536	142.536
F3.0	−64	−64.
F8.3	1.66543	1.66543
F6.4	+16698	1.6698

Note that the plus sign (+) may be omitted but the minus sign (−) must be included. Note also that the sign, if included, must be counted as part of the field width. If a decimal point is punched on the data card, it overrides the location of the decimal point given in the field description code.

If an insufficient number of columns is specified for output of a number, digits (and sign) are lost from the left (some compilers differ in this respect). For example, if the INTEGER number −996682 is stored, the following table shows the appearance of the number in output as described by several field specifications.

Field description	*Output appearance*
I7	−996682
I6	996682
I4	6682
I10	bbb−996682

In the table, "b" represents a blank column. Note that it is the most significant digits that are lost. No warning is given by some computer systems when this loss of digits occurs. The programmer is therefore cautioned always to allow sufficient space for output. The maximum value of an INTEGER variable (in most computers) has precision to 11 digits, thus the specification I12 is safe, since it allows for the 11 digits, plus a sign. In printing REAL numbers the field must be large enough to accomodate the sign, the digits left of the decimal point, the decimal point, and the digits right of the decimal point. Thus, assuming one digit to the left of the decimal, the smallest possible field width is 3. Failure to provide enough room for the whole part of the number will cause the program to fail in execution in some computer systems. A number of systems print a warning for insufficiently large fields. A common warning is the printing of asterisks in the place of digits if the field is too small to print the entire number.

Suppose we wish to describe three fields, having 10, 15, and 6 columns, respectively. If the fields are adjacent, it is simply a matter of placing the field descriptions together, separated by commas. If the first two fields are REAL and the third INTEGER, the description

F10.3, F8.5, I6

would define three fields as shown for the punched card in Figure VI.1. The fields are assigned from left to right, in the order that they are described in the series of field descriptions. The same rule holds whether we are dealing with input or output, or cards or paper, within the limitations on the total number of columns available.

The information describing fields for input or output is used by the program in transmitting the information in the list of the executable I/O statement. This information is provided by writing a FORMAT statement of the general form:

n FORMAT $(f_1, f_2, \ldots, f_k)$

where n is the statement number and f_1, f_2, ..., f_k are the field specifications. Other types of information may be included in the FORMAT statement (e.g., line spacing); these are introduced in the following sections and chapters as the occasion demands.

Skip Fields. Suppose that the fields are not adjacent. That is, that they are separated by some blank columns. In reading cards these columns are to be skipped. In output nothing is to be printed in those columns. In either case certain sets of columns simply are to be skipped. These sets of skipped columns are specified by defining them as a "skip field." A skip field may be thought of as a field type different than I. or F, designated by a field code X. To produce 10 blank columns between each of the three numeric fields described above, a ten-column X field is introduced between them. The description would be

F10.3, 10X, F8.5, 10X, I6

and the fields would appear

******.***bbbbbbbbbb**.*****bbbbbbbbbb******

where **** indicates a numeric field and bbbb indicates a blank field. Notice that the number of columns in a skip field is given by an integer value before the field code X. The assignment of fields always takes place from left to right. All columns to the left of a given field must be accounted for. If all the columns to the right of a given field are blank or ignored, it is not necessary to specify them with an X field. All that is needed is the description of all the fields, starting from the left, up through the last non-X field. All remaining columns will be skipped automatically, even though they are not declared in a skip field.

Numerical Field Descriptions and I/O Lists. Once the fields are described by the FORMAT statement, information as to what variable is associated with a field is communicated by the list. The first variable in the list is associated with the first field description, the second variable with the second field description, and so forth. In general, there must be the same number of field descriptions in the FORMAT statement as there are items in the list. This is not a hard and fast rule, as we point out below.

The principles can be illustrated by some examples. First, read three numbers for the values of variables X, Y, and I. Assume that the value of X will be up to nine digits including the sign. In order to make room for the decimal point, if it is punched, ten columns (to accomodate a decimal point punch) must be assigned to the field in which the value of X is punched. Imagine that X generally will have three digits after the decimal point and that only occasionally will the decimal point occur elsewhere. The appropriate field designation for X is therefore F10.3. Similar reasoning might indicate that the field for the Y value can be specified by F8.3. Finally, if we assume that the largest integer value we wish to input as the value of the variable I is 999999 the specification would be I6. No decimal point is ever punched for an INTEGER variable value. If we wanted to input the three values 40.29, 11.111, and 999 for X, Y, and I, respectively, the card could be punched as shown in Figure VI.3*a*. If the number of digits after the decimal point in Y exceeds three, as in 1.907463, the card would be punched as shown in Figure VI.3*b*. If the decimal point is punched in REAL numbers in card input, the location of the number in the field is not important, as long as all of the digits are within the field. However, the INTEGER conversion permits no latitude: the digits must be all the way to the right of the field. When the digits are on one side or the other they are said to be "packed right" or "packed left" depending on which side of the field is involved. INTEGER fields are always packed right.

If the FORMAT statement to read the

a:

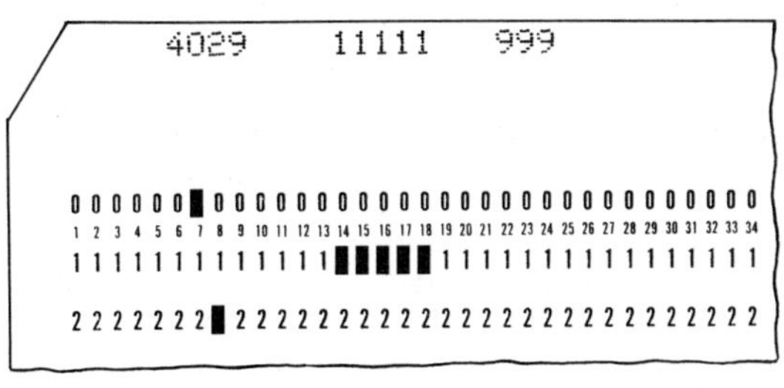

b:

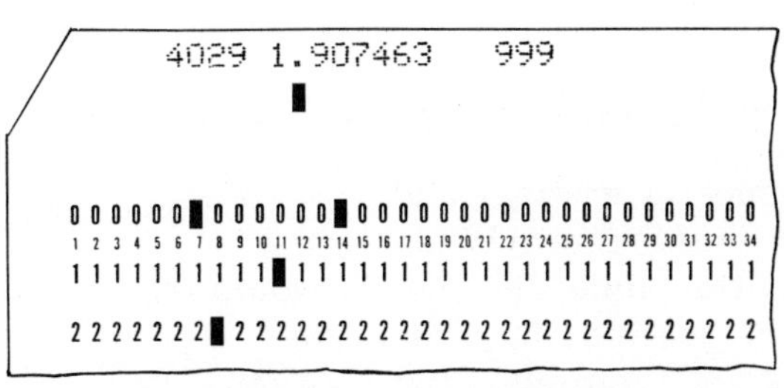

Figure VI.3 Punched card illustration.

cards in Figure VI.3 is statement number 103 the following pair of statements will cause, on execution of the compiled program, either of the two cards to be read.

```
    READ (5, 103) X, Y, I
103 FORMAT (F10.3, F8.3, I6)
```

The result of the execution of these statements is the storing of the values 40.29, 11.111 (or 1.907463 for the second illustration), and 999 for the values of variables X, Y, and I, respectively.

If the values of the same variables are to be printed, but with the values spaced out across the page, the statements would be

```
    WRITE (6,105) X, Y, I
105 FORMAT (F10.3, 15X, F8.3, 15X, I6)
```

The execution of the compiled program would produce paper output having the following form (assuming the values are 40.29, 11.111 and 999):

```
bbbb40.290bbbbbbbbbbbbbbb11.111bbbbbbbbbbbbbbbb999
```

Where the number of digits plus decimal point and sign (if negative) is smaller than the field, columns on the left of the digits remain blank and columns on the right of the digits are assumed to be equal to zero. The actual appearance of the line just indicated would be

```
    40.290               11.111                999
```

with the first number beginning in column 5 of the printed page.

In the program YOU DO the variables in the input list, X1, . . . , X8, are all represented with the same field structure, ten columns per field in consecutive sets of ten columns. The designation of the eight fields in a FORMAT statement might be

```
FORMAT (F10.4, F10.4, F10.4, F10.4, F10.4, F10.4, F10.4, F10.4)
```

However, a convenience in writing field specifications is built into Fortran. When adjacent fields have the same field description they may be specified by writing an INTEGER constant in front of the field designation indicating how many times the designation is to be repeated. In the example from YOU DO the eight F10.4 field designations can be specified by 8F10.4. This repetition of field designations applies to output as well as input. The repetition must refer to adjacent fields. If there are intervening fields with different specifications, two fields with a given specification will have to be represented separately in the FORMAT statement. To represent the field specifications

```
F10.4, F10.4, I6, I6, I6, F10.4, I6, I4
```

with repeated field specifications the statement would be

```
FORMAT (2F10.4, 3I6, F10.4, I6, I4)
```

In output, the insertion of blank fields between fields of data does not permit this economy, although at a slightly more advanced level of programming other methods permit grouping of field representations. These methods will be introduced in Chapter 9.

Record Spacing. This section introduces two additional features that allow more flexibility in programming.

The character "/" may be used in FORMAT statements to produce spacing. Unless otherwise instructed by the programmer, each execution of a WRITE statement produces one line of print, with all of the values specified in the list appearing on that line. When / appears in a FORMAT statement used for ouput, a new line of print is produced. Thus, the statements

```
  WRITE (6,2) X, Y, Z
2 FORMAT (F10.2/F10.2/F10.2)
```

would result in the printing of the values of X, Y, and Z on separate lines. Note that when a / is used to separate field descriptions, commas may be omitted.

When the character / appears in a FORMAT statement used in reading cards, the input tape moves to a new card image. As an example, suppose that three values are to be read from data cards, A and B from one card and C from a second card. The following statements would accomplish the reading.

```
   READ (5,10) A, B, C
10 FORMAT (2F4.0/F4.0)
```

The field description 2F4.0 describes two fields on the first card, containing A and B, respectively. The slash indicates a new card, and F4.0 describes the form in which the value for C appears on that card.

While the slash is used to move the page from one line to the next, it is the first character on the line that actually controls the printer carriage. The first character on a line is never printed, but may have an effect on the printer before the line is printed. The characters that are used for printer control vary according to the computer installation. However, the table below gives a widely used set of such characters.

Character	*Causes ... before printing*
Blank	Single space
0	Double space
+	No space
1	Skip to top of next page
2	Skip to next half-page
4	Skip to next fourth-page
6	Skip to next sixth-page

The most common method of introducing carriage control into a FORMAT statement is by inserting the characters 1H*c* as the first specification for a new line of print, where the symbol *c* indicates any of the carriage control characters from the table above. For example, by writing

```
FORMAT (1H1, ...)
```

a skip to the top of a new page of paper is produced. Likewise, the use of 1H*b* will produce a single space, etc.

To print the value of X, Y, and Z, starting with X at the top of a new page, and with one-sixth page between each value, the statements

```
   WRITE (6,10) X, Y, Z
10 FORMAT (1H1, F10.2/1H6, F10.2/1H6, F10.2)
```

will produce the output page schematized in Figure VI.4.

I/O WITH SUBSCRIPTED VARIABLES

In discussing the READ and WRITE statements the list was introduced as an explicit listing of variables to be input or output. When the material to be input or output is an array, this method is inefficient. One procedure to solve the problem should be clear to the reader—the use of a DO enclosing the I/O statement. For example, a DO loop to print out the array $X_1, \ldots, X_{50}$ without listing all fifty designations in the list of the PRINT statement might be

```
    DO 123 I = 1, 50
    WRITE (6,321) X(I)
321 FORMAT (1Hb, F5.2)
123 CONTINUE
```

This expedient has the unfortunate drawback of giving a long list of numbers one number per line: fifty lines, each containing one number. The solution is provided by an implied DO in the list of the I/O statement.

The Implied DO. When an array, or a portion of an array, is to be transmitted (either input or output) it is not necessary to list each element individually in the I/O statement. Suppose X(1), ..., X(50) is to be transmitted. This can be written in the Fortran list as

```
(X(I), I =1, 50)
```

This element of an I/O list is interpreted in the same manner as a DO would be; it defines an index (I in the example) that takes on certain specified values as though the index were in a DO loop. Values of the variable named in the im-

```
*******.**    ← field containing X

              ← 1/6 page

*******.**    ← field containing Y

              ← 1/6 page

*******.**    ← field containing Z
```

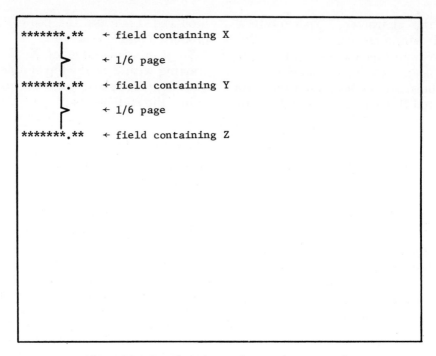

Figure VI.4 Sample output using carriage control.

plied DO, e.g., X, are transmitted, using the index as a subscript.

As an example, suppose that values of X, Y, Z, and SAM(1), ..., SAM(10) are to be read from cards. The format of the cards is described in a statement numbered 108. The read statement could be

READ (5, 108) X, Y, Z, (SAM(I), I = 1, 10)

Note that the implied DO is enclosed in parentheses, and that the entire sequence of symbols thus enclosed constitutes an element in the list.

If an entire array is to be transmitted by an I/O statement, an abbreviated list is allowed. If the array Q is to be transmitted, the statement may be

READ (5,110) Q

assuming that the array Q has been dimensioned. If Q is declared by the statement

DIMENSION Q(100)

then the 100 elements of Q may be read by either of the following two statements:

READ(5,119) Q

or

READ(5,119) (Q(I), I = 1, 100)

In either case, the format statement numbered 119 must describe 100 numeric fields for the values of Q.

In reading an entire array by the abbreviated list, care must be taken to have the data cards for the entire array as dimensioned. Hence, if P is dimensioned by

DIMENSION P(523)

the implied DO that is implicit in

READ (5,115) P

covers all 523 elements in the abbreviated list. The more general implied DO does not have to involve all of the dimensioned array. In the array P above it may be desired to read only the first 19 elements. The abbreviated form cannot be used unless the rest of the dimensioned array is "dummied" (e.g., with blank cards). However

(P(I), I = 1, 19)

in the list causes only the first 19 values,

that is P(1), ..., P(19), to be transmitted.

A single READ statement may be used to read parameters, and also to make use of the parameters in an implied DO. For example, the statement

```
READ (5,100) N, (X(I), I = 1, N)
```

reads N, and then uses the newly read value as an indexing parameter for the implied DO.

Any number of variables may be specified in a single list. However, the associated FORMAT statement must specify the same number of fields as there are items in the list. If more fields are specified than there are items in the list, the remaining fields are ignored.

The input section of U DO 2 is illustrative of the use of the implied DO in input. Up to 500 values of the array X may be input. However, no provision is made to input the number of values, N. N is determined within the loop containing the READ. Eight fields (i.e., a complete card) at a time are read by the statements

```
      READ (5, 10000) (X(J), J = I, K)
10000 FORMAT (8F10.0)
```

The READ statement causes data to be read from a card into locations named X(I), ..., X(K) where I and K are calculated just before the READ. This statement is equivalent to the READ statement

```
READ(5,10000) X(I), X(I+1), X(I+2),
X(I+3), X(I+4), X(I+5), X(I+6),X(I+7)
```

since K = I + 7.

A slight modification leads to a simpler input procedure in the program. Imagine that the programmer is always able to tell how many values are to be read into the array so that he can include in the data deck a card with that number punched on it. This parameter card is placed first in the deck punched, say, with an I3 field. The remaining data cards are punched in the same manner as in U DO 2. The appropriate READ and FORMAT statements are then

```
      READ (5, 10000) N, (X(I), I=1, N)
10000 FORMAT(I3/(8F10.0))
```

The FORMAT in the last example involves a use of parentheses to designate repetition. This is analogous to enclosing a FORMAT within a FORMAT. If a field or set of fields is enclosed in parentheses within the primary parentheses of the FORMAT statement, the enclosed set is repeated until the list is entirely transmitted. The interior right parenthesis acts like a / in the FORMAT. If the enclosed field is to be repeated a fixed number of times and then successive fields are to be used, an integer in front of the parenthesis indicates the number of repetitions. For example, the field specification

```
(I3, 2(F6.2, I4), F10.0)
```

is equivalent to

```
(I3, F6.2, I4, F6.2, I4, F10.0)
```

If a right parentheses, i.e.,), is encountered before the entire list is transmitted, the field description next used is the description just right of the left parenthesis paired with the right parenthesis. This is repeated indefinitely except when a number of repetitions is specified as above. The end of a parenthesis acts like a slash by causing input of the next card or output of the next line. In the FORMAT specification

```
(I3/ (8F10.0))
```

the list is read with the first card transmitting only one three digit INTEGER number and then succeeding cards are read, each transmitting eight ten-digit REAL numbers.

TWO-DIMENSIONAL ARRAYS

In the previous chapter it was shown how the learning score data could be handled by working with a single subscript, or a one-way, array. It is more natural to work with these data by conceptualizing the subjects as one dimension or subscript and the trials as the second dimension or subscript. Many situations in behavioral science call for a two-way layout of data. For example, a two-way layout is involved when several subjects are observed in each of several experimental conditions, or from each of several populations, or several levels of an independent variable. In Fortran such an arrangement is called a two-dimensional array. The word dimensional refers to the fact that the data are arranged along two axes, or by rows and columns. One of the dimensions might refer to the subjects (e.g., rows) and the other dimension might refer to the population from which the subjects were sampled (e.g., columns).

Suppose we have scores for N subjects in an anthropological study in which each subject was scored on K different measuring instruments. The K different scores are referred to as variables. The basic data sheet for such a collection of data might appear like those presented in Figure VI.5. Note that we may designate any particular row as the *i*th row and any column as the *j*th column. Thus, any value in the table may be designated as X_{ij}, where i gives the row number and j the column. For example, the score of subject 1 on variable 1 is designated X_{11}, and has the value 99 in Figure VI.5. Likewise, the score of the same subject on variable 2 (that is, X_{12}) is 26. The score of the *i*th subject on the *j*th variable is designated X_{ij}. The values of i and j must be stipulated before the value of X_{ij} can be specified.

The Fortran notation for double subscripted variables is similar to that for single subscripted variables. The subscript for the row is indicated first, followed by a comma and then the subscript for the column. Thus, the element in the array at the intersection of the *i*th row and the *j*th column is designated X(I,J). Specific columns or rows are designated by specifying the column or row number rather than the index name. The *j*th element in the first row is indicated by X(1,J). The 104th element in the *i*th column is indicated by X(104,I).
The actual index used in an abstract identification of an element in an array must be a number before the specific element is identifiable. However, the number may be determined by a calculation outside of the element designation. For example, the loop below will cause the sum of the fourth row of a two-way array X (N rows, K columns) to be summed into

Subject	Variable 1	Variable 2	...	Variable j	...	Variable K
1	99	26		X_{1j}		128
2	75	31		X_{2j}		97
.						
.						
.						
i	X_{i1}	X_{i2}		X_{ij}		X_{iK}
.						
.						
.						
N	93	34		X_{Nj}		77

Figure VI.5 Scores (X) of N hypothetical subjects on K variables.

the one-way array element ROWSUM(4)

```
      I = 4
      ROWSUM(I) = 0.0
      J = 1
   99 ROWSUM(I) = ROWSUM(I) + X(I,J)
      J = J+1
      IF (J - K) 99, 99, 100
  100 CONTINUE
```

Statement number 99 does not explicitly state the values of the indices I and J. The replacement statements before and after statement 99 result in the numerical definition of I and J.

If we want to take the sum for each of the N rows of the two-way array the loop could be written so that as soon as one row sum had been determined another could be found. This would make a loop within a loop. The following coding gives just such an analysis.

```
      I = 1
   88 ROWSUM(I) = 0.0
      J = 1
   99 ROWSUM(I) = ROWSUM(I) + X(I,J)
      J = J + 1
      IF(J - K) 99,99,111
  111 I = I + 1
      IF(I - N) 88,88, 222
  222 CONTINUE
```

A flow chart of this loop within a loop coding is shown in Figure VI.6. The coding for a column summation program is given below. This coding should be studied carefully and flow charted by the reader—make close comparison with the row summation coding. Both calculations require that the arrays X, COLSUM, and ROWSUM have proper DIMENSION statements.

```
      J = 1
   11 COLSUM(J) = 0.0
      I = 1
   22 COLSUM(J) = COLSUM(J) + X(I,J)
      I = I + 1
      IF(I -N) 22, 22, 33
   33 J = J + 1
      IF(I - K) 11, 11, 44
   44 CONTINUE
```

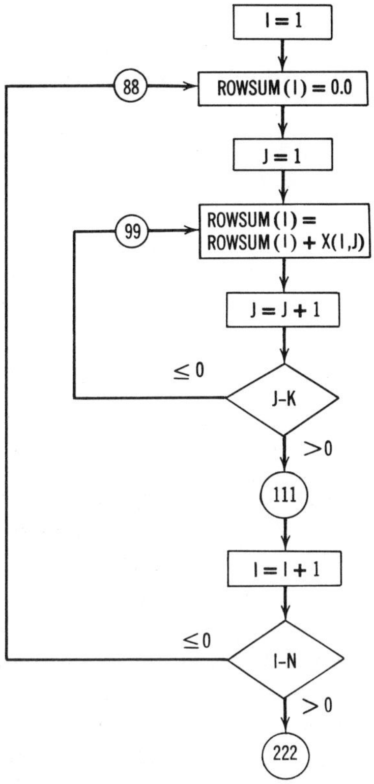

Figure VI.6 Flow chart of coding to find sums of rows in two-way layout.

NESTED DO STATEMENTS

The nesting of DO statements, one within the range of another, is useful in executing the same type of problem. For example, the row summation and the column summation separately may be done with the following coding:

```
      DO 123 I = 1, N
      ROWSUM(I) = 0.0
      DO 123 J = 1, K
      ROWSUM(I) = ROWSUM(I) + X(I,J)
  123 CONTINUE
      DO 321 J = 1, K
      COLSUM(J) = 0.0
      DO 321 I = 1, N
      COLSUM(J) = COLSUM(J) + X(I,J)
  321 CONTINUE
```

The flow chart for the row summation part of this coding is shown in Figure

VI.7. The same calculation can be done in another way that illustrates a different combination of coding to perform the same task.

```
      DO 555 I = 1, N
  555 ROWSUM(I) = 0.0
      DO 666 J = 1, K
  666 COLSUM(J) = 0.0
      DO 777 I = 1, N
      DO 777 J = 1, K
      COLSUM(J) = COLSUM(J) + X(I,J)
      ROWSUM(I) = ROWSUM(I) + X(I,J)
  777 CONTINUE
```

When one DO occurs within the range of a previous DO the interior DO is completely executed every time the outside DO goes through one loop. Thus, in the accumulation loops of the coding above J is run from 1 through K for each value of I from 1 through N.

The full set of rules governing the DO statement are discussed in Chapter 8. However, one rule must be stated here to permit the reader to use the DO without making a common mistake of beginning programmers. The end of an interior DO must be no further than the end of an exterior DO. That is, the statement specified in an inner DO must come before (or be the same) statement specified in the outer DO.

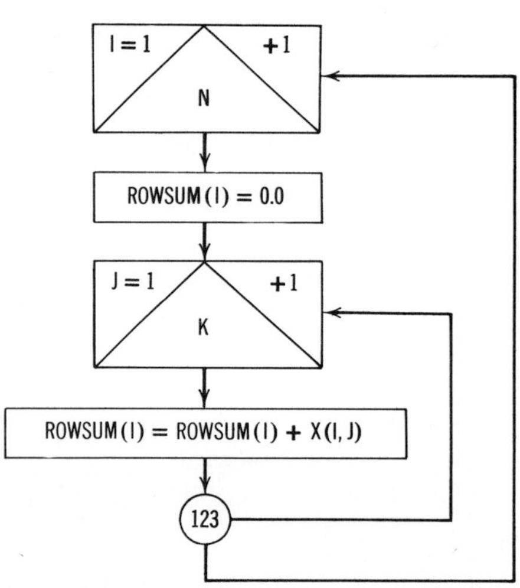

Figure VI.7 Partial flow chart for row summation.

Implied DO in Two-Dimensional Arrays. The implied DO used in input or output of a one-dimensional array may be generalized to the two-dimensional array. An M by N array (M rows, N columns) might be read by the following statement:

```
READ(5,101) M, N, ((X(I,J), I=1,M), J=1,N)
```

The order in which the indices are specified defines the form of the array as it appears in memory after transmission. The list implied by the elements in the parentheses is made up of N times M elements. The N times M elements may be read into the computer either by rows or by columns. The first subscript in the variable designation, e.g., I in X(I,J), defines the rows of the array, and the second subscript defines the columns of the array.

As an example, consider the 3 by 4 array X illustrated in Figure VI.8. Suppose that the array is punched by rows, that is, the first card contains X(1,1), X(1,2), X(1,3), and X(1,4). The second card contains X(2,1), X(2,2), etc. The implied DO describing this array must indicate that all elements in row 1 are to be read first, followed by all elements of row 2, and finally all elements of row 3. To put the matter in a different way, in reading across a card, the values of X punched there are arranged in such a way that the second subscript varies most rapidly.

In writing the implied DO for a two-dimensional variable, the index (I or J) that has its values defined in the position closest to the variable name varies most rapidly. Thus, the implied DO to read X should be

```
((X(I,J), J = 1,4), I = 1,3)
```

The innermost index definition (innermost meaning closest to the variable name) defines J, the subscript that is to vary most rapidly. This indicates that the value of J is to be varied from 1 to 4, and then I is to be increased by 1, and

		Column 1	Column 2	Column 3	Column 4
Row	1	X(1,1)	X(1,2)	X(1,3)	X(1,4)
	2	X(2,1)	X(2,2)	X(2,3)	X(2,4)
	3	X(3,1)	X(3,2)	X(3,3)	X(3,4)

Figure VI.8 A 3x4 array X to be read.

then J varied from 1 to 4 again, and so on. The process is parallel to having two DO loops, one nested inside the other as is illustrated in Figure VI.7. The implied DO for reading might be flow charted as shown in Figure VI.9. The inner index is always varied through all of its values before the outer index (the farthest from the variable name) is increased to its next value.

Suppose that the array X had been punched by columns rather than by rows, so that the first card contained X(1,1), X(2,1), and X(3,1); the second card contained X(1,2), X(2,2), and X(3,2), and so on. Here it is the first subscript that varies most rapidly. In this example, the indexing information for the first subscript (I) must be placed closest to the variable name in the implied DO. The implied DO is written

((X(I,J)), I = 1,3), J = 1,4)

which specifies I, the row (or first-named) index as that which varies most rapidly.

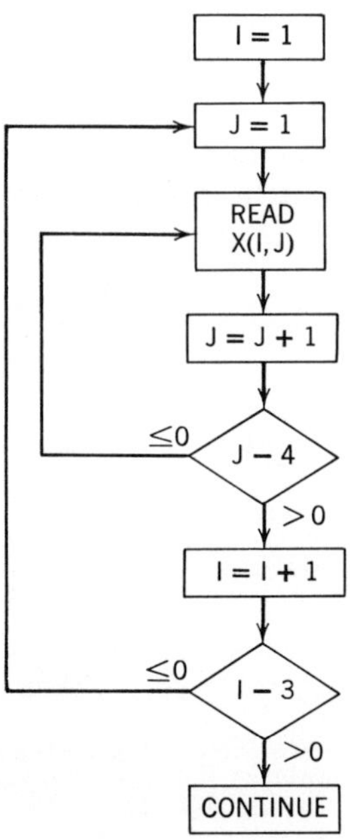

Figure VI.9 "Flow chart" for two-dimensional implied DO.

Great care must be exercised in writing implied DO elements of I/O lists. It is extremely easy, even for experienced programmers, inadvertently to interchange subscripts. When this happens, chaos generally results. For example, if the array X had been punched as rows, but read with the implied DO for columns given above, only the first value of X (X(1,1)) would be placed correctly in memory. Some of the values of X would not be read at all; the others would be placed in the wrong locations.

COMMON ERRORS IN ELEMENTARY I/O PROGRAMMING

Of all of the possible ways to make errors in Fortran programming, I/O probably offers the most fertile area for creative mistake making. An I/O error of a very simple kind can make the program fail to execute, or lead to the incorrect conclusion that it is operating incorrectly. Most of the errors are logical in nature, i.e., they are rarely diagnosed by the compiler as syntax errors.

Syntax errors are usually caused by carelessness or omission. A misplaced or omitted comma or parenthesis can cause an error indication; this kind of error is usually simple to correct. A more subtle kind of syntax error is illustrated by the following pair of statements:

```
   WRITE (6,99) A, B, (ISUM(I), I = 1, 10)
99 FORMAT (12F5.2)
```

Here the mode of variables is in effect "mixed" across two statements. The WRITE specifies two REAL numbers and 10 INTEGER numbers, while the FORMAT describes 12 REAL fields. The FORMAT statement and the I/O list must agree precisely in number and type of information.

Another kind of error is represented by the following:

```
    READ (5,110) A, B, C, D, E, F
110 FORMAT (F2.0, 3F5.1, F2.0)
```

There are more items on the list for the READ than there are fields described in the FORMAT statement. The outcome of this kind of error is unpredictable but rarely happy. Depending upon the particular Fortran implementation, there may be an error message, or there may not be. If there is not, the program may be allowed to execute but will do so incorrectly; in this case, the value of F will be read with an F2.0 but from the next card if there is one in the deck. If there is no card the execution error message may be something like "end of record found in input tape." The converse error (listing fewer items than fields) is usually not inconvenient since fields that have no variables assigned to them are ignored.

The most common logical error for input programming probably is an incorrect FORMAT statement—one that does not correctly describe the card to be read. Suppose, for example, that the following statements were executed:

```
   READ (5,66) N, (X(I), I = 1, N)
66 FORMAT (I3/(F5.0))
```

The FORMAT describes a card containing a three-digit integer number in the first three columns—the value of N. But suppose that the card containing N were actually punched in a four-column field, packed right, i.e., bb25, representing 25 as the value of N. Such a card read with an I3 FORMAT results in the number 2 being transmitted. Since N is used to control additional reading of data, and probably for other purposes, serious errors can result. An error like this will be undetected by the compiler as the statements are syntactically correct. The error usually is detected by comparing the output of the program with what is expected. The program will appear to be operating incorrectly when it may in fact be logically correct except for one minor error on a data card (or in the FORMAT).

A frequent output error is that of not allowing sufficient space for printed characters to appear. The result of this kind of error is dependent upon the particular implementation of Fortran, and the local computing center rules. Making such an error results in incorrect (or missing) output, although there *may not* be any indication that the answers are wrong, and the program may otherwise be logically sound.

Table VI.1 lists some common error messages resulting from I/O errors. Some of these messages result from syntax er-

Table VI.1

Common I/O Error Messages

Message	Cause
SUBSCRIPT (IBM)	An incorrect number of subscripts was used in a statement. For example, the DIMENSION statement might read X(10,10) and the reference might be SUM=SUM + X(I)
AN INTEGER IS MISSING FOLLOWING I OR F IN THE FORMAT. (UNIVAC)	Self-explanatory
THERE IS NO LABEL ON THE FORMAT. (UNIVAC)	A statement number was omitted. A parallel message will probably be produced in connection with the executable I/O statement which refers to a nonexistant statement.
THE I/O STATEMENT LIST HAS A BAD USE OF (. (UNIVAC)	Either a parenthesis has been inadvertantly inserted or there is an error in an implied DO.
THE FORM FOR (I=A,B,C) IS BAD. (UNIVAC)	Error in the implied DO.

rors diagnosed by the compiler, and others are produced by the executive system during the execution of a program containing an error.

EXERCISES

1. Write the executable I/O statements in Fortran to do each of the following. The input tape is 5, output is on tape 6.
   (a) Read values of SAM, JOEY, and GLENN from a card image.
   (b) Print the values of variables JEAN, SARA, and MARY.
   (c) Write out the values of the variables X, BIG, Y(1), Y(2), Y(3), Y(4) and LITTLE.
   (d) A data card contains the values of the variables CORR(1), CORR(3), D65, and CORR(2). Read the card.
2. Correct each of the following Fortran statements
   (a) READ(5,21), X, Y, BIGGST SMALST
   (b) WRITE(6 22) F101, I, J,
   (c) RAED(5,103 JUMP, GO, STOP, WHEN
   (d) READ(5 B(1,2) B(1,3), B(1 4)
   (e) WRIGHT (,26) WHAT, 66, Y6(2)
3. Correct the following pairs of Fortran statements. Where insufficient information is given, indicate why you cannot correct the statement.
   (a)
   ```
       READ (5, 1), N, X, Y, Z
     2 FORMAT (I5, F6.5 F7.9, F6.6)
   ```
   (b)
   ```
       WRITE (6, 6) Q, R, JOHN, JIM
     6 FORMAT (I6, F6.3, F1.0)
   ```
   (c)
   ```
       WRITE (6,), N, X(1), X(2), X(3)
   198 FORMAT (I3.1, 4F3.0)
   ```
4. The following variables have the values as shown. Sketch the appearance of the output page resulting from each of the pairs of WRITE and FORMAT statements:

F = 11.683	Z(1) = 99.2	N = −7775
X = .0032	Z(2) = 1.063	M = −1
Y = 1992.8	Z(3) = −.06	K = 10005
I = 999	Z(4) = 116.0	L = −10005
J = 102	Z(5) = .3322	

   (a)
   ```
        WRITE(6,99) F, I, Z(2)
     99 FORMAT (F6.3, 3X, I3, 10X, F5.3)
   ```
   (b)
   ```
        WRITE (6,103) (Z(I), I = 1,4)
    103 FORMAT (1H1, 4F7.3)
   ```
   (c)
   ```
        WRITE (6, 9999) K, L
   9999 FORMAT (2I5)
   ```
   (d)
   ```
        WRITE (6,1) Y, (Z(I), I=1,5), N, I
      1 FORMAT (1H1, F6.1/1Hb, 5F10.4, 8X/1H6, I6)
   ```
   (e)
   ```
        WRITE (6, 73) N, J, Y
     73 FORMAT (2I3, F8.2)
   ```
   (f)
   ```
        WRITE (6,12) X, M, F
     12 FORMAT (F3.2, I6, F10.3)
   ```
5. Write all necessary Fortran statements to accomplish each of the following. Sketch the card and/or printed page fields. Compile and execute a program containing the statements.
   (a) Read in values for A, B, C, and D. All are real numbers. Assign the number of columns for each and locate the decimal within the field in any way you feel appropriate, but be sure that there is at least enough room in each field for 4 digits and a sign.
   (b) The following list of numbers gives the scores of 10 subjects on an IQ test. Show how you would set up the data card and write the statements necessary to read the card. The values are to be stored in a vector called X. Also read in N, an integer number giving the number of scores.

Subject	*Score*
1	98
2	128
3	76
4	85
5	111
6	103
7	81
8	99
9	121
10	90

   (c) Print out the values for the following variables. Each is real and will have no more than 8 significant digits. Have them spaced neatly across the page.

X_1
X_2
.
.
.
X_7
XMEAN
XMODE
RANGE

6. The Fortran statements below are intended to read values of X, Y, BIG, and N from a card. The card is arranged so that X and Y each are punched as 4-column real numbers, with two digits in front of the decimal and two following. The variable BIG is located in columns 12–18 and has one digit following the decimal point. N is a 6-digit integer starting in column 53. Correct the statements so that they read the card properly:

```
    READ (5, 110) Y, X, BIG N
110 FORMAT 2F4.0, 7X, F7.1, 16X, 15.2)
```

7. Flow chart and code a program that accomplishes the following.
   (a) Read the values of 5 variables, named V1, V2, V3, V4, and V5. V1 and V2 are punched on one card; each a real number with no decimal part, requiring 5 digits, and V1 separated from V2 by three blank columns on the card. The remaining three variables are on a second card; each a 6-digit real number, each with two digits following the decimal point.
   (b) Calculate the following:

$$\text{ALPHA} = \text{V1}+\text{V2}-\text{V1}*\text{V5}$$

$$\text{BETA} = \frac{\text{ALPHA}^2-\text{V3}-\text{V4}}{\text{V3}^2-\text{V5}^3}$$

$$\text{GAMMA} = \text{ALPHA} + \text{BETA}\ (\text{V3} - \text{V4}/6)$$

   (c) Print the values of the variables calculated. Have them printed at the top of a new page, on separate lines, and separated by exactly one blank line.

8. Construct a flow chart for a program to read six numbers, X_1, X_2, ..., X_6 to find their mean (XBAR) and variance (SCATER) where we define

$$\text{XBAR} = \frac{1}{6}\sum_{i=1}^{6} X_i$$

$$\text{SCATER} = \frac{1}{6}\sum_{i=1}^{6} X_i^2 - (\text{XBAR})^2$$

Write the program you flow chart and indicate how you would punch the data card(s) needed. Print the six values, along with XBAR and SCATER.

9. An array X has 10 rows and 20 columns. The data have been punched by rows, each row taking two cards. Each data value occupies 6 columns, with the decimal to be understood as being between the fourth and fifth columns in each field. Write the Fortran statements necessary to read the array.

10. Assume that the array X in Exercise 9 has been punched by columns, one column per card in the format of Exercise 9. Read the array.

11. An array Y has been dimensioned as 10 by 25. The data cards have been punched by rows, each row requiring three cards. The first two cards for each row contain 9 values each, and the third contains 7 values. All values are in 6-column fields, with the decimal always explicitly punched. Write the statement necessary to read the array.

12. ALPHA is a two-dimensional array with 50 rows and 25 columns. Each value of ALPHA will require two columns on a card, with the decimal following the second column but not punched. Input is to be by rows. Arrange the format for the data cards and indicate it in a sketch of a typical card. Write the FORMAT statement describing the data cards. Then write the Fortran coding required to read the cards. Do the coding in two ways—by using a DO loop over rows with an implied DO across columns, and by using a nested implied DO over both rows and columns. Write the Fortran code to print the array, 50 rows of 25 columns. Compile and execute the program.

CHAPTER 7 FORTRAN IV: DECLARATIONS

The largest part of the material already presented deals with operations expressed in Fortran, such as arithmetic operations and looping. Other types of statements, like the DIMENSION statement, do not result in computer operations but provide information to the compiler, or to the program itself during execution. This is an important distinction between two general kinds of statements. Statements that are only informative to the compiler or to the program during execution are called nonexecutable statements or declarations. Statements that directly result in operations being performed during execution of the program are called executable statements.

There are several varieties of nonexecutable statements in Fortran. The FORMAT statement is an example of a statement that provides the program with information during execution. The information in the FORMAT specification actually becomes part of the compiled program and is used by the input/output parts of the program during execution. Another example is the DIMENSION statement which is used by the compiler to assign space to arrays. The information in a DIMENSION statement does not appear directly in the assembled program but is reflected by the addressing established for operations in the program. In general, a nonexecutable statement in Fortran that causes the compiler to define operations of one sort instead of another is called a declaration, or a declarative statement. This chapter is devoted to a discussion of declarations.

In the previous chapters, variables and constants were regarded as either INTEGER or REAL. While these are the most frequently used kinds or types of internal representations, Fortran programs can deal with a variety of other representations of data. It would be more correct to say that the Fortran language is built to aid the user in interpreting and operating on the contents of storage locations and registers in a manner that may be interpreted as nonnumerical. For example, in computing Project 3, Automatic Diagnosis (Chapter 3), the programmer might make use of what is known as a "logical" variable. Such a variable may assume only two values, "yes" and "no" (or "true" and "false"). In carrying out the diagnosis for a given patient, the program could assign a "yes" if a particular syndrome were present and a "no" if it were absent.

Other sorts of variables are defined in Fortran. Alphabetic and other Fortran characters (e.g., *,+.=/) may be input and output. Although mathematical manipulation of these characters is not a common need, the ability to move them around in storage and to output them in printed form is a valuable aid in visual presentation of the results of a computer application. Plotting, for example, is frequently carried out by using special characters such as a blank and a * in the place of numbers. Projects 6 and 7 in Chapter 3, call for the use of these features of Fortran. This type of representation is useful when the program is to deal with data such as lists of names, or when it deals with symbolic material such as samples of English language text. Chapter 9 presents example programs to deal with alphabetic data, as is often needed when applying computers to verbal materials from behavioral science research.

Although behavioral scientists do not generally use magnitudes too large for the storage accuracy of the modern computer, the need occasionally arises for very large magnitudes with a high degree of accuracy. This need can be served by the use of the "double precision" mode in storing numbers. Two words are set aside for one double precision value, increasing the number of bits available to represent a number. In the same general category are the complex numbers involving two parts, a real part and a part multiplied by $\sqrt{-1}$.

The major part of this chapter is devoted to the discussion of arrays, their definition, storage, utilization in calculations, and input/output characteristics. When an array is introduced into a program at least two things must be specified: the type of information to be stored in the array, and the magnitude of the array. The type of information stored is defined in two ways: either implicitly by the first letter of the array name, or by a "type" statement. Arrays may be specified to have a number of dimensions. We previously discussed one-dimensional arrays and two-dimensional arrays. In this chapter, arrays of three dimensions and more are introduced, along with more information about the DO statement, and additional characteristics of input/output of arrays. Finally, this chapter spells out the manner in which Fortran programs cause information to be stored and cross-referenced.

TYPE STATEMENTS

The two most frequently used types of variables are REAL and INTEGER. Up to this point we have made use of the first letter of the variable name to designate the type of the variable. In this scheme, variables with names beginning with I, J, K, L, M, or N are considered INTEGER, and variables with names beginning with any other letters are considered REAL. This manner of specifying the type of variable is called "implicit typing" since the type is implicitly designated by the first letter of the variable name.

For many applications in programming implicit typing of variables is adequate. There are occasions, however, when the programmer wishes to use a variable the name of which implies a type other than that intended. Fortran permits the declaration of a variable to have a type different than the implicit type of the variable. The declaration is accomplished by the type statement, the general form of which is

$m\ v_1, v_2, \ldots$

where m is the designation of the type and v_1, v_2, ... are the names of variables. If the variables with names IFILE and N are to be declared REAL, the type statement

```
REAL IFILE, N
```

must appear in the program before any reference to the variables is made in an executable statement. For example, in calculating the mean of a set of observations from the number of observations, N, and the sum of the observations, SUM, the replacement statement

```
AVER = SUM / N
```

is a mixed expression under the implicit typing of the variables involved and hence illegal. If N is declared a REAL variable, the statement is correct. The declaration must be made before N appears in any executable expression.

In a similar manner, variables that are REAL under the implicit typing rules may be declared INTEGER. For example, the variables SCORE and TALLY may be declared INTEGER by the statement

```
INTEGER SCORE, TALLY
```

Unless a variable appears in a type statement it is considered INTEGER or REAL under the rules of implicit typing. It is therefore wasted motion to declare a variable if it is already typed appropriately by the first letter of the variable name.

In addition to declarations specifying variables as REAL or INTEGER, several other types of variables may be declared in type statements: DOUBLE PRECISION, COMPLEX, LOGICAL, and EXTERNAL. DOUBLE PRECISION and COMPLEX variables are not discussed in this book because of their limited use in behavioral science programming. Those interested will find descriptions of these types of variables in Fortran IV manuals. The chapter on control statements contains a discussion of the meaning and use of LOGICAL variables.

A variable declared REAL cannot be used as an INTEGER anywhere in the program. This extends to the reading of the values of the variable. If N is declared by

```
REAL N
```

and an attempt is made to read N by an I conversion field in the FORMAT statement, e.g.,

```
FORMAT (I4)
```

an error will occur and the execution of the program will be stopped. Likewise if the declared REAL variable N is used as an index or the upper value in a DO, as in

```
DO 333 I = 1, N
```

the compiler will refuse the code or an execution error will occur (depending on the computer). Additional care is often called for in avoiding mixed expressions when type declarations are used freely since the first letter is no longer an effective cue to type.

THE DIMENSION STATEMENT

The DIMENSION statement was introduced in Chapter 5. In this section the basic definition is reviewed, the statement generalized, and the actual storage of an array is presented.

When a variable is an array, that is, specified by a variable name and one or more subscripts, the compiler must be informed of two facts about the array. First, the number of dimensions in the array must be communicated. The number of dimensions may be one, two, or three (as high as seven in some implementations of Fortran). Second, since the compiler assigns space for the array, the number of storage locations must be transmitted. Both of these items of information are communicated to the compiler by means of the DIMENSION statement, which has the general form

DIMENSION $v_1(n_1), v_2(n_2),\ldots$

where v_i is the name of a subscripted variable, and n_i is a series of one, two, or three (or more if allowed) integer constants, separated by commas. The values n_i specify the maximum value of the respective indices.

The variable XMEAN may refer to a one-dimensional array of means. If the largest number of variables to be entered into the array is 50, the statement

```
DIMENSION XMEAN(50)
```

will cause the compiler to set aside 50 locations for XMEAN and permit the variable XMEAN to be used with subscripts up to 50. The DIMENSION statement implies a one-dimensional array by the fact that there is only a single element inside the parentheses.

At a slightly more complex level, two-dimensional arrays are specified by indicating the largest values of the index for both rows and columns of the array. If the array X has at most 100 rows and 50 columns the declaration of the array would be

```
DIMENSION X(100,50)
```

If the program is written with both the variables XMEAN and X as dimensioned arrays, one statement may be used to declare both arrays:

```
DIMENSION X(100,50), XMEAN(50)
```

In many applications it is convenient

to conceptualize data as forming a three-dimensional array. In computer Project 5, for example, the data form a three-dimensional array, one of which is defined by subjects. A similar application is the analysis of variance for a factorial design. In this example, the basic design may be conceived as, for example, a three by four array (2 dimensions) where rows represent drugs and the columns represent diagnosis in a study of the effects of drugs on the behavior of hospitalized mental patients. An illustration of the design layout is shown in Figure VII.1. Each cell of the array contains a number of subjects, e.g., ten in each cell of the design. The array might be introduced into the program as a three by four by ten array. If the dependent variable in the investigation is a score on a test for anxiety, the array might be declared in a DIMENSION statement

```
DIMENSION ANXITY(3, 4, 10)
```

ANXITY is the name of the array and the scores of the patients will be entered as the values of the elements of the array in accordance with the three-way classification by drug, disease, and patient.

Elements in a subscripted array are referred to in other Fortran statements. In the example above the element ANXITY(I,J,K) refers to the Ith drug, the Jth diagnostic category and the Kth subject. The order of appearance of the index in a reference to a dimensioned variable determines which dimension is involved. The actual index variable named in a reference is of no importance as long as there is consistency in the use of the index names. The specific element in the array is not identified until the indices are set to specific values, either within the reference as in ANXITY (3, 2, 7), or outside of the reference as in

```
I=3
J=2
K=7
X=ANXITY(I,J,K)
```

The same element is referenced in the statements

```
I=7
J=3
K=2
X = ANXITY(J,K,I)
```

illustrating the principle that it is not the name of the index but its value and the location of the value in the reference indexing that specifies the element of the array.

Subscripted variables may be used in Fortran expressions in any way that nonsubscripted variables are used. However, the specific elements of arrays may be determined by the assignment of values to the indices outside of the expression, or explicitly in the expression. Hence, the statement

```
SUM = X(1,1) +X(1,3) + X(15,38)
```

is the same as the statements

```
IA = 1
IB = 3
IC = 15
ID = 38
SUM = X(IA,IA) + X(IA,IB) + X(IC,ID)
```

In addition to specifying elements in

		Diagnostic Category			
		Category A	Category B	Category C	Category D
Treatment	Drug 1				
	Drug 2				
	Drug 3				

Figure VII.1 A 3x4 factorial design.

arrays by the use of variables and constants as the subscripts, an element may be indexed by an INTEGER expression inside the parenthesis, within certain constraints. If I is any unsigned, nonsubscripted INTEGER *variable*, and C and D are any two unsigned INTEGER *constants*, then the following are the types of expressions that may be used as subscripts:

```
I
C
D
I + C (or I + D)
I − C (or I − D)
C *I
D *I
C *I + D
C *I − D
```

The programmer must use care in writing expressions that are to be used as subscripts or indices. For example, the expression 5*I is allowed, but I*5 is not. The reader is advised to learn the rule that, with respect to subscripts, the constant appears first in multiplication, but the constant appears last in addition or subtraction.

Only one variable may be expressed in an index. That single variable must be the unsubscripted integer variable. If the value of an index is zero or negative when evaluated the program will fail (on most computers). Thus, the indices formed by IA + IB is illegal (two variables) and the index formed by I − 2 is illegal if I is ever equal to or less than 2. The following subscript expressions are valid:

```
X(I)
Y(4)
BETA(J+3)
SUM(5*ICOUNT)
ARRAY(8*JMAX − 16)
```

The following are illegal subscript expressions:

```
A(6.5)        (not an INTEGER constant)
B(ICOUNT*6)   (incorrect order)
C(19−J)       (incorrect order)
```

The DIMENSION statement must appear in the Fortran program prior to any reference in executable statements to the variables declared in that statement. The general practice is to place DIMENSION statements in the program above (before) any executable statements.

Several arrays may be declared in a single DIMENSION statement with as many continuation cards as allowed in the system. Any number of DIMENSION statements may be present.

STORAGE OF ARRAYS

The way in which Fortran stores an array variable deserves a good deal of attention. The beginning programmer frequently makes errors in input/output and in calculation unless he has a basic understanding of the storage of elements in arrays.

In one-dimensional arrays the elements of the array are stored in consecutive storage locations. If the array Y has been declared in a DIMENSION statement, such as

```
DIMENSION Y(75)
```

the storage for Y is in sequential locations beginning at a given location and ending 74 locations later. The storage might be diagramed schematically as:

Y(1)	Y(2)	Y(3)	Y(4)	. . .	Y(75)

In the case of a two-dimensional array, a somewhat different procedure is followed—the array is actually converted into a "one-dimensional" form for storage. A two-dimensional array has the general form shown in Figure VII.2 when written in the conventional manner as a matrix.

Consider the example where $n = 3$ and $m = 4$ so that the matrix is a 3 by 4 arrangement declared by

```
DIMENSION X(3,4)
```

and illustrated in Figure VII.3. The array is converted to a one-dimensional form by dealing with one column at a time. The first column is stored, followed column number

row number	1	2	j	m
1	X_{11}	X_{12} ...	X_{1j} ...	X_{1m}
2	X_{21}	X_{22} ...	X_{2j} ...	X_{2m}
⋮	⋮	⋮	⋮	⋮
i	X_{i1}	X_{i2} ...	X_{ij} ...	X_{im}
⋮	⋮	⋮	⋮	⋮
n	X_{n1}	X_{n2} ...	X_{nj} ...	X_{nm}

Figure VII.2 Illustration of a two-dimensional array.

by the second, ..., and finally the fourth. The arrangement may be diagramed as

X(1, 1)	X(2, 1)	X(3, 1)	X(1, 2)	X(2, 2)	. . .	X(2, 4)	X(3, 4)

The first subscript varies most rapidly, reading across the storage locations. An array stored this way is said to be stored columnwise. The compiled Fortran program increments the location number in memory while the indices of the array are incremented. The second index is held at a given value while the first index is incremented throughout its entire range. After the first index has reached its maximum value, it is set back to one and the second index is incremented. Then the first index is incremented through its range again. This process is repeated until all of the elements to be entered are entered. Thus, it is always possible to find the precise location of a word in memory by making use of the knowledge of the storage characteristics of the language.

column number

row number	1	2	3	4
1	X_{11}	X_{12}	X_{13}	X_{14}
2	X_{21}	X_{22}	X_{23}	X_{24}
3	X_{31}	X_{32}	X_{33}	X_{34}

Figure VII.3 A 3x4 array.

All of the elements in the array are reserved by the Fortran compiler even if only a portion of them are used when the program is executed. Thus, if an array X is dimensioned

DIMENSION X(5,5)

and a smaller array is stored in the locations of X, some of the reserved locations will be unused. If the actual array in the computation is

$$\begin{matrix} X_{11} & X_{12} & X_{13} \\ X_{21} & X_{22} & X_{23} \end{matrix}$$

it will be stored as if it were

$$\begin{matrix} X_{11} & X_{12} & X_{13} & X_{14} & X_{15} \\ X_{21} & X_{22} & X_{23} & X_{24} & X_{25} \\ X_{31} & X_{32} & X_{33} & X_{34} & X_{35} \\ X_{41} & X_{42} & X_{43} & X_{44} & X_{45} \\ X_{51} & X_{52} & X_{53} & X_{54} & X_{55} \end{matrix}$$

giving the relative memory locations of the actual array as

Location:	1	2	3	4	5	6	7	8	...	16	17	...
Contents:	X_{11}	X_{21}	( )	( )	( )	X_{12}	X_{22}	( )	...	X_{14}	X_{24}	...

where the ( ) indicates the unused locations.

If Y is dimensioned

DIMENSION Y(3,2)

and the program refers to it as a 2 by 3 array, reversing the subscript roles, serious errors occur. The array is defined in the DIMENSION statement as

$$\begin{matrix} Y_{11} & Y_{12} \\ Y_{21} & Y_{22} \\ Y_{31} & Y_{32} \end{matrix}$$

but the references are to an array

$$\begin{matrix} Y_{11} & Y_{12} & Y_{13} \\ Y_{21} & Y_{22} & Y_{23} \end{matrix}$$

The storage order as defined in the DIMENSION statement is

$$Y_{11}, Y_{21}, Y_{31}, Y_{12}, Y_{22}, Y_{32}$$

The order of the elements as referred to (i.e., as in a 2 by 3 array) is

$$Y_{11}, Y_{21}, Y_{12}, Y_{22}, (), ()$$

where ( ) refers to an undetermined quantity. Note that Y_{31} and Y_{32} are not referenced.

The order of an array may be larger than actually needed. Hence, if a program computes an N by M matrix X the values of N and M may be larger than the original application calls for. If N = 5 and M = 10 in the original application, but applications with N = 50 and M = 100 are in prospect, the matrix may be dimensioned

```
DIMENSION X(50,100)
```

to cover all general cases where N ≤ 50 and M ≤ 100.

When more than one array is declared in a DIMENSION statement the arrays are located in adjacent locations in core. Thus, the statement

```
DIMENSION REAL(50), INTEGR(10)
```

results in sixty locations being set aside for the two arrays, the first fifty locations for REAL and the next ten locations for INTEGR. If a reference is made to REAL(55), the location involved is the location 55 locations beyond the first element location of REAL. Consequently, the reference will be in error. Depending on the type of operation involved the error may or may not cause the program to fail in operation. For arithmetic operations the program will treat REAL(55) as a REAL number (unless otherwise declared in a type statement) even though the actual data representation at that location is an INTEGER representation of the number in the location.

Utter confusion can result in referencing two-dimensional arrays with indices not in accord with the DIMENSION declaration. For example, the data array SCORES with

```
DIMENSION SCORES(10,12)
```

is stored into a set of 120 storage locations. If reference is made to SCORES with the second subscript greater than 12 the program can reference a location beyond the confines of the locations allocated to SCORES. If the reference is SCORES(8,13) the 8th row of the array, the 13th element in that row, is specified. The location of the element is 10*12+8 = 128 from the first element in the array —clearly outside of the allocated storage.

The key to understanding the location of an element in an array is the identification of the two parts of the address of an element. The first part is the base of the array, the address of the first element in a one-dimensional array is the base of the array. The address of the (1,1,1) element in a three-dimensional array is the base of the array. The second part of the address is the number of locations beyond the base. The Ith element in a one-dimensional array is just I − 1 locations beyond the base. Imagine an array CAN with

```
DIMENSION CAN(20)
```

The element CAN(I) with I = 10 has an address equal to the address of CAN(1) plus I−1 = 9.

In an array BOX with

```
DIMENSION BOX(10,15)
```

the element BOX(I,J) with I = 4 and J = 6 has an address equal to the address of BOX(1,1) plus a quantity dependent on the number of rows and the values of I and J. In general, if r is the number of rows in the array the location is given by the address of the base plus $r(J - 1) + (I - 1)$ where J is the column index variable and I is the row index variable. In the example the address is given by the address of BOX(1,1) plus $10(6 - 1) + (4 - 1)$.

The formula for the address of an element depends on the way array storage is allocated. The entire first column (*r* elements in each column) is allocated before the second column is allocated (all *r* elements) and so on. Therefore the location of the 1st element in the second column is a full *r* locations beyond the base of the array. The fourth element in the second column is a full *r* plus 4 elements beyond the base of the array.

Confusing locations by exceeding the maximum index is an error often occasioned by a programmer reversing the role of the indices or reversing the upper value of an index. For example, in zeroing out an array prior to using it as a repository for calculated values, the index of the DO may be turned around erroneously. The correct coding is given by

```
      DIMENSION ARRAY(100, 10)
      DO 1111 I = 1, 10
      DO 1111 J = 1, 100
      ARRAY(J,I) = 0.0
 1111 CONTINUE
```

If the indices I and J are reversed the result will be the zeroing out of the locations outside of ARRAY that may contain needed information. If B is the address of the base of ARRAY, i.e., ARRAY(1,1), then

```
      DIMENSION ARRAY(100, 10)
      DO 1111 I = 1,10
      DO 1111 J = 1,100
      ARRAY(I,J) = 0.0
 1111 CONTINUE
```

will zero out addresses B, B + 100, B + 200, B + 300, ..., B + 9900, B + 101, B + 201, ..., B + 9901, B + 102, ..., B + 9902, ..., B + 109, B + 209, ..., B + 9909. In another type of reversal of indices the following coding will result in similarly undesirable results:

```
      DIMENSION ARRAY(100,10)
      DO 1111 I = 1, 100
      DO 1111 J = 1, 10
      ARRAY(J,I) = 0.0
 1111 CONTINUE
```

This will zero locations B through B + 9, B + 100 through B + 109, B + 200 through B + 209, ..., B + 9900 through B + 9909. Clearly this is an undesirable outcome of the loop. A careful analysis of the elements in subscripted arrays is necessary in order to keep these sorts of errors out of the program. Be sure that the indices indicated are the indices for the locations for which the operations are intended. A quick check of the DO statement and the DIMENSION can usually catch such errors.

For most purposes the programmer is not concerned with the arrangement of arrays in storage. In some error conditions, and for the use of the EQUIVALENCE statement (see below), an understanding of array storage is essential. The Fortran compiler establishes all of the necessary linkage between location and the subscripts used by the programmer. What is usually of concern is the total number of storage locations used by an array. This may be obtained as the product of the maximum subscript values given in the DIMENSION statement.

In order to illustrate the use of two-and three-dimensional arrays; the analysis of variance example used earlier in this chapter is partially programmed here. One aspect of the analysis of variance is the calculation of the sum of squares of observations within cells, for each of the treatment conditions across all of the other treatment conditions and for the total sample. The entire data set corresponds to a three-dimensional array, say X(I,J,K) where I indicates drug treatment conditions, J represents disease category, and K refers to subjects within a specific I,J combination. If we restrict the program to this specific design with a limited number of subjects in each cell, say N = 100, the program can be simplified considerably over what would be required for a general analysis of variance program. It will be assumed that each cell has the same number of subjects. In addition to X, a two-dimensional array will be needed to store the cell sums of squares, and two one-dimensional arrays to store the treatment sums of squares (one for rows and one for columns). A single variable is sufficient to store the total sum of squares.

It is convenient in this example to read a card indicating the number of observations in each cell, N. A simple way to input the data for such a design is to read N cards, each with a replication for the entire design. That is, N cards, each containing the score for one subject for each cell. The order of the data on the card is a columnwise input order, A1, A2, A3, B1, B2, B3, C1, C2, C3, D1, D2, D3, where for example B3 refers to category B and drug 3. The program listing for a simple program ANOVA is shown in Figure VII.4.

If we let CELSUM be the array into which the sums of squares within cells

```
CANOVA
CANOVA  AN EXAMPLE PROGRAM USING A THREE DIMENSION ARRAY. THE SUMS OF
C       SQUARES FOR CELLS AND LEVELS ON TWO FACTORS (3BY4)
C       ARE CALCULATED AND OUTPUT. THE PROGRAM
C       ASSUMES EQUAL NUMBERS OF OBSERVATIONS IN EACH
C       CELL, N. N MAY BE NO LARGER THAN 100.
C
C       INPUT.. THE FIRST CARD CONTAINS N IN AN I3
C       FIELD. THE DATA ARE READ BY REPLICATION, EACH
C       CARD CONTAINING THE SCORE FOR ONE SUBJECT FOR
C       EACH CELL IN THE ORDER A1, A2, A3, B1, B2, B3, C1, C2
C       C3, D1, D2, D3 FOR CATEGORIES A, B, C, AND D AND DRUGS 1, 2, AND 3
C       SCORES ARE PUNCHED IN 12F6.2 FORMAT.
C
C       OUTPUT. SUMS OF SQUARES ARE OUTPUT FOR EACH
C       CELL OF FIGURE VI.1, AN FOR EACH DRUG AND EACH
C       DIAGNOSTIC CATEGORY AND FOR THE TOTAL SAMPLE OF
C       OBSERVATIONS.
C
        DIMENSION X(3,4,100),CELSUM(3,4),DRGSUM(3),CATSUM(4)
        DO 1 J=1,4
        CATSUM(J)=0.0
        DO 1 I=1,3
        CELSUM(I,J)=0.0
      1 CONTINUE
        DO 2 I=1,3
        DRGSUM(I)=0.0
      2 CONTINUE
        SUMTOT=0.0
        READ(5,100)N
    100 FORMAT(I3)
        DO 3 K=1,N
        READ(5,101)((X(I,J,K),I=1,3),J=1,4)
    101 FORMAT(12F6.2)
      3 CONTINUE
C   OUTPUT LOCATIONS ARE ALL ZERO AND DATA ARE ALL IN NOW.
C
C
        DO 5 I=1,3
        DO 5 J=1,4
        DO 4 K=1,N
        CELSUM(I,J)=CELSUM(I,J)+X(I,J,K)**2
      4 CONTINUE
        TOTSUM=TOTSUM+CELSUM(I,J)
        CATSUM(J)=CATSUM(J)+CELSUM(I,J)
        DRGSUM(I)=DRGSUM(I)+CELSUM(I,J)
      5 CONTINUE
        WRITE(6,103)
    103 FORMAT(1H1)
        DO 6 I=1,3
        WRITE(6,104)(CELSUM(I,J),J=1,4),DRGSUM(I)
    104 FORMAT(//4(5X,F15.4),15X,F15.4)
      6 CONTINUE
        WRITE(6,102)(CATSUM(J),J=1,4),TOTSUM
    102 FORMAT(/////4(5X,F15.4),15X,F15.4)
        STOP
        END
```

Figure VII.4 Program listing for the ANOVA.

are stored, DRGSUM be the array into which the sums of squares of drug treatment levels (rows) are stored, and CATSUM be the array into which the sums of squares of diagnostic categories (columns) are stored, then the appropriate dimension statement is

```
DIMENSION X(3,4,100), CELSUM(3,4),
DRGSUM(3), CATSUM(4)
```

First the output arrays are zeroed so that they can be used as accumulators. Two DO loops are useful and efficient here. First let J run from 1 through 4 resetting CATSUM. Nested in the first loop, a second loop with I running from 1 to 3 is used to set CELSUM to zero. In this way the program does not have to establish an independent index for looping through DRGSUM. However, it is not possible for the program to take advantage of the loop on I to set DRGSUM, without setting it four times over as the loop was repeated within the loop on J. It is more efficient to set up another DO and run through I from 1 to 3 to set DRGSUM. The array CATSUM might have been dealt with outside of the first nested DO statements but this would have required four passes through the loop instead of the three passes for DRGSUM. Since the nested DO statements involve a total of 12 cycles (4 times 3) anyway to zero out CELSUM, we take advantage of as many of these passes as possible to do other work, in this case the zeroing of CATSUM. The variable TOTSUM is set to zero next.

The input of N is simple. The input of X, however, must follow the form of the punching that has been selected. Actually the form of punching was selected because of the simplicity of the input algorithm that it made possible. The input is imbedded in an explicit DO ranging over K = 1, N. The actual list of the READ statement is defined by an implicit DO ranging over the indices I and J. The result of imbedding the implicit DO within an explicit DO is a nesting of DO statements three deep in the reading of data.

The actual calculation takes place in a triply nested DO. The outer pair of DO statements are indexed on I and J standing for the drug treatments and the diagnostic categories, respectively. Within the outer two DO statements is the DO to accumulate the cell sums for each I and J combination. Once a cell sum is completed for a given pair of values of I and J the cell sum is added into the sums for the category and drug treatment and to the total sum of squares. The second level of the two outer loops steps through its range, completing one row sum, i.e., drug treatment sum, each time through the loop. As the outer loop is executed the column sums are completed. It should be noted that the values are squared only once and that the accumulated within-cells squares are then accumulated for row and column sums. The program could have been written so that it would step through all 3×4×N scores for each of the sums of squares. Such a program would be several times less efficient than the present coding, where each sum within cells is added to the appropriate treatment level and the total.

The output is very nearly as simple as the input. The cell sums and the row sums are printed out row by row followed by the column sums and the total.

THE EQUIVALENCE STATEMENT

In large programs there is sometimes insufficient space to store all of the variables. This is particularly likely when large arrays are needed for data analysis or bookkeeping for calculations. If the program deals with an array early in the program but never again, the locations of that array can be used for another array later in the program. This is done by indicating, with the EQUIVALENCE statement, that the two arrays are to occupy the same storage locations. Imagine that two arrays X and Y are used, X first and then Y. Once Y is defined X is never needed again. The array locations can be made equivalent by the statement

```
EQUIVALENCE (X,Y)
```

The general form of the EQUIVALENCE is

EQUIVALENCE ($v_1, v_2, \ldots$), ($w_i, w_j, \ldots$), ...

where v_1, v_2, ... and w_1, w_j, ... are variable names, including subscripted variables. Each pair of parentheses encloses an equivalence set. This means that each variable, or element of an array, named in the equivalence set, refers to the same location in core. Thus, the same locations may be referred to by different names. If members of an equivalence set are elements of array variables, it means that the arrays overlap in such a way that the elements in the equivalence set refer to the same location. If a variable is not mentioned in an EQUIVALENCE statement, it is assigned to a unique location in memory.

Variables named in an EQUIVALENCE statement may be elements of arrays, implying that the arrays overlap. For example, the statements

```
DIMENSION X(10), Y(10)
EQUIVALENCE (X,Y)
```

allocate storage space so that the two arrays occupy the same locations in core:

X(1)	X(2)	...	X(10)
Y(1)	Y(2)	...	Y(10)

The EQUIVALENCE statement does not deal only with first elements of arrays. Arrays may be defined as overlapping in virtually any manner. The statements

```
DIMENSION X(10), Y(15)
EQUIVALENCE (X(2), Y(5))
```

cause the storage to be arranged as

		X(1)	X(2)	...	X(10)		
Y(1)	...	Y(4)	Y(5)	...	Y(13)	Y(14)	Y(15)

Imagine that we wanted to find the standardized values of a very large number of observations, say 20,000. Since there is not room for two arrays of 20,000 elements in memory we use the EQUIVALENCE statement to permit the calculations to be performed using two different variable names, one for the variable and one for the standardized values of the variable. Let the input observations be a variable X and the output observations, the standardized values of X, be a variable XPRIME. X and XPRIME will have the same dimensions:

```
DIMENSION X(20000), XPRIME(20000)
```

In addition, we want X and XPRIME to use the same space in the computer. This calls for an EQUIVALENCE statement:

```
EQUIVALENCE (X, XPRIME)
```

Assume that the data, X, have been input to the program. The mean and standard deviation are calculated by loops. If these two statistics are named XMEAN and STDEV, respectively, the equation for the *i*th value of XPRIME is

```
XPRIME(I) = (X(I) - XMEAN)/STDEV
```

If this statement is put in a DO with I = 1,20000 the values of XPRIME will replace the values of X. This could also be accomplished by the statement

```
X(I) = (X(I) - XMEAN)/STDEV
```

without the EQUIVALENCE of X to XPRIME—XPRIME would not be necessary. The advantage of XPRIME equivalenced to X is the clarity of statement in the program.

A more interesting example is the following. Imagine that the data variable OBS is dimensioned with 27,000 locations. We wish to modify the variable so that only the integer part of the values of OBS is retained for some calculations. Defining an integer variable IOBS and writing

```
DIMENSION OBS(27000), IOBS(27000)
EQUIVALENCE (OBS, IOBS)
```

permits the programmer to use the *same* 27,000 locations for storage of INTEGER *and* REAL values. The type of value stored by a READ or a replacement statement determines the internal representation of the value. For example, the statement

```
READ (5, 99)(OBS(I), I = 1, 27000)
```

places the REAL values of OBS into the 27,000 locations. The following statement, later in the program, replaces OBS with IOBS

```
IOBS(I) = OBS(I)
```

This places INTEGER values into the 27,000 locations as I is stepped through 1 to 27,000 in a loop.

THE COMMON STATEMENT

Another Fortran declaration is effective in the allocation of space to variables. The COMMON statement causes the space allocated to have a special designation that permits easy transmission of information from one part of a program to another when the two parts are compiled separately.

Since the use of the COMMON statement is meaningful only in the context of separately compiled programs, subroutines, or subprograms, discussion of COMMON will be reserved for Chapter 10.

SOME APPLICATIONS

We turn now to a brief presentation of two practical examples of subscripted variables in Fortran. Not only do these demonstrate the use of arrays but they illustrate some general concepts of use to behavioral science programmers. The first example is a program to rank N values of a subscripted variable. The program shifts the values of a variable from one location to another depending on the relative magnitudes of the values. The second example is the calculation of a matrix of correlations illustrating the use of simple matrix operations in dealing with two-dimensional arrays.

Simple Ranking. Imagine an array SCORE with N values in arbitrary order. We want to modify the order and output the list of ranked values and the corresponding observation number. Two arrays are needed, one for the scores and one for observation number. The arrays are restricted to 100 elements in the example, a restriction that is not necessary. The arrays are dimensioned by

```
DIMENSION SCORE(100), NUMBER(100)
```

The two arrays are read at the same time from cards that have the number of the observation and the score punched in alternating fields—the number of the first score punched and the value of the first score, the number of the second score punched and the value of the second score, etc. The numbers of the scores may be subject numbers, observation order numbers, or any other identifying numerals. The numbers are INTEGER and the scores are REAL.

We want to sort the largest observed values into the locations of SCORE with the largest subscripts and the smallest observed values into the locations of SCORE with the smallest subscripts. When an observed value is transferred in SCORE, its number must be transferred to the corresponding location in NUMBER.

The method to be used is referred to as the exchange method. The first observed values are compared. If the one with the larger subscript is smaller the two values are exchanged. If the observed value with the larger subscript is larger, the two values are not exchanged. The element with the next larger subscript is then compared in the same way with the larger of the first two observed values. This process is repeated until all N observed values have been examined. The largest value will be in the Nth location of the array at the end of the string of comparisons. Every time a value is exchanged, the observation number is exchanged in the array NUMBER. The process is repeated beginning with the small subscripts again. At the end of the second time through the loop, the second largest value will be in the next to last location in the array. The search need not proceed beyond the N − K element on the K + 1 search. Therefore, (N − 1) (N)/2 searches are all that are required, each search extending only to the N − K location in the array.

Let the variable MOST be the largest number of elements involved in the Kth search, i.e., N − K, and IBIG be the highest index value which on the last time through the search led to an exchange. IBIG is set initially to 1. If an exchange of elements in the array is necessary the value of IBIG is changed to the value of the index of the smaller of the two exchanged elements. If IBIG is still 1 at the end of the first search the implication is that all of the elements in the array are in numerical order. The value of IBIG, if greater than 1 after the search, indicates the subscript beyond which all of the elements are in numerical order. Consequently for IBIG greater than 1 the next search need only cover the first IBIG − 1 elements in the array.

The program is called RANK and is listed in Figure VII.5. A flow chart for RANK is shown in Figure VII.6. The reader should be sure to understand the role played by setting IBIG to 1 initially for any pass through the primary DO loop. The setting of IBIG to I within that loop is a device to keep the program from searching through the part of the array already in rank order. If the entire array is in rank order IBIG will remain unchanged with a value of 1. If IBIG is 1 either after the first search or after any other search, the array is in rank order and no further work is required.

Note the use of the two temporary storage variables BAG and BOX. Since SCORE(I+1) is to be stored in SCORE(I) the contents of SCORE(I) must be saved until it can be put into SCORE(I+1).

Correlation Matrix. In this example of array use, we shall depend on some knowledge of simple matrix algebra. The reader unfamiliar with matrix terminology and operations is referred to any standard text on matrices.

A simple program such as CORDEM is adequate for calculating a single correlation coefficient. When a larger number of variables is involved, the simple approach is inadequate. Consider, for example, the data given in Table VII.1. These data give values of three variables—the time spent in the start box, runway, and goal box, respectively, by 10 rats in a

```
CRANK
      DIMENSION SCORE(100),NUMBER(100)
      WRITE(6,1001)
 1001 FORMAT(1H1)
      READ(5,1000) N, ((NUMBER(I),SCORE(I)),I=1,N)
 1000 FORMAT(I3/(8(I4,F6.2)))
      MOST=N-1
   10 IBIG=1
      DO 1 I=1,MOST
      IF(SCORE(I)-SCORE(I+1))1,1,2
    2 BAG=SCORE(I)
      SCORE(I)=SCORE(I+1)
      SCORE(I+1)=BAG
      BOX=NUMBER(I)
      NUMBER(I)=NUMBER(I+1)
      NUMBER(I+1)=BOX
      IBIG=I
    1 CONTINUE
      IF(IBIG-1)3,3,4
    4 MOST=IBIG-1
      GO TO 10
    3 DO 5 I=1,N
      WRITE(6,1002) NUMBER(I),SCORE(I)
 1002 FORMAT(20X,I4,10X,F10.5)
    5 CONTINUE
      STOP
      END
```

Figure VII.5 Listing of program RANK.

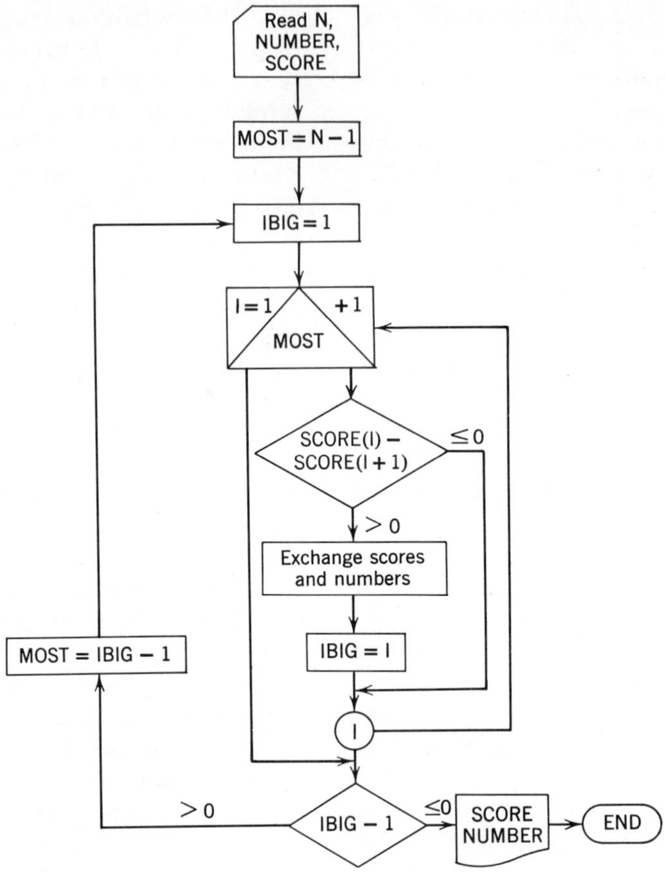

Figure VII.6 Flow chart for program RANK.

study on motivation.* If we wish to calculate the intercorrelations among the variables, only three correlations are involved (start-runway, start-goal, and runway-goal). If there were M variables, the number of intercorrelations would be $M(M-1)/2$, and matrix techniques would be much more efficient.

The data of Table VII.1 will be used to illustrate the computational steps to be followed. The resulting procedure and Fortran program can be generalized easily to applications where more than three variables or 10 observations are involved. We shall consider only the simplest case of correlation matrix calculation—where the raw score matrix has been standardized. (Recall the discussion of error in numerical calculation in connection with CORDEM.)

*We thank D. A. Leach for providing these data.

Call the original score matrix **X**. **X** may be standardized by calculating the mean and standard deviation of each variable (column). The standardized equivalent of each entry x_{ij} in the **X** matrix can be computed by

$$z_{ij} = \frac{x_{ij} - \bar{x}_j}{s_j}$$

where $\bar{x}_j$ is the mean of column j, and s_j is the standard deviation of column j. The matrix $\mathbf{Z} = [z_{ij}]$ calculated from the matrix **X** is shown in Table VII.2.

For simplicity, only the matrix **Z** is considered in the program segment which follows. Actually, the computation of **Z** from **X** would most likely be accomplished by the program as well.

Table VII.1

Time spent in parts of runway by 10 rats, in seconds

Rat	Start box	Runway	Goal box
1	0.25	0.90	0.40
2	0.35	1.36	0.60
3	0.22	0.83	0.42
4	0.29	0.79	0.35
5	0.49	3.14	3.66
6	0.21	0.79	0.46
7	0.24	1.03	0.83
8	0.31	0.81	0.39
9	0.31	0.99	0.37
10	0.27	0.82	0.34

Assume that the 10×3 array **Z** is in memory, having been either computed previously or read from cards. The matrix equation for computing the correlations is

$$\mathbf{R} = \frac{1}{N}\mathbf{Z}'\mathbf{Z}$$

where **R** is the 3×3 matrix of correlation coefficients, **Z**′ is the 3×10 transposed **Z** matrix, and $1/N$ is a scalar equal to the reciprocal of the number of observations; $N = 10$ in this example.

The first step is the calculation of **Z**′. This is accomplished in the program by the statements

```
    DO 100 I = 1,10
    DO 100 J = 1,3
100 ZT(J,I) = Z(I,J)
```

The transposed **Z** matrix is shown in Table VII.3. Next, each element of **Z**′ is multiplied by the scalar (i.e., divided by N)

```
    DO 101 I = 1,10
    DO 101 J = 1,3
101 ZT(J,I) = ZT(J,I)/N
```

Table VII.2

Matrix of standard scores, [Z], from scores of Table VII.1

-0.50	-0.37	-0.39
0.75	0.31	-0.19
-0.88	-0.47	-0.37
0.00	-0.53	-0.44
2.50	2.92	2.97
-1.00	-0.47	-0.34
-0.63	-0.17	-0.05
0.25	-0.50	-0.40
0.25	-0.24	-0.42
-0.25	-0.49	-0.45

Table VII.3

Transpose of matrix [Z], [Z]'

-.50	.75	-.88	.00	2.50	-1.00	-.63	.25	.25	-.25
-.37	.31	-.47	-.53	2.92	-.47	-.17	-.50	-.24	-.49
-.39	-.19	-.37	-.44	2.97	-.34	-.05	-.40	-.42	-.45

This array is shown in Table VII.4. Finally, now that $\mathbf{Z}'$ has been divided by N, the equation for the correlation matrix reduces to

$$\mathbf{R} = \left(\frac{1}{N}\mathbf{Z}'\right)\mathbf{Z}$$

The following Fortran statements carry out the matrix multiplication.

```
        DO 102 J = 1,3
        DO 102 I = 1,3
        R(I,J) = 0.0
        DO 102 K = 1,10
    102 R(I,J) = R(I,J) + ZT(I,K) * Z(K,J)
```

Illustrative calculations for the first two entries in **R** are shown in Table VII.5. The complete **R** matrix is presented in Table VII.6. The Fortran program calculating the matrix of intercorrelations is presented in Figure VII.7.

COMMON DECLARATION ERRORS

Several kinds of errors are made in writing declaration statements. These fall into three broad classes, each of which has been previously discussed and illustrated. These kinds of errors are: multiple dimensioning (declaring the same array in two or more places), syntax errors in the declaration statements themselves (e.g., leaving out necessary punctuation), and subscripting errors. While the latter category does not deal directly with declaration statements, the incorrect use of subscripts is often a result of the lack of coordination of use of subscripted variables and the declaration statements for those variables.

Table VII.7 presents some illustrative error messages produced by three compilers.

Table VII.4

Matrix resulting from the operation $\frac{1}{N}[Z]'$

-.050	.075	-.088	.000	.250	-.100	-.063	.025	.025	-.025
-.037	.031	-.047	-.053	.292	-.047	-.017	-.050	-.024	-.049
-.039	-.019	-.037	-.044	.297	-.034	-.005	-.040	-.042	-.045

Table VII.5

Calculation of r_{11} and r_{21}

$$r_{11} = (-.050)(-.50) + (.075)(.75) + (-.088)(-.88) + \ldots + (.025)(.25) + (-.025)(.25) = 1.000$$

$$r_{21} = (-.037)(-.50) + (.031)(.75) + (-.047)(-.88) + \ldots + (-.024)(.25) + (-.049)(-.25) = .86$$

Table VII.6

The correlation matrix, R

1.00	.86	.81
.86	1.00	.89
.81	.89	1.00

EXERCISES

1. Write the declaration(s) necessary for the following:
   (a) Variables BAG, BOTTLE, FLASK, JUG and REVNUR are to be treated as integers.
   (b) WHICH, WHAT, and WHERE are real variables and WHO and WHY are integers.
   (c) UP, DOWN, and AROUND are integers. UP is a one-dimensional array needing 50 storage locations.
   (d) HIM and HER are integer variables. WEEONE and BIGONE are single subscripted variables with the maximum value of the subscript being 100. HIM is likewise subscripted and requires 1000 locations of core.
   (e) LIST is a real array, 5×12×6.
   (f) COEFF is a real array, size 11×10. Its last column is the same as the variable YNOT.
   (g) The integer array DECK has 4 columns and 13 rows. Each column is to have an alternate name as follows:
   Column 1: SPADES
   Column 2: HEARTS
   Column 3: DIAMDS
   Column 4: CLUBS

```
CRMAT
C
C RMAT. A CORRELATION MATRIX PROGRAM.
C
C **** EXAMPLE--CHAPTER VI.****
C
      DIMENSION R(3,3),Z(10,3),ZT(3,10)
      READ(5,1001)((Z(I,J),J=1,3),I=1,10)
 1001 FORMAT(3F3.2)
      WRITE(6,104)((Z(I,J),J=1,3),I=1,10)
  104 FORMAT(3F8.3)
C TRANSPOSE Z AND STORE AS ZT.
      DO 100 I=1,10
      DO 100 J=1,3
      ZT(J,I)=Z(I,J)
  100 CONTINUE
      WRITE(6,1002)((ZT(I,J),J=1,10),I=1,3)
C
C MULTIPLY ZT BY 1/N.--ACTUALLY, DIVIDE ZT
C     BY N.
C
      DO 101 I=1,10
      DO 101 J=1,3
  101 ZT(J,I)=ZT(J,I)/10.0
C
C  PREMULTIPLY Z BY ZT, FORMING R MATRIX.
C
      DO 102 J=1,3
      DO 102 I=1,3
      R(I,J)=0.0
      DO 102 K=1,10
      R(I,J)=R(I,J)+ZT(I,K)*Z(K,J)
  102 CONTINUE
C
C  PRINT ZT AND R
C
      WRITE(6,1002)((ZT(I,J),J=1,10),I=1,3)
 1002 FORMAT(1H1,(10F8.3))
      WRITE(6,1003)((R(I,J),J=1,3),I=1,3)
 1003 FORMAT(1H2,(3F8.3))
      STOP
      END
```

Figure VII.7 Correlation matrix program RMAT.

Table VII.7

Some compiler diagnostics for declarations

Message	Cause
OD-DIMENSION statement order (CDC)	An array has been referenced prior to being named in a DIMENSION statement. On some compilers this is an error, on others it is not.
SB-Subscript (CDC)	Format error in subscript of an array reference. Usually this is due to using an expression in the subscript, and writing the expression incorrectly. It may also be due to a DIMENSION statement which was unrecognized by the compiler.
NON-COMMON EQUIVALENCE ERRORS (IBM)	A conflict between two or more EQUIVALENCE statements—both defining the same variables but in a contradictory way.
THE ARRAY ... HAS AN ILLEGAL SUBSCRIPT FORM (UNIVAC)	Any of several kinds of errors in writing a subscript expression.
THE ARRAY ... IS TOO LARGE (UNIVAC)	The assignment of storage for this array would require more words of storage than are available; or the size specified contains numbers larger than the allowable values of subscripts.

2. Modify the program RANK so that it sorts on the basis of subject numbers rather than scores. (*Hint*: only one statement need be changed.)
3. Modify the program RMAT so that it is more efficient. The program need not physically store the matrix ZT but can determine it by referring to Z with the subscripts reversed. The entire correlation matrix may be calculated in one set of DO loops. Note also that R is a symmetric matrix—that is, its transpose is R itself. Does this suggest a way to make RMAT more efficient?
4. Modify the program that you wrote for Exercise 3 or that it will calculate the correlation matrix for up to 10 variables. The actual number of variables and observations are to be read as data.
5. Modify RANK so that it sorts in reverse order—that is, high scores placed in the locations of SCORE with *low* subscripts.
6. Complete the program you wrote in Exercise 4 so that it is useable—that is, write the input and output as well.

CHAPTER 8 FORTRAN IV: CONTROL STATEMENTS, LOGICAL EXPRESSIONS, AND OPERATIONS

Fortran contains several statements that permit the programmer to control the flow of operations through a program. These statements do not cause any calculation directly nor are they executed in the same sense as arithmetic statements. There are three broad classes of control statements: conditional control, unconditional control, and iterative or loop control.

Unconditional control statements cause some specific condition to be established in the computer. For example, the PAUSE statement causes the computer to halt its operation. It is used to permit the computer operator to perform some manual action, such as mounting a tape on a tape drive. Other unconditional control statements cause a transfer of control from one portion of the program to another whenever that statement is reached. For example, the GO TO statement causes the program to transfer without conditions. (Recall the TRA transfer command discussed in Chapter 2.) Other unconditional control statements are END, STOP, and RETURN. These will be discussed in detail in this chapter.

Conditional control statements are similar to the unconditional control statements, except the operation of the statement depends on some specified condition in the execution of the program. The most often used conditional control statement is the IF, which is dependent on an arithmetic or logical (see below) expression. Depending on the value of the expression, the IF causes a transfer to a location in the program designated in the IF statement. The IF statement is similar in operation to the transfer commands TMI and TPL discussed in Chapter 2.

There are two forms of the IF control statement, the arithmetic IF statement and the logical IF statement. The arithmetic IF provides a choice among three alternative paths of program direction or control depending on the relative value of the arithmetic expression. One alternative is executed when the expression is evaluated as less than zero (negative), the second alternative is executed when the expression is evaluated as exactly zero, and the third alternative when the expression has a value greater than zero.

The logical IF statement is conditional on a logical expression. A choice is made between executing a statement specified in the IF statement or passing on to the succeeding statement, depending on the truth or falsity of a logical relationship. The logical relationship is specified in a logical expression according to rules that are spelled out below.

A conditional GO TO defined in Fortran permits the conditional use of a direct transfer to locations that must be specified during the course of execution of the program. There are two varieties of conditional GO TO statements—the COMPUTED GO TO and the ASSIGNED GO TO. These statements cause transfer to one of a list of specified statements depending on the value of a variable that is set as a result of a computation or that is set by the ASSIGN statement.

Perhaps the most useful and powerful control statement in Fortran is the DO statement. This statement has been discussed in the preceding chapters. Even so, the entire character of the DO has not been developed. This chapter reviews the material already presented and presents a complete description of the DO statement.

LOGICAL VARIABLES AND LOGICAL OPERATIONS

A logical variable in Fortran takes on only two values or states: true and false. A logical variable is not in any way an arithmetic variable. The operations that may be applied to logical variables are not the operations of addition, subtraction, etc., but rather they are parallel to logical conceptualizations, such as conjunction, disjunction, greater than, or equal to.

Our interest in logical variables and operations stems from the use of Boolean algebra, symbolic logic, and relational logic in the construction of sophisticated programs. The possibility of using logical propositions in the computer widens the scope of applications rather significantly. It is not our purpose here to discuss logic—the reader unfamiliar with logic should refer to a basic text on symbolic or Boolean logic. A particularly attractive introduction for behavioral scientists is Kemmeny, Snell, and Thompson (1956). We illustrate in this chapter the application of symbolic logic in one area of experimental psychology and indicate the way in which a computer can be of assistance in manipulating logical expressions.

Another, and probably the most frequent, use of logical variables in programming is in connection with branching procedures. Up to this point, we have used the arithmetic IF to introduce branching into a program. Once logical variables and expressions are understood, another powerful branching procedure can be employed.

Logical Variables. Any Fortran variable name may be used for a logical variable. If a variable is to be so used, it must be declared by a type statement having the general form

LOGICAL $v_1, v_2, \cdots$

where v_i is the name of the variable. If a variable is not defined by a type statement, the variable name will be interpreted by the compiler as having an implicit arithmetic designation (i.e., REAL or INTEGER).

Logical constants and variables have two values in Fortran. As with arithmetic variables, values of logical variables can be set internally during execution, they may be input, or they may be stated as constants in the program. The two logical values are

.TRUE.
.FALSE.

The preceding and following periods must be included in the value of the variable. When input/output for logical variables is discussed again in Chapter 9, we shall point out circumstances in which the letters T and F could be used for the two values.

Replacement statements may be used to set the logical state of a logical variable. For example, the statement

TEST = .FALSE.

stores the value .FALSE. as the value or state of the variable TEST. This statement presumes that TEST has been declared previously as a logical variable.

Mathematical Relations as Logical Relations. Mathematical relations are used in making comparisons of two arithmetic variables or expressions. The result of such a comparison is the value of a logical variable. That is, a comparison such as

$$A < B$$

in effect asks the question, "is A less than B?" The answer is either true or false, depending upon the values of A

and *B*. This comparison can be written in Fortran (where RELATE has previously been declared LOGICAL):

```
RELATE = ALPHA .LT. BETA
```

The logical variable RELATE takes on the value .TRUE. if the expression is true, or .FALSE. if the expression is false.

The mathematical relations defined in Fortran, the Fortran notation for them, and an example of each are shown below.

Relation	*Notation*	*Example*	*Mathematical Statement*
Equal to	.EQ.	A .EQ. B	$A = B$
Not equal to	.NE.	C .NE. D	$C \neq D$
Less than	.LT.	E .LT. F	$E < F$
Less than or equal to	.LE.	G .LE. H	$G \leq H$
Greater than	.GT.	I .GT. J	$I > J$
Greater than or equal to	.GE.	K .GE. L	$K \geq L$

The mathematical relations need not express, or ask about, the relationship between single variables. The relationship may be expressed between any two arithmetic expressions. Thus, the general form of the relation can be shown as

```
A .R. B
```

where A and B are arithmetic expressions and .R. is one of the mathematical relations defined above. Examples:

A + B / C .LE. D*E means $A + \frac{B}{C} \leq DE$

SQRT (A+D*COS(Q)) .GT. F means $\sqrt{A + D(\cos Q)} > F$

We consider the place of the mathematical relations in the discussion of the hierarchy of operations below, but for now it suffices to know that they are below the arithmetic operations, so that all arithmetic expressions are evaluated before the comparison is carried out. A relation takes the value .TRUE. or .FALSE. depending on the value of each of the expressions at the time the comparison is made.

When a variable has been defined as a logical variable, it may take on a value depending upon the result of a relational comparison. For example, suppose that the logical variable defined by

```
LOGICAL OK
```

is to be used in the program as a test of a relational condition expressed as

$$X^2 + Y^2 \leq Z^3 - \frac{X}{4}$$

If this inequality is true we wish to set OK to .TRUE. and if it is false we wish to set OK to .FALSE.. The Fortran statement

```
OK = (X**2 + Y**2) .LE. (Z**3 - X/4.)
```

will result in the desired state of the variable OK. The variable OK will be assigned the value .TRUE. if the inequality is true and the value .FALSE. if the inequality is false. Note that the parentheses are unnecessary.

Logical Operations. Logical operations are used to link two or more relational expressions. For example, if we want to determine the truth or falsity of the following, we would use a Boolean operation for linkage.

$X \leq 5$ (at the same time) $Y \neq Z$

The Fortran expression would be

```
(X .LE. 5) .AND. (Y .NE. Z)
```

The logical operations defined in Fortran are shown below. In the table, *a* and *b* represent relational expressions of the type just discussed or other logical expressions. In all cases, the entire logical expression is assigned a value of .TRUE. or .FALSE. depending upon the values of the variables and constants in the expression.

Symbol	*Meaning*
.NOT. *a*	Logical *negation.* If the expression *a* is .TRUE., then the entire expression has the value .FALSE.. If *a* is .FALSE., then the expression is .TRUE..
a.AND.*b*	Logical *and.* The entire expression will have the value .TRUE. only if both *a* and *b* are .TRUE.. If either *a* or *b* is .FALSE., or both are .FALSE. then the entire expression is .FALSE..
a.OR.*b*	Logical *or.* If either *a* or *b*, or both, are .TRUE., then the entire expression is .TRUE.. The expression will have the value .FALSE. only if both *a* or *b* are .FALSE..

The preceding and following periods must be present.

A logical expression may be defined as a string of logical constants, logical variables (which may be subscripted), references to logical functions (see below), and arithmetic expressions, separated by the logical or relational operators defined above. All variables in a logical expression must be of the same mode.

Parentheses may be used to enclose any part of a logical expression. Unless specified otherwise by parentheses, evaluation of a logical expression follows a clearly defined compiler-specified order. From highest to lowest priority, the following list shows the order of computation.

Priority	*Operation*
1	Function reference (e.g. SQRT)
2	**
3	* , /
4	+ , −
5	.GT., .GE., .LT., .LE., .EQ., .NE.
6	.NOT.
7	.AND.
8	.OR.

Within a given priority, evaluation proceeds from left to right in the expression. Parentheses play the same role in logical expressions as they do in arithmetic expressions.

The rules of order operate as illustrated in the following examples. Assume that A = 5.6, B = 10.0, and C = .005. The examples show the steps in the evaluation of the logical expressions. The final step gives the logical value of the entire expression.

```
Example A   A .LT. B
  Step 1     .TRUE.
Example B   B .GT. C .AND. A .LT. 4.9
  Step 1     .TRUE.            .FALSE.
  Step 2             .FALSE.
Example C   A + 10.3 .NE. 25.0 .OR. C*10.0 .GT. 1.0
  Step 1       15.9                        .05
  Step 2             .TRUE.                    .FALSE.
  Step 3                        .TRUE.
Example D   B+6.0 .EQ. 16.0 .AND. .NOT.(C .LT. 1.0)
  Step 1       16.0
  Step 2          .TRUE.                   .TRUE.
  Step 3                          .FALSE.
  Step 4                      .FALSE.
Example E   A + B .GE. .05 .OR. C .NE. .005
  Step 1     15.6
  Step 2          .TRUE.             .FALSE.
  Step 3                     .TRUE.
```

The examples also illustrate several other rules concerning the construction of logical expressions. These rules will be stated here without elaboration.

1. The logical operator .NOT. must be followed by a relational or logical expression, or an expression involving .AND. or .OR.. That is, the expression

```
.NOT. 15.8
```

is illegal. If the expression following the .NOT. operator contains two or more quantities it must be enclosed in parentheses. If the variable ALPHA had been declared as a logical variable the expression

```
.NOT.ALPHA
```

would be legal. If the variable were any other type of variable than logical the expression would be illegal. If the variable BETA were defined as a REAL variable the expression

```
.NOT.(BETA.LT.15.8)
```

would be legal.

2. Two logical operators may not be placed side by side unless one of them is .NOT., e.g.

```
(A.LT.10.).AND..NOT.(X.NE.27.8)
```

3. Two periods may be placed together only if one of them is a decimal point and the other a part of a logical or relational operator, or if both are parts of logical operators. Thus, the expression

```
C.NE..005
```

is legal.

4. The logical operators .AND. and .OR. must be preceded and followed by logical expressions.

An Example, Truth Tables. We conclude this section with an illustration of the use of logical variables and operations in a program to construct and evaluate truth tables. One of the growing fields of interest in contemporary psychology is concept formation, the process by which persons learn to place stimuli in categories that may be given convenient labels. For example, a young child may be shown an apple. He will not know what it is at first. But after considerable experience he will develop the concept "apple" which includes the following attributes as some of its defining characteristics: roundish, red (but not always), small, sweet tasting, etc. Once the concept "apple" has been learned, the child can identify a given stimulus object, and say whether or not it is an instance of that concept.

Psychologists studying concept formation typically make use of abstract objects, and combine them in arbitrary ways to form artificial concepts. Suppose, for example, we wish to teach the concept "red and square." We might construct a variety of stimulus patterns such as those shown in Figure VIII.1 and present them to the subject one at a time. The subject would be required to indicate whether or not the pattern was an instance of the concept. Of course, only those patterns that are marked * in the figure qualify. We might also want to teach the concept "either red or square, or both." In that case, the patterns labeled ** are instances of the concept.

In general, the various dimensions along which stimulus patterns vary take on either of two "values," i.e., red or green, square or triangle, large or small. These can be conveniently noted as "red or not-red," "square or not-square," etc. If we let T (or .TRUE.) stand for the presence of the attribute and F (or .FALSE.) for its absence, we can begin to see how logical variables in Fortran can be of assistance.

A basic tool for analyzing concepts is the truth table. Such a table lists the possible values for the stimulus, and indicates whether the stimulus is an instance of the concept. The truth table for the concept "red and square" is given in Figure VIII.2. This truth table can be written in Boolean notation as

$$\text{red} \wedge \text{square}$$

In Fortran, it would appear as

```
RED  .AND.  SQUARE
```

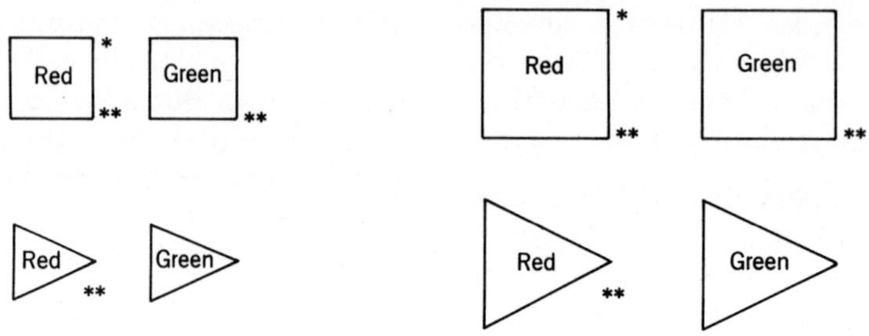

Figure VIII.1 Some stimuli used in concept formation.

assuming that both RED and SQUARE had been defined as logical variables. The expression would have the value .TRUE. only if both RED and SQUARE were .TRUE..

The reader should note that the truth table presents all the possible combinations of T and F for the two stimulus attributes. It follows, then, that a truth table can be constructed by listing the possible stimulus configurations, and determining which meet the requirements of the concept as stated in a logical expression. Let us write a program to determine the truth table for the concept "red or square or both." This program is a trivial example, but it serves to introduce the basic notions from which we shall proceed to write a program to generate truth tables for three variable (or attribute) expressions using complex expressions.

Figure VIII.3 presents the flow chart for the program. We define three logical variables COLOR, SHAPE, and TRUTH. The program will construct the truth table one row at a time, starting with the condition where both the color and shape attributes are true. Thus, we begin by setting both COLOR and SHAPE equal to .TRUE.. We then calculate the value of TRUTH, which is the truth value for

Stimulus attributes

Red	Square	Concept instance?
T	T	T
T	F	F
F	T	F
F	F	F

Figure VIII.2 Truth table for "red and square."

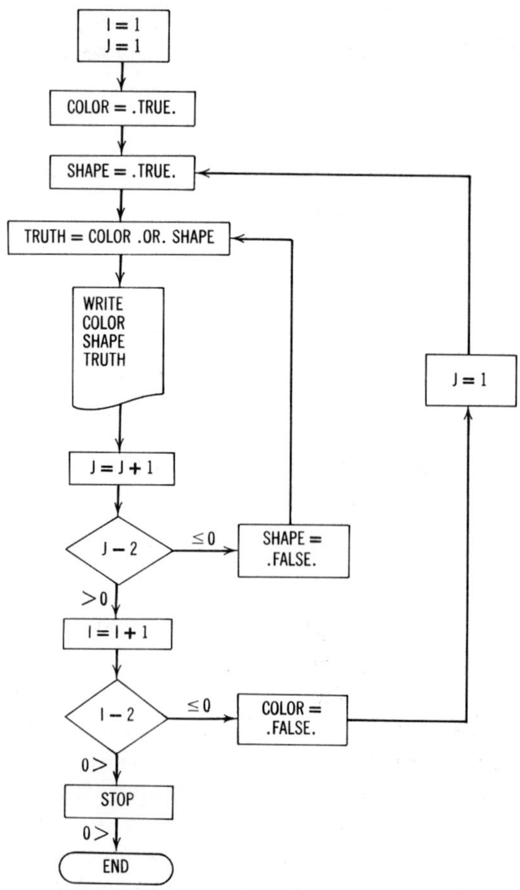

Figure VIII.3 Flow chart for truth table generation program.

the combination of the attributes of the concept. In this particular program, since the concept is "red or square, or both," the calculation of the truth value is accomplished by the statement

TRUTH = COLOR .OR. SHAPE

The program next prints the value of COLOR, SHAPE, and TRUTH, forming the first row of the truth table.

After the first line is printed, the program tests the condition of one of the two indicators (I and J) that control the loops in the program. If J = 2, the program sets the value of SHAPE to .FALSE., returns to calculate TRUTH, and then produces the second row of the table. At this point, J = 3, and the program tests I. If I = 2, the program sets COLOR to .FALSE., SHAPE to .TRUE., and returns to calculate TRUTH, producing the third row of the table. Finally, SHAPE is again set to .FALSE., TRUTH is calculated again, and the final row of the table printed. The Fortran program written from the flow chart is presented in Figure VIII.4. The student is urged to punch the program and run it.

The program uses only one unfamiliar operation. In the FORMAT statement, the output field is specified as a logical field, described by an L1 designation. This output specification will be described in detail in Chapter 9. The specification L1 describes a one-column logical field. The output will consist of one of the letters T or F, depending upon the value of the logical variable.

As a final demonstration of truth table generation, a second program is developed, TRUTH2. This program, an elaboration of TRUTH1, deals with three logical variables. We call the variables A, B, and C. They could stand for color, shape, and size, or any other three stimulus attributes in a concept learning investigation. To illustrate the ability of Fortran to evaluate complex logical expressions, the concept involved can be defined by the logical expression

$$(A \wedge B) \vee (A \wedge C') \vee (B \wedge C)$$

or, in Fortran, the expression would be

TRUTH = (A.AND.B).OR.(A.AND..NOT.C).OR.(B.AND.C)

```
CTRUTH1
C   TRUTH1. A TRUTH TABLE GENERATOR.
C
C   CALCULATES A TRUTH TABLE FOR TWO LOGICAL VARIABLES
C   USING THE .OR. OPERATION
C
      LOGICAL  COLOR, SHAPE, TRUTH
      WRITE (6,100)
  100 FORMAT (1H1)
      I=1
      J=1
      COLOR=.TRUE.
    1 SHAPE=.TRUE.
    2 TRUTH = COLOR .OR. SHAPE
      WRITE (6,101) COLOR, SHAPE, TRUTH
  101 FORMAT (10X, 3(L1,5X))
      J=J+1
      IF(J-2) 10,10,11
   10 SHAPE = .FALSE.
      GO TO 2
   11 I=I+1
      IF(I-2)20,20,21
   20 COLOR = .FALSE.
      J=1
      GO TO 1
   21 STOP
      END
```

Figure VIII.4 Truth table program for .OR. operation.

where A, B, and C are logical variables.

The truth table will have 8 rows, each row representing one of the combinations of .TRUE. and .FALSE. values of the three variables. Figure VIII.5 is a listing of TRUTH2. The program TRUTH2 departs from the logic of TRUTH1. TRUTH1 uses a clumsy method of changing the values of COLOR and SHAPE for the analysis of the logical expression. The juggling of the counters I and J can be avoided by the use of an array to store the values .TRUE. and .FALSE.. TRUTH2 uses a three-deep nest of DO statements. This is a straightforward extension of nesting from the two-deep examples already used in previous chapters. The reader is urged to construct the flow chart for TRUTH2 so that he will more clearly understand the program. The output of TRUTH2 is illustrated in Figure VIII.6.

COMMON ERRORS WITH LOGICAL VARIABLES

Probably the most common error with logical variables and expressions, and the simplest to correct, is to omit the type statement. With REAL or INTEGER variables, no great problem is involved since programmers readily learn to use first-letter codes to distinguish among types of variables. With logical variables, on the other hand, there is no means for implicitly assigning the type and it must be done with a LOGICAL statement.

A very simple syntax error, and one usually detected by the compiler, is to omit a period (.) in writing one or more relational or logical operators. Such an error is likely to cause a compiler error message, indicating that a variable name is too long or that some variable name contains an illegal character.

For example, in the UNIVAC compiler the statement

TRUTH = COLOR OR SHAPE

might produce the message

THE NAME CONTAINING COLORO
HAS MORE THAN 6 CHARACTERS.

In this case, the string of characters COLORORSHAPE has been interpreted as a single variable name since the punctuation was omitted, and the first six characters were listed in the message.

We wish to stress again the importance of careful writing of expressions so that they correctly reflect the intent of the programmer. The introduction of the logical expression introduces additional complexities into the concept of an expression in Fortran, in that two or more *arithmetic* expressions can be combined by relational operators into quite complicated *logical* expressions.

CONTROL STATEMENTS

Although a number of the control statements defined in Fortran have been introduced already, all of them are re-

```
CTRUTH2
C--TRUTH2
C
      LOGICAL A, B, C, L, TRUTH
      DIMENSION L(2)
C
      L(1) = .TRUE.
      L(2) = .FALSE.
      DO 1 I=1,2
      A=L(I)
      DO 1 J=1,2
      B=L(J)
      DO 1 K=1,2
      C=L(K)
      TRUTH = (A.AND.B).OR.(A.AND..NOT.C).OR.(B.AND.C)
      WRITE (6,101) A,B,C,TRUTH
  101 FORMAT (10X, 4(L1,5X) )
    1 CONTINUE
      STOP
      END
```

Figure VIII.5 Program coding for TRUTH2.

Values of variables			Truth value
A	B	C	
T	T	T	T
T	T	F	T
T	F	T	F
T	F	F	T
F	T	T	T
F	T	F	F
F	F	T	F
F	F	F	F

Figure VIII.6 Truth table produced by TRUTH2; headings are not produced by the coding shown in Figure VIII.5.

viewed or discussed in detail in this chapter. The next three sections of this chapter cover control statements—unconditional control, conditional control, and iteration control.

UNCONDITIONAL CONTROL

Unconditional GO TO. The unconditional GO TO causes a transfer to a specified statement regardless of circumstances. When the GO TO is executed, control is immediately transferred to the designated statement. The GO TO has the form

GO TO *n*

where *n* is the number of the statement to which control is transferred. Statement *n* must be an executable statement—GO TO cannot refer to a FORMAT or declaration statement.

The PAUSE Statement. This statement is never used by beginning programmers. It is used only in advanced programming and then, in general, only rarely. The statement assumes one of two general forms, either

PAUSE

or

PAUSE *n*

where *n* is an unsigned octal (or hexadecimal) constant of from 1 to 5 digits.

The effect of either of the two forms is to stop the computer from further processing. When the operator subsequently presses the START button on the control unit, the program begins again with the next instruction. If a value of *n* is given in the statement, it will be displayed in a register on the console of the computer. This is useful if there are several different PAUSE statements in the program, and it is essential that the operator be able to distinguish among them. The PAUSE is commonly used when the operator is required to mount a particular reel of tape, or place a new disc in the disc unit, during the execution of the program. An output message to the operator's console requests operator intervention. This statement is discussed in Chapter 9, but it, too, is used only in advanced programming applications. In this example the message may refer to a tape reel number and a tape unit and request the operator to place the tape reel on a tape unit and start the computer.

The STOP Statement. The general form of the STOP statement is

STOP

This statement terminates the execution of the program. As distinguished from the PAUSE, execution cannot be resumed by pressing the start button on the console. It causes the termination in one of two ways, depending upon the executive system. It may return to the executive system, thus allowing the executive to continue with the next job on the input device. Alternatively, the STOP may simply cause the computer to halt without a return to the executive. There must in this case be operator intervention to resume processing under executive control. When the latter situation holds, the STOP should not be used. A programming advisor should be consulted before using STOP. Where STOP does not return to the executive, the statement

```
CALL EXIT
```

is usually used to return to the executive system.

The END Statement. The general form of the END statement is

```
END
```

This statement marks the physical end of the program and *must* be the last statement in the program deck. When this card is encountered, the compiler stops reading cards and completes compilation.

The RETURN Statement. This statement marks the point at which a subroutine returns control to the calling program. It has the general form

```
RETURN
```

The use of RETURN is illustrated in the material on subroutines in Chapter 10.

CONDITIONAL CONTROL

The Arithmetic IF. The arithmetic IF provides a three-way branching process in Fortran. The general form of the arithmetic IF is

IF (a) n_1, n_2, n_3

where a is an arithmetic expression and n_i is a statement number. The execution of the statement causes a transfer to statement n_1 if a is negative, to n_2 if a is equal to zero, and to statement n_3 if a is positive. Assuming that A = 5.2, B = 10.9, and C = .5, the statement

```
IF (B*C-A) 10, 20, 15
```

would cause a transfer to statement 15, since the expression B*C−A is positive.

Imagine that we wished to execute a different set of calculations on a variable X depending on the value of an index. Specifically, imagine that we wished to set $Y = X^2$ if $I < 2$, $Y = X^3$ if $I = 2$, and $Y = X$ otherwise ($I > 2$). A single arithmetic IF and a couple of GO TO statements comprise this program segment:

```
      .
      .
      .
      IF (I - 2) 10, 11, 12
   10 Y = X**2
      GO TO 15
   11 Y = X**3
      GO TO 15
   12 Y = X
   15 CONTINUE
```

The Computed GO TO. The computed GO TO has the general form

GO TO $(n_1, n_2, \ldots, n_m), j$

where n_i is a statement number and j is a nonsubscripted integer variable. The statement causes a transfer to n_i when $j = i$. For example, if the statement were

```
GO TO (15, 16, 28, 10), K
```

the transfer would be to statement 15 when K = 1, to 16 when K = 2, to 28 when K = 3, and to statement 10 when K = 4. The value of the integer variable j cannot be larger than m, the number of statement numbers inside the parentheses.

The Assigned GO TO. The assigned GO TO, along with the ASSIGN statement (see below) permits a GO TO statement to refer to different values during the execution of the program. The unconditional statement

GO TO n

is fixed with n as a constant. The assigned GO TO, on the other hand, allows the number n to change. The assigned GO TO has the general form

GO TO $j, (n_1, n_2, \ldots, n_m)$

where j is a nonsubscripted integer variable that previously has appeared in an ASSIGN statement, and $n_1, \ldots, n_m$ are statement numbers. The statement

```
GO TO K, (10, 20, 30, 40)
```

causes a transfer to one of the four statements whose numbers appear in the parentheses. One of the numbers had been previously "assigned" to the variable K by an ASSIGN statement.

The ASSIGN Statement. This statement is used with the assigned GO TO. The general form is

ASSIGN *n* TO *j*

where *n* is a statement number, and *j* is the name of an integer variable that appears in an assigned GO TO statement. The two statements must be used in parallel. The ASSIGN appears first, followed (either immediately or separated by a block of programming) by the assigned GO TO. For example,

```
ASSIGN 10 TO J2
```

in effect gives the value 10 to the variable J2. If at some later point in the program, the statement

```
GO TO J2, (5, 10, 24)
```

appears, the transfer at that point in the program is to statement 10. The other statement numbers that may be assigned to the variable J2 are 5 and 24 in this example.

As an example of the use of the ASSIGN and assigned GO TO statements, consider the following problem an extension of the program segment introduced in the section above on the arithmetic IF. A block of program statements is to be executed several times, but never in precisely the same form. The following statements illustrate the program segment

```
      ASSIGN 10 to I
      .
      .
      .
    1 GO TO I,(10, 11, 12)
   10 Y = X**2
      ASSIGN 11 to I
      GO TO 15
   11 Y = X**3
      ASSIGN 12 to I
      GO TO 15
   12 Y = X
      .
      .
      .
   15 CONTINUE
```

Sometime before entering the block of programming, the value 10 is assigned to I. Statement 1 marks the assigned GO TO. The first time the statement is encountered, I has the value 10, so control passes directly to the next statement, which defines Y as equal to X^2. Following that operation, a new value is assigned to I and control is transferred to statement 15. Statement 15 may be a single statement, or it may represent an entire block of programming. Eventually, control is returned to statement 1. At this point, I has the value 11 and control transfers to statement 11 which cubes X and stores it in location Y. Then 12 is assigned to I and control passes again to statement 15. Control eventually returns to statement 1, and the assigned GO TO has the value 12, so that the transfer is to statement 12.

The same operations could be written in another way, using the computed GO TO statement. The following Fortran coding shows how this would be accomplished.

```
      I = 1
      .
      .
      .
    1 GO TO (10, 11, 12), I
   10 Y = X**2
      I = 2
      GO TO 15
   11 Y = X**3
      I = 3
      GO TO 15
   12 Y = X
      .
      .
      .
   15 CONTINUE
```

These programs can be expressed easily by using the arithmetic IF. The flow chart of Figure VIII.7 indicates the flow of the program segment using the IF. The student is urged to write the Fortran coding, using the arithmetic IF, to conform with the flow chart.

The Logical IF. This statement is one of the more powerful and versatile statements in the Fortran language. It allows for a branching operation depending on the value of a logical expression, with one branch taken when the expression is .TRUE. and the other when .FALSE.. In the past, we have used the arithmetic IF statement for branching. In constructing a loop, for example, we might use the statement

```
IF (I - N) 10, 11, 11
```

to test whether or not we are through the loop. The coding of the entire loop might be

```
   I = 1
12 .
   .  statements in body of loop
   .
   IF (I - N) 10, 11, 11
10 I = I + 1
   GO TO 12
11 CONTINUE
```

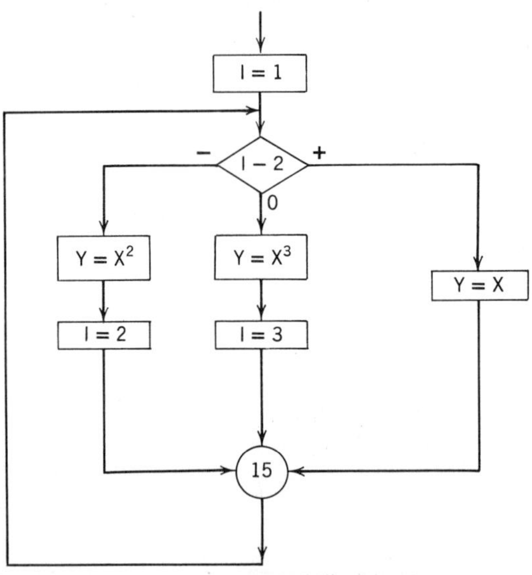

Figure VIII.7 Flow chart of an example program segment illustrating the principle of the computed and assigned GO TO.

In the test for this loop, we perform a subtraction, and take one of two alternate courses of action depending upon the sign of the result. Using a logical IF statement, the loop may be programmed as

```
   I = 1
12 .
   .
   .
   IF (I .GE. N) GO TO 11
   I = I + 1
   GO TO 12
11 CONTINUE
```

The logical IF statement, written as

```
IF (I .GE. N) GO TO 11
```

in this example, provides a transfer if the loop has been completed, just as the arithmetic IF does. The programming is slightly simpler in the sense that the logic is clearer, even though the number of statements is the same. In this case, if the logical expression

```
I .GE. N
```

is .TRUE., the GO TO is executed. If the expression is .FALSE., the GO TO is ignored and the program proceeds to the next statement which increases I by 1.

The general form of the logical IF statement is

IF *(L) S*

where *L* is any logical expression (i.e., capable of being evaluated as either .TRUE. or .FALSE.), and *S* is any other executable (or control) statement (i.e., not a declaration), *except* a DO statement or another logical IF. When the logical IF is executed, statement *S* is executed only if *L* is .TRUE.. If *L* is .FALSE., *S* is ignored and control passes to the next statement following the IF statement.

As an example of the use of the logical IF statement, consider a part of the program for Project 3, the automatic diagnosis program. A patient is represented by an array of four scores called *X*. Each value in *X* is the score on one diagnostic test. For this example, only the diagnosis for the Sarbin Syndrome is considered. It suffices to recall from Chapter 3 that a patient can fall into one of three categories with respect to the disease—either he has it, does not have it, or cannot be classified. The housekeeping chores performed by statements that are concerned with records of the diagnostic categories for each patient, for each disease, and keeping totals of the numbers of patients having each disease, are not discussed here. For our purposes, the program transfers to one of three points depending upon the diagnostic category.

The diagnostic rule for Sarbin Syndrome is as follows.

> If ($X_1 > 14$, $X_2 < 10$, $X_3 = 1$, and $X_4 < 10$) or if ($6 \leq X_i \leq 14$ for all $i = 1, 2, 3, 4$), then Sarbin's Syndrome is present. Otherwise, Sarbin's Syndrome is not present, unless all scores are in excess of 15 in which case the patient is not classifiable with respect to the syndrome.

The first step in the coding of the diagnostic routine is to write the IF corresponding to the two positive indicators. If either of these are failed by a patient (disease) the routine is to transfer to a housekeeping segment of the program to record this information. If the patient passes the first indicators, the question of whether the patient is classifiable or not must be determined. If the patient is classifiable, the implication is that he is free of the disease. Otherwise the fact that the patient passed the positive indicators is ambiguous. Figure VIII.8 is a listing of statements from a program that applies the diagnostic routine to a single patient. The first statement indicates the truth or falsity of the first indicator. If this first indicator is true, the patient has the disease and no further tests are necessary. However, if the patient passes this first test, there is another contingency leading to the conclusion that the patient has the disease. This is tested by the DO loop. If any score of the patient is outside the defined range, the patient is clearly free of the disease. If all four scores are within the range, additional testing is needed, and the program proceeds to test the proposition that none of the scores are less than or equal to 15. If

```
        •
        •
        •
        IF(X(1).GT.14..AND.X(2).LT.10..AND.X(3).EQ.1..AND.X(4).LT.10.) GO TO 100
        DO 8 J = 1,4
      8 IF(X(J).GE.6..OR.X(J).LE.14.) GO TO 9
        GO TO 200
      9 DO 10 J = 1, 4
     10 IF(X(J).LE.15.) GO TO 200
        GO TO 300
        •
        •
        •
    100 statements to record that patient has disease
        •
        •
        •
    200 statements to record that patient is free of disease
        •
        •
        •
    300 statements to record that patient is not classifiable
        •
        •
        •
```

Figure VIII.8 Program segment for Project 3.

any score is found to be less than or equal to 15, the patient is clearly free of the disease. If all scores are greater than 15, the final conclusion is that the patient is not classifiable with respect to this disease.

Appendix B presents a complete implementation of the automatic diagnosis program. In that program, it will be noted that the tests that were programmed as two logical IF statements in the above example, have been broken down into several separate statements. The reason for this is efficiency in the execution of the program. A single large logical IF, as used above, is perfectly correct and acceptable to the Fortran compiler. However, careful reading of the diagnostic condition indicates that if *any* of the separate parts of the condition are not true, then the entire expression must be false since all the connectives are .AND.. For this reason, it is more efficient to test each of the four conditions sequentially, rather than have the computer evaluate the entire expression.

The executable or control statement in the logical IF cannot be another IF or a DO. However, if the logical expression in the IF statement is evaluated .FALSE. the next statement in the program can be any executable or control statement including the IF and the DO. Thus, logical IF's may follow one another and be "nested." As an example of this usage, suppose we wanted to read a series of numbers and sort them into four classes, depending upon the value of the number; we want the frequency of each of the four classes. Suppose that the values range from 1 to 20, inclusive, and the four classes are 1–5, 6–10, 11–15, and 16–20. Figure VIII.9 shows the flow chart of a program that sorts the numbers and tallies frequencies. Assume that the numbers to be sorted are REAL, and may require four columns on the data card. A number (N) is read from the first card; N indicates how many numbers are to be read. Each of the N numbers is considered individually and is called X. After X is read, a series of logical IF statements are executed, until the correct category for the number X has been found. The value of the counting variable for that category is increased by 1, and another value of X is read and the process repeated. The process repeats until the last card has been read and tallied, then the results are printed. The program written from the flow chart in Figure VIII.9 is listed in Figure VIII.10.

This coding of a sorting program is very awkward and inefficient. A more elegant and general sorting program is developed in the last part of this chapter.

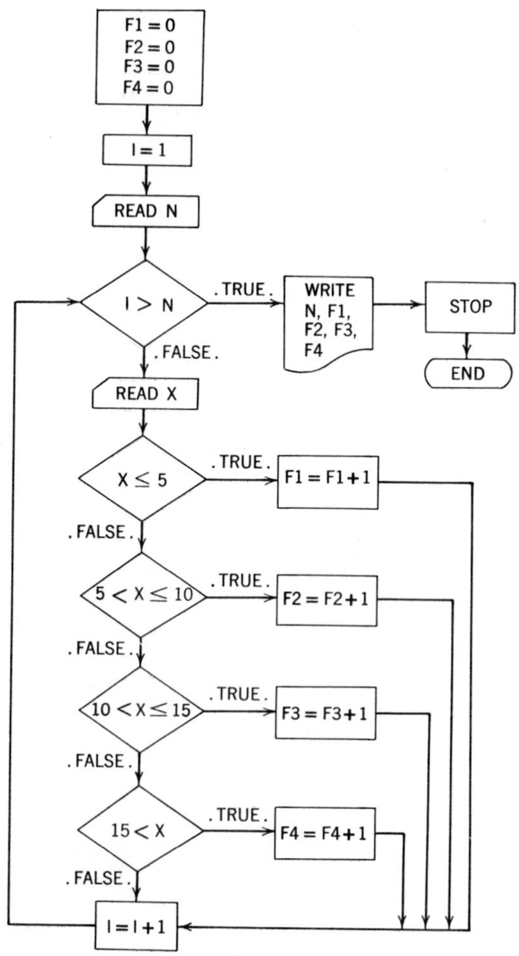

Figure VIII.9 Flow chart of an elementary sorting program.

```
CSORT1
C   ELEMENTARY SORT PROGRAM
C
      INTEGER F1, F2, F3, F4
      F1 = 0
      F2 = 0
      F3 = 0
      F4 = 0
      I = 1
      READ (5, 1) N
    1 FORMAT (I4)
   20 IF(I.GT.N) GO TO 100
      READ (5,2) X
    2 FORMAT (F4.2)
      IF(X.LE.5.0) F1=F1 + 1
      IF(X.GT.5.0.AND.X.LE.10.0) F2 = F2 + 1
      IF(X.GT.10.0.AND.X.LE.15.0) F3 = F3 + 1
      IF(X.GT.15.0) F4 = F4 + 1
      I = I + 1
      GO TO 20
  100 WRITE (6, 3) N, F1, F2, F3, F4
    3 FORMAT (1H1, I10////4I10)
      STOP
      END
```

Figure VIII.10 Elementary sort program.

COMMON ERRORS WITH CONDITIONAL CONTROL STATEMENTS

Any statement that disrupts the normal straight-through processing of a program is prone to logical errors.

One kind of error must be carefully guarded against—the infinite loop. The following coding illustrates such a loop:

```
  SUM = 0.0
1 SUM = SUM + X
  GO TO 1
  XMEAN = SUM/FN
```

There is no way to reach the statement following the GO TO. The result is an infinite loop. Fortunately, most compilers will detect this kind of error. Many infinite loops are not so simple—as for example

```
   ICOUNT = 15
99 I = ICOUNT - 5
   ALPHA = BETA**2 - GAMMA**3 - X(I)
   IF (I .LT. 10) GO TO 19
   ICOUNT = ICOUNT + 1
   GO TO 99
19 WRITE (6,100) ALPHA
```

There is an infinite loop embedded here, and it will never be detected by the compiler. The computer will simply continue performing the loop until the operator becomes suspicious and terminates the program. Most executive systems require, as a part of the information identifying a job, an estimate of the execution time. This is to guard against infinite loops—the system usually automatically terminates execution when the time estimate is exceeded. The beginning programmer is well advised to make small time estimates when debugging a program as endless loops are astonishingly easy to write.

Aside from simple syntax errors, such as incorrect punctuation, most of the errors that occur with control statements are logical in nature. As illustrated above, an error in a logical IF can cause a lot of grief. Great care must be exercised in writing logical expressions, and again the programmer is advised to "play computer" to test his logical statements. In many cases, if the program is not operating correctly, and the programmer suspects that some of his conditional control statements may be at fault, the use of a trace technique as discussed in Chapter 9 may be useful, or perhaps a selective or "snap-shot" dump as presented in Chapter 12 might be used.

ITERATION CONTROL

The CONTINUE Statement. Although the CONTINUE has more uses than merely the reference statement in a DO, e.g., the reference statement in a GO TO, it is included here for lack of a more natural place. The CONTINUE is a dummy statement and gives rise to no operations. It is used where an executable statement is needed but no operations are desired.

The DO Statement. The DO statement has been used extensively already in this book. Consequently, we go immediately to the full technical description of the DO. The full form of the DO is

DO n $i = k_1, k_2, k_3$

where n is the statement number of the last statement in the loop, i is a nonsubscripted integer variable (the iteration variable), and k_j is either an integer constant or a nonsubscripted integer variable: k_1 gives the initial value of the iteration variable i, k_2 gives the terminating value, and k_3 indicates the amount that the iteration variable is to be increased each time through the loop. The statement causes the statements up through and including the one numbered n to be executed several times. The first time, i has the value k_1. On the second iteration, i has the value $k_1 + k_3$, and so on until i has the highest value not exceeding k_2. At that point control passes to the statement following statement n. A simple addition loop may thus be programmed as

```
      .
      .
      .
      SUM = 0.0
      DO 5 I = 1, 50, 1
      SUM = SUM + X(I)
    5 CONTINUE
   10 -------
      .
      .
      .
```

Suppose that only the sum of the alternate elements of the X array had been desired, that is, X(1)+X(3)+. . .+X(49). The segment of the program could have been written as

```
      .
      .
      .
      SUM = 0.0
      DO 5 I = 1, 50, 2
      SUM = SUM + X(I)
    5 CONTINUE
   10 -----
      .
      .
      .
```

The only change is in the value of k_3. The statement specifies a starting value for I of 1, with an increase of 2 each time through the loop. Note that it is immaterial whether 49 or 50 is used as the terminating value. I can take on values of 1, 3, 5, ..., 47, 49, 51. The loop will terminate after 49 in either case, since the next value (51) would exceed the limit of either 49 or 50.

The several rules pertaining to the DO statement may be summarized as follows:

1. If k_3 is not stated explicitly, it is taken to be 1. Thus the statement

```
DO 158 I = 1, N, 1
```

is equivalent to

```
DO 158 I = 1, N
```

2. The value of the index variable i should not exceed $2^{15} = 32{,}768$ in many systems, although this restriction varies from machine to machine.

3. The value of the index or iteration variable i is available for computations within the loop. It may be used as an ordinary integer variable, or as a subscript. When the exit from the loop is normal, i.e., the criterion value of i (k_2) is exceeded, the value of i is no longer defined and may not be used for any purpose. When the value of i is needed for use outside the loop, and the exit is normal, a

statement like the second statement here

```
DO 158 I = 1, N
K = I
```

inside the loop will make the value of the iteration variable I available outside the loop as the ordinary integer variable K. If the exit from the loop is by means of a transfer out of the range of the DO statement, the value of i is available.

4. The range of a DO statement, is defined as all those statements between the DO statement itself and statement n (including statement n).

5. No statement or subroutine call executed in the range of the DO may redefine the value of the indexing variable i. Thus, the statement I=I+1 in the range of DO n I = k_1, k_2, k_3 is not permitted.

6. The last statement in the range of a DO cannot be an arithmetic IF statement, or any GO TO statement. If the last statement is a logical IF, the following rule holds: the statement is executed before the range is executed again if L is .TRUE.. If L is .FALSE., the range is executed without the statement being executed.

7. Statements within the range of a DO may be transfer statements (GO TO and IF) subject to Rule 6 above. Transfer may be made to outside the range of the DO. Transfer may never be made into the range of a DO.

A DO statement may occur within the range of another DO. Such configurations of statements are called *nested* DO's. Nested DO's must follow the rule that all statements within the range of the inner DO must also be within the range of the outer. Thus, the following two configurations are allowed

```
      DO 1 I = 1, 20
      DO 2 J = 1, 30
          .
          .
          .
    2 -----
    1 -----
```

```
      DO 5 I = 1, 30
      DO 5 J = 5, 10, 2
          .
          .
          .
    5 -----
```

The following is an illegal nested DO configuration

```
      DO 6 ICOUNT = N, M, 3
      DO 7 JCOUNT = K, L, 2
          .
          .
          .
    6 -----
    7 -----
```

In a flow chart, the initial value of the index is indicated in the upper-left corner. The increment to the index is indicated in the upper-right-hand corner. The terminal value of the index is indicated in the lower center of the box. The general flow chart representation of the general statement of the DO is as follows.

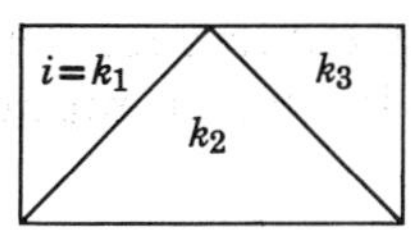

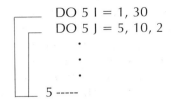

COMMON ERRORS IN DO STATEMENTS

Three kinds of errors are frequently made in the use of the DO statement, all of which have been mentioned in the previous discussion of rules.

An illegal terminal statement for a DO loop will usually be detected by the compiler. When the logic of the program requires that the last statement in the range of a DO be an arithmetic IF or GO TO, the CONTINUE must be used:

```
      DO 10 I = 1, 99
          .
          .
          .
      IF (X-Y(I)) 15, 15, 16
   10 CONTINUE
```

Care must be taken in writing a logical IF as the last statement in the range of a DO. When used properly, however, such programming can be very useful. In the program developed for Project 3 (Automatic Diagnosis—see Appendix B), the following statements are used to scan an array of scores. As soon as a score meeting the requirements for the diagnostic condition is met, a transfer is made. If a transfer is not made, i.e., if none of the scores satisfy the condition, the exit from the loop is normal and a transfer to 100 occurs:

```
  DO 8 J = 1, 4
8 IF (X(J).LT.6..OR.X(J).GE.14.) GO TO 9
  GO TO 100
```

Such programming can be used to scan an array and find some entry that meets some criterion. The transfer out of the loop with the logical IF as illustrated preserves the value of the index variable (J), allowing it to be used again outside the loop. J will have the value that it had when the exit from the loop occurred.

Redefining the index variable is sometimes inadvertently accomplished in a loop. Such an occurrence may be detected by the compiler, but it might not. In addition to modifying an index, modifying any of the other variables (the k_j) that appear in a DO statement is an error. For example, the following statements are illegal:

```
    DO 108 I = ISTART, IEND, 2
       .
       .
       .
    IEND = IEND + 3
108 CONTINUE
```

Another variety of error with the DO concerns illegal transfers. Aside from writing loops that have overlapping ranges, as discussed previously, illegal transfers are the easiest kind of error to make. A transfer into the range of a loop is illegal since there is no way of getting the loop initialized—i.e., setting up the values of the control constants. If a loop must be written that requires a transfer from outside into the range, it must be programmed without the DO statement by using IF statements and setting the controlling conditions. Table VIII.1 il-

Table VIII.1

Common compiler messages for control statements.

Message	Cause
THE DO INDEX....IS ALSO THE INDEX OF AN OUTER DO. (UNIVAC)	Self-explanatory.
THIS IS A BAD USE OF .NOT. (UNIVAC)	A syntax error in a logical expression containing .NOT. Most likely the expression following the .NOT. operator is not a logical expression and therefore cannot be negated.
THE DO-INDEX...IS BEING DEFINED VIA INPUT. (UNIVAC)	The compiler has detected a READ statement within the loop containing the DO index as an element of its list.
THIS DO HAS NO END, OR IS BADLY NESTED (UNIVAC)	The statement number referenced in the DO cannot be located, either due to being absent or to improper nesting of loops.
THERE IS A GO TO...BUT NO ASSIGN XX TO ... (UNIVAC)	The ASSIGN statement was not located, either due to its absence, or to improper punching.
THERE IS A TRANSFER INTO THIS LOOP BUT THERE IS NO EXIT.BAD. (UNIVAC)	A transfer into the range of a DO occurred, but there can be no exit since indexing information is not available.
DO YOU REALLY WISH TO COMPARE THE VALUE OF CONSTANTS. (UNIVAC)	A logical expression compares two constants and is therefore incorrect or unnecessary.
THERE IS A LOGICAL OPERATOR BETWEEN NON-LOGICAL VARIABLES (UNIVAC)	Self-explanatory.

lustrates some common compiler messages for control statement errors.

SORT2, A SORT PROGRAM

An elementary sorting program was developed earlier in this chapter. Only the class frequencies were computed by SORT. The behavioral scientist often wishes to isolate all subjects in a sample who have a common characteristic and count their numbers in order to make an analysis on the subgroups in the sample. For example, each subject may be observed on two variables, say X and Y. The variable Y is a simple classification variable with 10 coded values, say 1, 2, ..., 10. We wish to sort the subjects into ten subgroups in terms of the Y value and inspect the X values for each subgroup. On the input side we want to read scores for each subject, as well as a subject number, in whatever order they appear. On the output side we want to list all subjects, subject number, X, and Y, organized so that all subjects having the same Y values are together; subjects with Y = 1 first, subjects with Y = 2 second, etc. Imagine that there are N subjects.

Two simple procedures are suggested immediately. First, we could loop through the subjects 10 times, printing the data when Y = 1 on the first loop, the Y = 2 data on the second loop, etc. This would give a simple ordered output listing. However, if we are to do more than list the data this algorithm is inadequate—it simply lists the data without leaving any record of the groupings of the data. Also it requires N times 10 passes at the data. The second suggestion is to set up 10 arrays in which to store the data associated with each distinct Y value. Each such array would have to accomodate the entire sample in the event that all subjects have the same Y value. Consequently, this method is inefficient in the use of memory, requiring 10 times as much space as is actually needed (K categories on Y would call K times as much space) to store the data.

A much more efficient sort procedure can be devised. The program SORT2, listed as Figure VIII.11 is an example of this procedure. Imagine our data are like those shown in Figure VIII.12 and that we store them in an array ARRAY organized like that illustrated in Figure VIII.13. The first three columns of ARRAY, i.e., J = 1, J = 2, and J = 3, represent subject number, X score, and Y score. The fourth column of ARRAY plays a role explained below.

All of the subjects having a given Y value are interspersed throughout ARRAY. The trick of SORT2 is to find the first subject with the given Y value and keep a record of where he is in ARRAY and then let the value of the fourth column of ARRAY for that subject indicate the location of the next subject having the same Y value. The value in the fourth column is called the link, i.e., it links a subject to the next subject with the same Y value. Let the location of a subject in ARRAY be called his index, say I, which corresponds to the row number in ARRAY. The first subject in ARRAY having the given Y value is assigned the link to the next subject, etc. The index of the first subject is given in a table constructed by the program as the array TAB. The first row of TAB is used to record the first subject index for each Y value, the Y values corresponding to the column indexes of TAB. The index of the first subject having Y = 6 is stored in TAB (1,6), etc. The index of the second subject having Y = 6 is stored in ARRAY(TAB(1,6),4). Figure VIII.14 illustrates this principle. The last subject in ARRAY having the given Y value is assigned a link referring to his own index. Thus, if I = 46 were the last index with Y = 6, the link for the 46th subject in ARRAY would be 46.

In the process of assigning link values to subjects, SORT2 considers a subject with a given Y value as the last such subject until the next is found. When a new subject is found the link of the previous subject is changed to the index value of the new subject. The index value of the previous subject is kept in the sec-

```
CSORT2
      DIMENSICN ARRAY(100,4), TAB(2,10)
      INTEGER ARRAY, TAB
      L = 3
      READ(5,1)N,((ARRAY(I,J), J=1,3), I=1,N)
    1 FORMAT (I3,/,(3I4))
C   SET UP TAB AND SET LINKS
  100 DO2I=1,2
      DO2J=1,10
    2 TAB(I,J)=0
      DO3I=1,N
      K=ARRAY(I,L)
      IF(TAB(1,K))4,4,5
    4 TAB(1,K)=I
      TAB(2,K)=I
    5 KK=TAB(2,K)
      ARRAY(KK,4)=I
      ARRAY(I,4)=I
      TAB(2,K)=I
    3 CONTINUE
C  PRINT SUBLISTS
      WRITE(6,15)
   15 FORMAT(1H1)
      DO6I=1,10
      WRITE(6,14)
   14 FORMAT(////)
      WRITE(6,7)I
    7 FORMAT(10X,25H SUBJECTS WITH KEY CODE =,I4,///)
      K=TAB(1,I)
      IF(K)8,8,9
    8 WRITE(6,10)
   10 FORMAT(10X,4HNONE,/////)
      GOTO6
    9 DO12J=1,N
      WRITE(6,13)(ARRAY(K,JJ),JJ=1,3)
   13 FORMAT(3(10X,I4))
      IF(K.EQ.TAB(2,I)) GO TO 6
      K=ARRAY(K,4)
   12 CONTINUE
    6 CONTINUE
      STOP
      END
```

Figure VIII.11 Program listing for SORT2.

Subject	number	X	Y
1	10	3	3
2	69	2	3
3	71	2	1
4	104	1	1
5	03	9	3
6	52	4	5
7	24	8	1
8	18	7	6
9	70	6	4
10	89	4	7

Figure VIII.12 Data for SORT2 problem.

	J = 1	J = 2	J = 3	J = 4
I = 1	10	3	3	2
I = 2	69	2	3	5
I = 3	71	2	1	4
I = 4	104	1	1	7
I = 5	03	9	3	8
...	...	...	...	...
I = 10	41	4	1	
I = 11				
I = 12				
etc.				

Figure VIII.13 Data of Figure VIII.12 as stored in ARRAY including the link values after sorting.

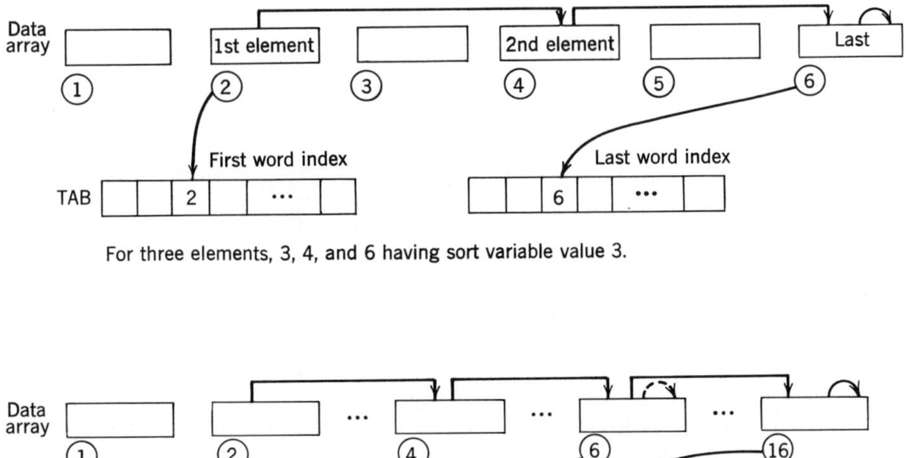

For three elements, 3, 4, and 6 having sort variable value 3.

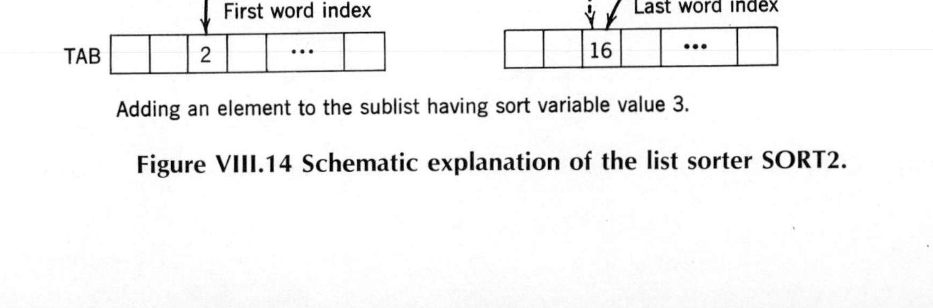

Adding an element to the sublist having sort variable value 3.

Figure VIII.14 Schematic explanation of the list sorter SORT2.

ond row of TAB. Thus, when a new subject is found with Y = 6, say with index value 94, ARRAY(TAB(2,6),4) = 94, ARRAY(94,4) = 94, and TAB(2,6) = 94, SORT2 stores the link to the new subject for the previous subject and sets up the new subject to play the role of the last subject. Figure VIII.14 illustrates the expansion of a sublist of subjects. Figure VIII.15 illustrates the changes to TAB and ARRAY with the processing of the subjects listed in Figure VIII.12. The final link values are shown in Figure VIII.13 as ARRAY(I, 4).

The output portion of SORT2 is started once all subjects are processed by the linkage portion. The subjects having a given Y value are all identifiable without checking the Y value of the subjects. The first subject has an index stored in TAB(I,Y), the second has an index given by ARRAY(TAB(I,Y),4), the third has an index given by the link in the second, etc. The list for a given value of Y is ended when the link is equal to the value in TAB(Z,Y). The program takes cognizance of the fact that there may be no subjects with a given Y value—TAB(I,Y) will be equal to zero for that value of Y. Figure VIII.16 illustrates output from SORT2.

SORT2 can be generalized to permit sorting on a number of variables. This generalization can take several forms, two of which will be indicated here. The first is to rearrange the data in ARRAY so that it is in physical order of the first sort variable. For example, transfer all elements in the sample to another array, first all the elements with Y = 1, then all the elements with Y = 2, ..., etc. But store them sequentially into the second array. Now apply the SORT2 algorithm

	1	2	3	4	5	6	7	8	9	10	
Step 1: After Subject 10	0	0	1	0	0	0	0	0	0	0	ARRAY(1,4) = 1
	0	0	1	0	0	0	0	0	0	0	
Step 2: After Subject 69	0	0	1	0	0	0	0	0	0	0	ARRAY(1,4) = 2
	0	0	2	0	0	0	0	0	0	0	ARRAY(2,4) = 2
Step 3: After Subject 71	3	0	1	0	0	0	0	0	0	0	ARRAY(3,4) = 3
	3	0	2	0	0	0	0	0	0	0	
Step 4: After Subject 104	3	0	1	0	0	0	0	0	0	0	ARRAY(3,4) = 4
	4	0	2	0	0	0	0	0	0	0	ARRAY(4,4) = 4
Step 5: After Subject 03	3	0	1	0	0	0	0	0	0	0	ARRAY(2,4) = 5
	4	0	5	0	0	0	0	0	0	0	ARRAY(5,4) = 5
Step 6: After Subject 52	3	0	1	0	6	0	0	0	0	0	ARRAY(6,4) = 6
	4	0	5	0	6	0	0	0	0	0	
Step 7: After Subject 24	3	0	1	0	6	0	0	0	0	0	ARRAY(4,4) = 7
	7	0	5	0	6	0	0	0	0	0	ARRAY(7,4) = 7
Step 8: After Subject 18	3	0	1	0	6	8	0	0	0	0	ARRAY(8,4) = 8
	7	0	5	0	6	8	0	0	0	0	

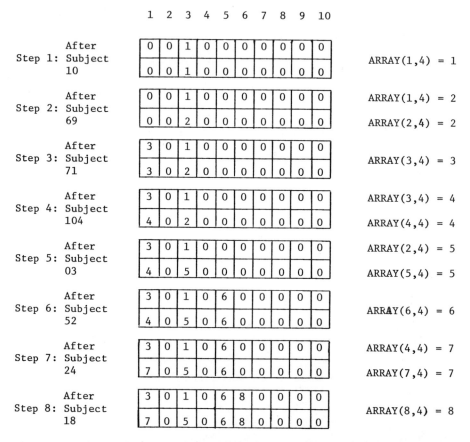

Figure VIII.15 Entries in TAB and in ARRAY (I,4) after subject number 18 is sorted.

```
SUBJECTS WITH KEY CODE =    1

     71          2          1
    104          1          1
     24          8          1



SUBJECTS WITH KEY CODE =    2

NONE



SUBJECTS WITH KEY CODE =    3

     10          3          3
     69          2          3
      3          9          3


SUBJECTS WITH KEY CODE =    4

     70          6          4
```

Figure VIII.16 Illustrative output from SORT2.

to the second array but use the second sort variable. The sorted array will thus be sorted. Note that the resulting listing will be ordered first in terms of the second sort variable and within the second variable categories according to the first sort variable.

A second generalization of SORT2 is to define a table like TAB but containing enough columns to represent all of the joint values of the two sort variables. Sort on the subordinate sort variable first. If this subordinate variable has k categories, the TAB table will have k columns. If the second sort variable has p categories, each of the k categories in the first sort will be split up into p subcategories. Hence, the two-level sort will need a TAB table with $p \times k$ columns.

EXERCISES

1. In each of the following problems, a verbal statement is given, along with a completed or partially completed flow chart.

Complete the flow chart where necessary and write the Fortran statements to carry out the operations.

(a) If X is positive but not zero, add X and Y. If X is negative or zero, go on.

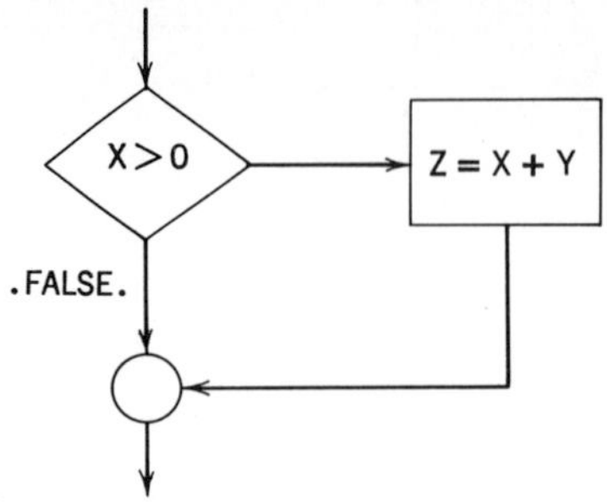

(b) If ALPHA is larger than 58, move either A or B, whichever is smaller, to location C. If ALPHA is less than or equal to 58, set ALPHA to 58.

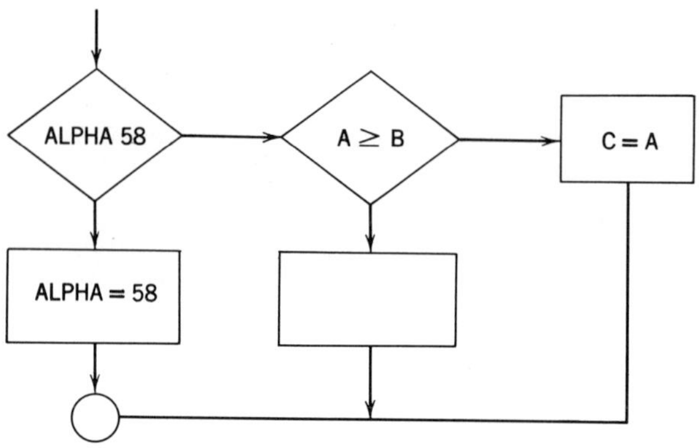

(c) If X+5 is greater than or equal to Y/3, and at the same time Z=15, store the product of X, Y, and Z at P. Otherwise, store the product of X and Y in P.

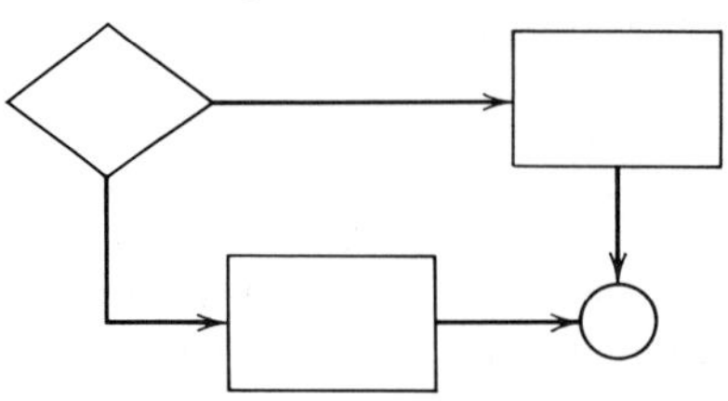

(d) If X is greater than Y, replace X with Y+2, or if Y = X, replace X with Y+X, or if X is less than Y, replace X with Y.

(e) Solve the problem in 1*d* using one IF statement.

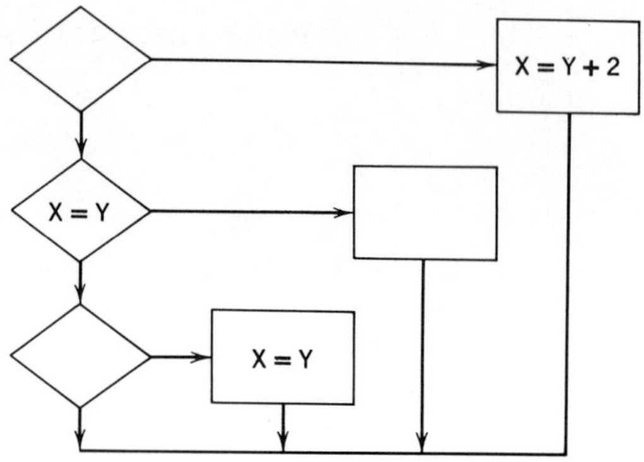

2. Correct the following Fortran statements so that they correctly accomplish what is asked.

(a) Transfer unconditionally to statement 25

GO TO, 25

(b) WHERE is an integer variable that may assume the values 1, 2, 3, 4, and 5. When WHERE = 1, control is to be transferred to statement 18; when WHERE = 2, the transfer is to be to 6; when 3, to 99; when WHERE = 4, to 158; and when WHERE = 5, to statement 56.

GO TO (56,18, 99, 6, 158) I

(c) Transfer to statements 10, 20, or 30, depending upon whether the value of

$$\frac{X + Y}{2(Z^2 - X^2)}$$

is negative, zero, or positive, respectively.

IF (X + Y / 2* ((Z**2) – (X**2)), 10, 30, 20

3. Complete the flow chart and write the Fortran statements for each of the following problems.
   (a) Find the mean of the elements in a one-dimensional array CAR where N is the number of elements in CAR.

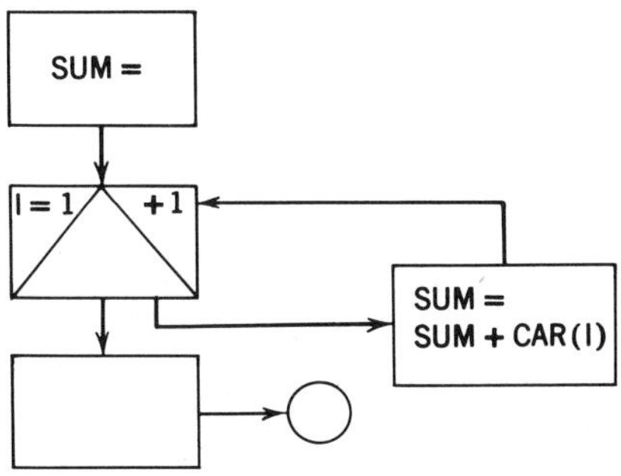

   (b) Find the sum of the odd numbered elements of the one-dimensional array Q where the subscript of Q has the maximum value QMAX.

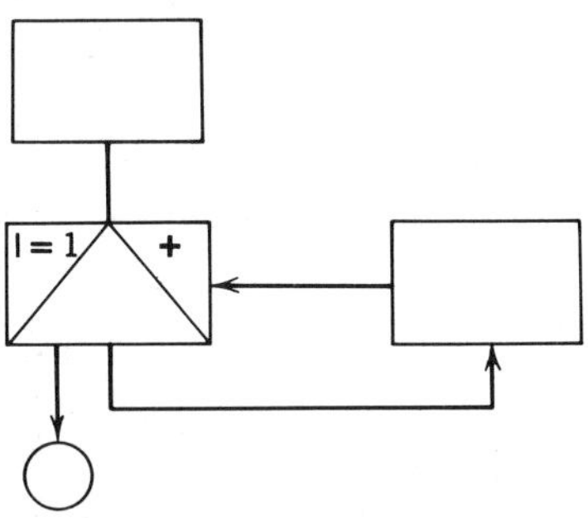

   (c) DOG is a two-dimensional array with M rows and N columns. TOTAL is a one-dimensional array of N elements. Set all elements of TOTAL to zero. Find the sum of each column and store it in TOTAL(J). *Hint.* Draw a sketch of the array DOG. It will help to visualize the problem. Let I be the row index and J the column index.

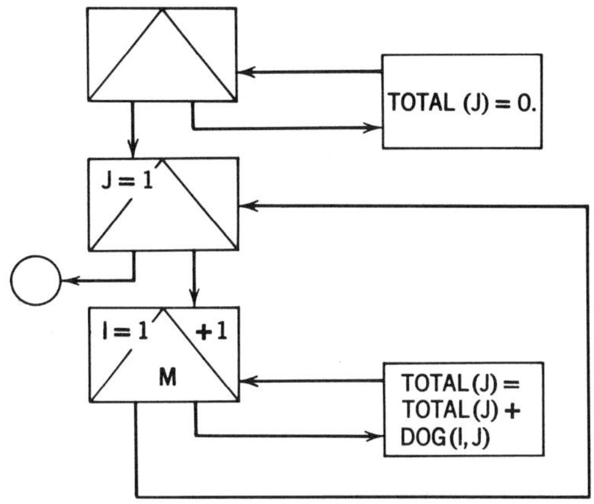

   (d) Store the value 1.0 in each cell on the diagonal of the two-dimensional square matrix COR. The dimensions of COR are N×N.
4. Express each of the following relations in Fortran notation.
   (a) $A < B$
   (b) $X_1 \geq X_2$
   (c) $A \neq B$
   (d) $A_5 + A_6 = A_7\, A_8\, B$
   (e) $Q_1 Q_2 \neq$ TOP
   (f) $A \times B \times C > \cos(D \times E + F)$
   (g) Y lies between 0 and $5X$, inclusive.
   (h) Either X exceeds A, or it exceeds B, or it exceeds C.
   (i) X exceeds Y and either P is less than 4, or Q is equal to 6, or both.
   (j) The absolute value of X is less than or equal to 5 times Q.
   (k) X lies between 6 and 9, inclusive, but Y does not.
   (l) A is greater than 5 while B is less than 15, or A is less than 15 while B is greater than 5.
   (m) The line segment from (X_1,Y_1) to (X_2,Y_2) is longer than the line segment from (X_1,Y_1) to (X_3,Y_3).

CHAPTER 9 FORTRAN IV: ADVANCED INPUT AND OUTPUT

Chapter 6 presented the notion that there are two essential features of I/O programming—the executable part and the FORMAT statement. While this simple distinction suffices for many applications, more information is needed to take full advantage of the capabilities of the computer system.

ORGANIZATION OF FORTRAN I/O

The organization of Fortran I/O is presented graphically in Figure IX.1. Up to this point we have been concerned only with the process designated in the figure as BCD (Binary Coded Decimal) hard copy. That is, we considered only reading from cards and producing printed output on paper. We have only alluded to the possibility of using other forms of numbers, and to the possibility of storing large quantities of information in a storage device other than the internal storage system of the computer. While a discussion of some of the more sophisticated I/O procedures is deferred until Chapter 12, a discussion and introduction of terms is appropriate at this point.

The Fortran I/O system may be con-

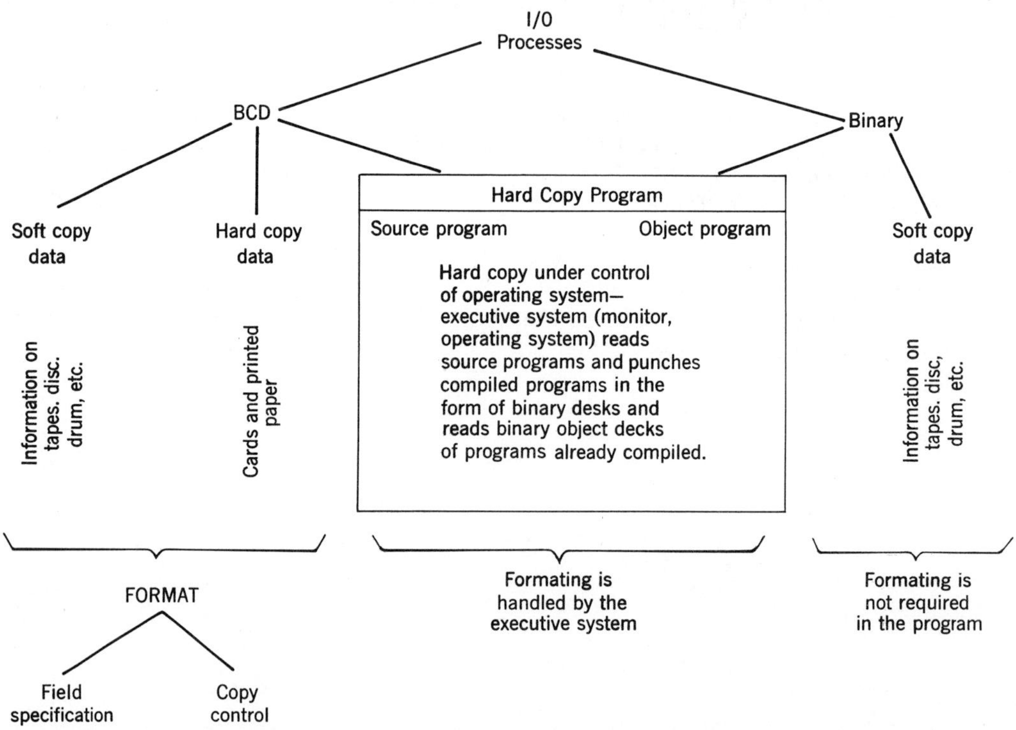

Figure IX.1 Basic organization of Fortran I/O.

sidered as comprised of three levels, as shown in Figure IX.1. At the first level, distinctions are made regarding the manner in which the information to be transmitted is coded—Binary Coded Decimal (BCD) or binary. At the next lower level, a distinction is made regarding the physical form of the transmitted information. Hard copy is that form of information which, in most cases, is readily readable by the programmer; soft copy is that which is ordinarily interpretable only by the computer. At the lowest level, the format of the information to be transmitted is specified. Where the programmer must be concerned about format there are two forms, field specification and copy control (e.g., spacing of lines on a printed page).

In addition to these levels of I/O processing, Figure IX.1 distinguishes data and program copy. For the most part, we are concerned only with data—information read by a program and the output produced by the program. For some purposes, however, we must consider forms in which programs exist. We discuss each of these several problems briefly, and then return to a discussion of the more common kinds of programming applications.

Transmission Mode. Information is transmitted in two modes by input and output statements. The first mode includes the familiar numeric information discussed in Chapter 6. This sort of information transmission is by way of binary code. In card input the code is familiar. A hole in a specified place in a punch card is a code for a specified number or other character. A punch card is an example of a simple binary device with 1 and 0 represented by punched and nonpunched spaces on the card. When the numeric decimal values of data are coded in binary form, the representation is called Binary Coded Decimal (BCD). In addition, other characters, such as the letters and symbols used in the Fortran language statements, are coded in conventional ways to correspond to octal numbers and subsequently to binary representation. Specific configurations of binary bits are taken to represent specific Fortran characters and numbers. Hence, the entire symbol set in Fortran, numbers, letters, punctuation, etc., may be represented in BCD. This representation can be in the physical form of cards, magnetic tape, disk, etc.

The second mode of information transmission is binary. Numbers and characters are represented without regard for the intent of the program or programmer. Both binary transmission and BCD transmission of information are actually in terms of binary words. However, if a binary word is known to be BCD, the word may be decoded, i.e., the BCD meaning of the binary code may be determined. If information in the binary mode is decoded under the mistaken assumption that it is BCD, the result will be nonsense. If one does not know that a binary word is BCD, the word is interpreted simply as a binary number representation. The code convention varies from computer to computer. Hence, if the BCD code is to be used, the programmer must know the code of the machine.

The executable I/O statement specifies the action to be taken (READ, WRITE) and the mode of the information to be transmitted. The content and form of the statement indicates which I/O unit is to be operated, the number of the statement containing the FORMAT when needed, and the list of information to be transmitted.

BCD representation on punch cards requires a full column of 12 rows per character. However, a Fortran character code requires only six binary bits of internal storage because there are fewer than 64 characters. Once the BCD information is translated into binary a great savings can be observed. This is particularly true when a single character per computer word is stored in BCD. If a word in memory is used to represent a number of characters in binary, the transmission of information between memory and soft copy devices is much more economical. If binary information is punched on cards, the savings are impressive in terms of sheer bulk of materials. Instead of storing 80 BCD characters on a card, one to a column, up to 160 characters can be stored on a card in the binary mode. Optimal use of a card implies use of all 80×12 bits. This degree of efficiency is nearly achieved by some parts of Fortran I/O, particularly soft copy binary output.

Types of Copy. The word "copy" is used here to refer to the physical representation of the information transmitted in I/O. Hence, "copy" refers to cards, printed paper, magnetic tape, etc. Two general kinds of copy are distinguished: hard copy and soft copy. Hard copy includes all the tangible input and output materials, such as cards, printed paper, and punched paper tape. Soft copy refers to input and output material that in general is not tangible or directly interpretable. Soft copy includes electromagnetic tape, disc, etc., on which input or output has been written by the computer or some computer-compatable device. Soft copy also refers to microfilm records made from cathode-ray tube (CRT) display devices. Display devices like the CRT's are also being used to communicate information directly to human observers in the form of messages or pictures.

The implications of the distinction between hard and soft copy are discussed in the following sections.

Format. BCD information is transmitted under the control of a FORMAT statement specifying the form and nature of the information. Each BCD word in the I/O list may be in a different mode than the succeeding word. This is in contrast to the transmission of binary information where the words in the string transmitted are not differentiated one from another. Each binary word is transmitted without any accompanying information regarding its nature—whether it is fixed or floating numeric, alphabetic, etc.

The FORMAT in BCD information transmission serves two general purposes: to specify the fields of information transmitted, and to control the spacing and appearance of the copy (copy control). Two types of fields were introduced in Chapter 6, namely, the I and F field designations for integer and real number fields. In addition, the FORMAT characters "X", "/" and "1H1" were introduced to permit spacing of characters on a line (or card) or to change lines (cards) in input and output, and to change pages in printed output. These characters permit the programmer to control the handling of the copy with which he is dealing. Additional field specifications are defined in Fortran and copy control is extended beyond the characters already introduced.

Program Transmission. The discussion up to this point has ignored two modes of hard copy information transmission, namely, BCD cards containing a Fortran program and binary cards containing a compiled machine language program. When a programmer has coded and punched a program the result is a deck of BCD cards—the source program. The program at this point cannot cause itself to be read into the computer for compilation. Likewise, the compiled (object) program has no means whereby it can cause itself to be punched out on cards for future execution. The input of the object program likewise cannot be executed by the program itself. All of these input and output functions dealing with the program itself are performed by the Fortran operating (or monitor) system without additional programming. Certain "system control" options, indicated by special cards placed in front of the program, are necessary to get the operating system to read and punch out the program in the source and object form. These system control cards vary from installation to installation, even when "identical" machines are involved. The programmer will have to consult the local computing center advisory personnel for the specific cards required and permitted.

EXECUTABLE I/O STATEMENTS

All input is accomplished by a READ statement. Two READ statements are defined, one for BCD and one for binary. The statements are:

READ *(i,n) list*

to read BCD information corresponding to *list* from I/O device or file number *i* by the FORMAT in statement number *n*; *i* is an integer constant or variable.

READ *(i) list*

to read binary information corresponding to *list* from I/O device or file number *i*; *i* is an integer constant or variable.

The BCD READ requires specification of an I/O device and a FORMAT statement while the binary READ requires only a device number. The FORMAT statement is not required in the binary READ because the format is always the same—a list of *k* binary words where *k* is the number of elements specified in the list. The device specified may be a physical device like a tape drive or a logical device like a sector on a disc. The term "file" is widely used to designate a logical device.

The binary and soft copy BCD READ statements are used when a Fortran program has written soft copy information on a disc, drum, or tape and the information is to be recovered. The writing may occur during the execution of the program or at some previous time (when a physical tape is used, the reel must be mounted on I/O unit *i* at the time the READ statement is executed).

Two output statements are defined:

WRITE *(i,n) list*

to record BCD information in *list* on input-output device number *i* in FORMAT specified in statement number *n*; *i* is an integer constant or variable.

WRITE *(i) list*

to record binary information in *list* on input-output device number *i*; *i* is an integer constant or variable.

The two WRITE statements correspond to the BCD READ and binary READ in the sense that the WRITE statements produce records of information that are read by the BCD READ or the binary READ. Two restrictions are imposed—a program cannot read the system output files or write on the system input files.

I/O FILES

Input/output statements for BCD information require two values [e.g., READ(5,117) or READ(INFILE,117) where INFILE has been set equal to the number of the input file]. The second of these two values refers to the number of a FORMAT statement that specifies the form that the BCD information assumes. The first of the two constants refers to an I/O file, a tape, disc, etc. Binary I/O statements require only the file specification. It is the purpose of this section to present additional information on the designation of I/O files.

Imagine that the computing center has eight tape units, a disc with 100 "sectors," and a drum with 150 sectors. Each of these 258 I/O "devices" or files can be assigned a number that is known as the symbolic file designation. If a given tape unit is assigned the number 4 then reference to a READ or WRITE statement in a program such as

```
READ(4,179)   or   WRITE(4,179)
```

causes a read or a write for that tape unit. The symbolic file designations are independent of the physical unit assignments as far as the programmer is concerned (at least for the level of programming we are discussing now). Hence, the programmer need not be concerned with the physical unit with which he is dealing. Symbolic file number 4 may be one physical tape unit in one execution of the program and another physical unit in another execution.

There are certain restrictions on the use of the symbolic file designations in connection with the operations of the computing center. Generally one or more files (e.g., tape units) are assigned to serve the functions of hard copy input and output. Thus, if the programmer wishes to input a deck of cards to the computer he will address the symbolic file designated by the computer center as the BCD system input file. If the programmer wishes to punch cards (hard copy card output) the file designated in the WRITE must correspond to the designation established by the computing center as the file for punched output. The standard conventions in IBM Fortran (which are not consistently observed) is to assign symbolic file 5 as the hard copy system input unit, symbolic file 6 as the printed hard copy system output unit, and file 7 as the hard copy punched card output unit.

An example of the assignment of eight units is as follows

Symbolic File	*Assignment*
1	Binary input-output (soft copy)
2	Binary input-output (soft copy)
3	Binary input-output (soft copy)
4	BCD input-output (soft copy)
5	BCD input (hard copy)
6	BCD printed output (hard copy)
7	BCD punched output (hard copy)
8	Binary output (hard copy)

THE LIST

The list of an executable I/O statement (hard copy as well as soft copy) is composed of the names of variables and arrays including implied DO's specifying subscripting. For example, the elements e_i in

READ (i,n) e_1, e_2, e_3, ...

may be the names of variables, the names of arrays that are to be transmitted in their entirety, or arrays in implied DO form. The complete extended implied DO includes the full form of the DO. The general form of the implied DO for a one-dimensional array is

$$(X(i),\ i = m_1, m_2, m_3)$$

where X is the array name and m_1, m_2, and m_3 have the same meaning as in the DO statement. For example, if every other element in the array X is to be transmitted the implied DO in the list will be

```
(X(I), I = 1, N, 2)
```

If every other column of two-dimensional array Y were to be transmitted the implied DO in the list would be

```
(Y(I,J), I = 1, N), J = 1, M, 2)
```

ADDITIONAL BCD FIELD SPECIFICATIONS

The F and I field specifications were introduced in Chapter 6. These permitted the transmission of real and integer values between memory and some I/O file. Several other modes of numbers have been discussed and we must present the means for transmitting information for variables that are of some type other than REAL or INTEGER. First, REAL numbers may be transmitted as a so-called E or exponential field that is useful for very large or very small values. Following the description of E fields three other field types are introduced: logical (L) fields for transmitting logical information, alphameric (A) fields for transmitting alphabetic and other characters, and Hollerith (H) fields for transmitting characters through FORMAT statements and for serving as copy control. A special formating control character, T, for transferring from one segment of a record to another is also introduced.

Exponential Fields. Many areas of science commonly express values as powers of 10 rather than as decimal numbers.

While this is more characteristic of physical sciences than of behavioral sciences, the exponential notation is sometimes useful, particularly when the relative magnitude of a value cannot be safely predicted or when it is likely to become very large or very small (hence, requiring a great many decimal places or significant digits).

Any REAL number may be expressed as a fraction multiplied by a power of 10. For example, the number 58.779 can be expressed as

$$.58779 \times 10^2 = .58779 \times 100$$

If this value were to be read by a Fortran program, the data card would be punched as

.58779E2

Note that the letter E takes the place of the notation

"× 10"

The Fortran statements to read the value, assuming that it were the value of the variable EVAR, would be

```
READ (5, 153) EVAR
153 FORMAT (E8.5)
```

The field description must be large enough to account for the entire field, including the exponent, the sign (if present), and the decimal point.

The general form of the E specification is

E*w*.*d*

where w is an integer constant giving the width of the entire field, and d is an integer constant giving the number of significant digits to the *right* of the decimal point, but *not including the exponent notation.*

An exponent may be either positive or negative. Table IX.1 gives some illustrations of card formats, the numbers represented by them, and the required FORMAT specifications. It is clear from the examples presented in Table IX.1 that the exponent and its sign are of critical importance in using an E specification. The sign of the number and the sign of the exponent obviously do not have to be the same.

Care must be taken in using the E field description so that space is allowed for the exponent. In addition, the usual cautions appropriate to the F field specification regarding decimal point and sign apply here.

In using E fields for output, a minimum field width of 8 columns is required. The output routines generated by the Fortran compiler assign one column to

Table IX.1

Some Illustrative cards read by E designations.

Field description	Field appearance	Value
E6.2	3355E3	33.55×10^{3} = 33,550.0
E7.2	12355E2	123.55×10^{2} = 12355.0
E8.2	-1.28E+4	-1.28×10^{4} = -12,800.0
E8.0	-1.28E+4	-1.28×10^{4} = -12,800.0
E4.2	99E2	$.99\times10^{2}$ = 99.0
E5.2	99E-3	$.99\times10^{-3}$ = .00099
E7.1	-105E-3	-10.5×10^{-3} = -.0105

the sign, one to the decimal, one for the letter E, and three columns for the value of the exponent. A field of E output may be diagrammed as

↓↓↓ ↓ ↓ ↓↓
±0.xxxxE±ee

where the x's are values of the variable being printed and the e's are positions for exponent values. The seven positions marked with an arrow (↓) are always required by the output routines. If the field is described as being a total of 8 columns in width, only one column is allowed for the value of the variable. Suppose that the field description is E8.1. The output field may be diagrammed as

±0.xE±ee

which leaves room for only one significant digit. The safest rule in using E fields for output is never to use less than a 10-column field width. It is suggested therefore, that the narrowest E output field be described as

E10.3

which describes a field

±0.xxxE±ee

allowing only a marginal amount of room for significant digits.

Logical Fields. Logical variables may be read or written with the format specification

L*n*

where *n* is the field width expressed as an integer constant. When the logical specification is used to read cards, the value .TRUE. will be stored if the first nonblank character in the group of *n* characters is a T, and .FALSE. will be stored if the first nonblank character is an F. If all *n* of the characters are blank, then the value .FALSE. will be stored. Thus, all of the following may be read with an L6 format specification, and will result in the value of .TRUE. being stored: bTRUEb, bbbbbT, bTbIbC, TACbbb, and bbbTOE. Any of the following, when read by L5 will result in .FALSE. being stored: FALSE, bbbbF, bbbbb, and bbFAR. In output, only the letter T and F are printed. If *n* is greater than 1, the letter will be preceded by *n*-1 blanks. Examples of logical field output are given in the two programs in the previous chapter, TRUTH1 and TRUTH2.

Alphameric Information. There are three ways in which the Fortran characters (including the alphabet and numeric characters, i.e., alphameric information) are transmitted by Fortran. The first of these is by the so-called alphameric mode involving an A field in a format statement. These fields are read by the program just as F and I numeric fields are read. Hence, A field information is treated as a manipulable variable within the memory of the computer.

The second way of transmitting alphameric information is by specifying it in the FORMAT statement at the time the program is coded. Information transmitted in this way is called Hollerith information. The characters are specified in the FORMAT and are not in general manipulable in the sense that A field characters are.

The third way of transmitting alphameric information is by compiling it into the program with a DATA statement. This type of statement is similar to a declaration, in that it establishes the information as a part of the program and actually causes no computations when the program is executed. The alphameric information is compiled into named variables (including arrays) and hence can be treated as variables in logical and arithmetic expressions. The DATA statement is dealt with in a separate section later in this chapter.

Alphameric Fields. A variable of any implicit mode may contain information transmitted by an A field FORMAT description. For example, the statements

```
   READ (5,1) NAME,(SCORE(I), I=1,5)
 1 FORMAT (A6, 5F3.0)
```

could read six letters of a person's name and his scores on five variables or tests from a card. The integer variable NAME would contain 6 characters of alphameric information, which may later be printed as a label. For example, the program might calculate MEAN, a real variable that is the average of the scores for an individual. The data are read by the previous statements from a card of the form

SMITHb100b96b54b68b97

The mean of the scores could be calculated, and the value of MEAN, and the contents of NAME printed by the statements

```
   WRITE (6,2) NAME, MEAN
 2 FORMAT (1H1, 10X, A6, F6.2)
```

The execution of these would result in the line

SMITHbb83.00

being printed at the top of a page of output, ten spaces from the left.

In general, a specification

Am

in a FORMAT statement indicates that *m* alphameric characters (an A field of *m* characters) are to be written from, or read into, a location in memory named in the I/O list. The number of characters that may be transmitted to or from memory depends on the particular computer. In the UNIVAC 1108, for example, only six characters may be stored in a single word. This rule arises from the fact that a 36 bit computer word can store only 6 alphameric characters. If it is desirable to use, say, 12 characters for the name, an array may be used or, alternatively, two variables. Thus, the coding may be either

```
   DIMENSION NAME (2)
99 READ (5,2) NAME(1), NAME(2)
 2 FORMAT (2A6)
   .
   .
   .
   WRITE(6,3)NAME(1),NAME(2),XMEAN
 3 FORMAT(1H1, 10X, 2A6, F7.2)
```

or we may write

```
99 READ (5,2) NAME1, NAME2
 2 FORMAT (2A6)
   .
   .
   .
   WRITE (6,3) NAME1, NAME2, XMEAN
 3 FORMAT (1H1, 10X, 2A6, F7.2)
```

The reader should note the difference in NAME(1) and NAME1 with respect to the formal properties of the variables involved and the required declarations.

On input, if *m* is less than the number of characters per word, the word of alphameric information is left-justified, and the remainder of the word filled out with blanks. Thus, if the specification is A3 in a 6 character word, and the data card field contains

BIG

the word is stored as though the characters BIGbbb are read. On the other hand, if *m* is greater than the number of characters per word, only the rightmost characters are stored (this may vary with machines). Then a card containing

GREATEST

read with an A8 specification results in the characters

EATEST

being stored, in a 6 character word.

For output of alphameric information, the following rules hold. If *m* is less than the number of characters per word, only the leftmost characters of the specified word are transmitted. For example, if the variable LABEL contains the characters BIGEST, then the specification A3 results in the transmission of the characters BIG. However, A6 transmits the full word, BIGEST. If *m* is greater than 6, the full word is transmitted, preceded by *m*-6 blanks, in a 6 character word machine. Thus, the printing of LABEL with a format specification of A10 results in

bbbbBIGEST

Hollerith (H) Fields. The second method of dealing with alphameric information does not treat it as a variable. The specification

```
mH________
  \___ ___/
      V
 m characters
```

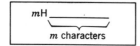

allows the placement of alphameric information in a FORMAT statement. This treatment of alphameric data is most frequently used for printing labels, and for output copy control. For example, it might be desired to have the printed output be of the form

bbSMITHbbMALEbbMEANbSCOREb=bbb83.00

The label "bbMEANbSCOREb=b" can be introduced into the FORMAT statement as shown below.

```
FORMAT (2X,A5,2X,A5,14HbMEANbSCOREb=b,F7.2)
```

An H field was introduced giving the characters to be printed. Note that the alphameric information is inserted directly into the FORMAT statement and that the count (14) gives the exact size of the H field, and that blanks are counted as legitimate characters. These characters in the H field ordinarily cannot be manipulated within the program.

As an additional example, suppose that the values of X, Y, SUM, and MEAN are to be printed. Each is to be labeled and printed on a separate line, with the first starting at the top of a new page. The following statements will accomplish the desired end.

```
   WRITE (6,1) X, Y, SUM, MEAN
 1 FORMAT (5H1Xb=b, F5.2,/5HbYb=b,F5.2,
1/7HbSUMb=b, F5.2, /8HbMEANb=b, F5.2)
```

Note that each of the variables is associated with a numeric field description (F5.2 in this case) and the labeling and carriage control is accomplished by H fields and slashes.

Suppose that we want to print out the 3×3 array X and we want the rows and columns labeled, so that the output appears as

	COLUMN 1	COLUMN 2	COLUMN 3
ROW 1	XX.XX	XX.XX	XX.XX
ROW 2	XX.XX	XX.XX	XX.XX
ROW 3	XX.XX	XX.XX	XX.XX

The general approach is to print the heading row giving the column numbers first, then go into a loop to print the matrix row by row. The program statements are presented below. The reader should draw a sketch of the output produced by these statements to aid in deciphering the format codes.

```
   WRITE (6,10)
10 FORMAT (20X,8HCOLUMNb1, 6X, 8HCOLUMNb2, 6X, 8HCOLUMNb3)
   DO 1 I = 1, 3
 1 WRITE (6,11) I, (X(I,J), J = 1, 3)
11 FORMAT (10X, 4HROWb, I1, 6X, 2(F5.2,8X), F5.2)
```

Note that FORMAT statement 10 contains no numeric fields, only Hollerith information. Consequently, the WRITE statement referring to FORMAT 10 has no list. This is perfectly acceptable—a list may be omitted when all the information to be transmitted is contained in the FORMAT statement.

Some implementations of Fortran allow a simpler form of the Hollerith field specification. In these systems, the nH notation does not have to be used, but the material to be printed can be enclosed in apostrophe marks (or asterisks). For example, the FORMAT statement given above to print a heading could be written as

```
10 FORMAT (20X, 'COLUMNb1' 6X, 'COLUMNb2' 6X, 'COLUMNb3')
```

The reader is advised to consult a programming advisor before attempting to use this feature since the apostrophe marks will cause a compiler message if this procedure is not allowed.

Thus far, only the use of H fields in output has been discussed. They may also be used in input, in a way that permits the programmer to set the contents of a Hollerith string from punched cards read where the program is executed. We illustrate the use of an H field in a common input application, labeling of the output in a general program. The specification *m*H in a FORMAT for a READ statement causes *m* characters to be read and those *m* characters to replace the *m* characters in the format statement itself. To read a title to be printed, the statements

```
   READ (5,26)
26 FORMAT (24Hbbbbbbbbbbbbbbbbbbbbbbbb)
```

may be used to cause 24 characters on the input card to be read. Supposing the card to be read contained the characters

bbbbbbANALYSISbb20bbbbbb

The output from the statement

```
WRITE(6,26)
```

referring to the FORMAT just used in the input will cause the characters

bbbbbbANALYSISbb20bbbbbb

to be printed just as if statement 26 had originally been written

```
26 FORMAT (24HbbbbbbANALYSISbb20bbbbbb)
```

The T Specification. This specification is not precisely a field description but an instruction to the computer (it is not available in all Fortran implementations). Suppose that a program is to process data cards for a number of subjects in a learning task. Each subject has N trials until he reached criterion, but N will vary from one subject to the next. The data consist of the number of errors made on each of the N trials; N never exceeds 35, and the number of errors on a trial never exceeds 99. Suppose that the data cards have been punched before the program was written and have the values arranged on the card with the N two-column fields beginning in column 1 and continuing up to column 2N. The value of N is punched in columns 71 and 72. By using the T specification N can be read first and then the N data values can be read.

In some Fortran implementations a READ can be begun at any specified column and then redirected to any other column of the card. The general form of the specification is

T*n*

where *n* is an unsigned integer constant representing one of the 80 columns on the card. The result is that the card is read beginning with column *n* and continuing until either the end of the FORMAT statement, or another T specification is encountered. As applied to the present problem, a T specification may be used to transfer to column 71 to read N, and then another T to transfer back to column 1 to begin reading X. The statements would appear as

```
    READ (5, 879) N, (X(I), I = 1, N)
879 FORMAT (T71, I2, T1, (F2.0))
```

The T specification may be used in output as well; *n* indicates an allowable print position on the paper.

BCD HARD COPY CONTROL

Controlling line spacing on the printer is much like controlling lines on a typewriter. The statement

WRITE (6, *n*) *list*

writes a record on the system output file 6 which is then converted to printed paper off-line. The statement may specify via the FORMAT statement number *n* that the record is to be printed in more than one line. The use of the character "/" to separate lines of output has already been introduced. While the slash causes the printer to move to a new line, it is the first character on the line that actually controls the carriage. The first character on a line generally is not printed, but may have an effect on the printer before the line is printed (see Chapter 6).

The most common method of introducing a carriage control character into a FORMAT statement is with a one-column Hollerith field. Thus, writing 1H1 as the first field specification in a FORMAT statement defines a one-column H field containing the numeral 1, causing a skip to the top of the next page.

One-column H fields may be combined with a slash to combine several lines in a single FORMAT statement. Thus

```
      WRITE (6,999) XMEAN, YMEAN, N
999   FORMAT (1H1, 12HMEANbOFbXb=b, F7.2/1H4, 12HMEANbOFb
     1 Yb=b, F7.2/1H4, 4HNb=b, I5)
```

causes the values of XMEAN, YMEAN, and N to be printed, labeled, and spaced down a fresh page. The slash gives a new line, and the first field defined on each line is for carriage control.

Consecutive slashes may be used, as has been shown in several previous examples, to produce any desired spacing. In general, *N* slashes will produce *N*-1 blank lines.

When the BCD copy involves cards, either in input or in output, the "spacing" is limited to the exchange of one card for the next in the deck. Thus, a Hollerith character in the first "column" of a card I/O FORMAT does not have any meaning. The slash, /, is interpreted in I/O for cards in such a way that for every /encountered the I/O proceeds to the next card.

Repetition of Fields. Field descriptions may be enclosed in parentheses to denote repetition. For example,

```
    WRITE (6, 101) N, SUM, (X(I), I=1, N)
101 FORMAT (I5, F6.1, (F3.0))
```

associates I5 with N, F6.1 with SUM, and F3.0 with all of the elements X(I). If a group of FORMAT specifications are to be repeated, they may be enclosed in parentheses and preceded by an integer constant denoting the number of repetitions. Thus

```
1 FORMAT (1H1, 2X, 3(5X, F1.0))
```

is equivalent to

```
1 FORMAT (1H1, 2X, 5X, F1.0, 5X, F1.0, 5X, F1.0)
```

FORMAT STATEMENTS READ IN AT EXECUTION TIME

In writing programs that are to be of general utility, it frequently is desirable to be able to read as data the format that is used to describe the data. Thus, the data do not have to be punched in accordance with a FORMAT statement written into the program, but the FORMAT statement may be read from cards by the program and then used to read data. The following statements illustrate the use of the variable format feature of Fortran.

```
    DIMENSION FORMT (12)
    READ (5, 199) (FORMT(I),I=1,12)
199 FORMAT (12A6)
    READ (5,FORMT) X,(Y(I),I=1,10)
```

The first statement defines a variable FORMT which requires 12 words of memory storage. The next statement reads 72 columns into the array FORMT using an alphameric specification. Thus, the contents of the card are stored directly into memory as the variable FORMT. The card contains the format statement for the data. The final statement uses the information in the array FORMT to read a data card containing the variables X, Y(1), ..., Y(10). The card read by the READ (5,199) statement might have the appearance

```
(F8.2, 10(F5.1))
```

The card containing the format information contains an actual FORMAT statement, except for the word "FORMAT." The parentheses enclosing the format description must be present, the first open parenthesis in the first column read.

A FORMAT variable may be of any mode. It must always be mentioned in a DIMENSION statement, even if it only requires a single word of storage (6 characters or less).

TRACE METHODS IN DEBUGGING

Many programs are written in such a way that a great deal of computation is done before any output is produced. In these cases, if the program fails before output, it is often very difficult to locate the source of the error, especially if the program is quite complex. In such an instance, the use of a trace is very valuable. The tracing procedure is a simple matter of inserting WRITE statements at several points so the programmer can follow the execution of the program.

Many programmers have made up sets of cards like the following

```
      WRITE (6,10001)
10001 FORMAT (4H ONE)
      WRITE (6,10002)
10002 FORMAT (4H TWO)
      WRITE (6,10003)
10003 FORMAT (6H THREE)
```

which they can insert in pairs into their programs. These of course cause the words ONE, TWO, THREE, etc. to be printed as output. The difficulty can be located more easily when the failure is more clearly localized.

To facilitate convenient use of trace cards, they can be punched in cards different from those normally used in punching a Fortran program (i.e., different color, different corner cut, etc.). This allows the trace cards to be removed easily from the deck when the program is operating correctly, thus eliminating the debug printing from the output.

It is also possible to eliminate tracing in another way, which is occasionally useful. A data card can be read at the beginning which indicates whether or not tracing is to be done. One way of doing this might be as follows

```
   LOGICAL TRACE
   READ (5, 99) TRACE
99 FORMAT (L1)
   .
   .
   .
   IF(TRACE) WRITE (6,10001)
   .
   .
   .
```

This would produce a trace only if the logical variable were read with the value .TRUE..

When tracing a loop, it is often useful to print the value of the index to count the number of executions of the loop. The following statements would accomplish this:

```
      DO 100 J = 1, 10
      IF (TRACE) WRITE (6,99999) J
99999 FORMAT (1X,3HJb=,I2)
      .
      .
      .
```

Any data that might be useful in following the operation of a program can be printed in the same way.

THE DATA STATEMENT

Named variables in memory may be preset by use of the DATA statement. This is particularly useful when certain constants need to be stored. It is also convenient for storing nonnumerical information, i.e., alphabetic characters and Fortran special characters, that may be printed as labels, etc. The statement has the general form

DATA $list/d_1, d_2, \ldots, d_n/, list/d_1, \ldots$

where the list contains the names of the variables being defined and d_i is a data item. The statement

DATA A,B,C/5.6, 8.39, 98.6/

accomplishes the same purpose as the three statements

A = 5.6
B = 8.39
C = 98.6

That is, it stores the numerical values at locations A, B, and C. However, the DATA statement does this during compiling. When the program begins execution, variables A, B, and C have already been defined as having specific values.

Subscripted variables may be used in the list. The subscript may be either an integer constant or an integer variable. If it is the latter, it must be under the control of an implied DO as in the list of an I/O statement. There must be a one-to-one correspondence between the list variables and the data values d_i. As an advantage to the programmer, if it is desired to repeat the data value d_i several times, say n, the data item may be preceeded by "n*" indicating repetition of the value. For example, the statement

DATA A, B, C, SAM /4*6.83/

places the value 6.83 in the locations A, B, C, and SAM. When data are compiled into an entire array by this option subscripting information may be omitted in the list. Thus, the statements

DIMENSION CONSTS (30)
DATA BIG, CONSTS, Y /990.6, 30*2.5, .005/

define values of 990.6 and .005 for BIG and Y, respectively, and preset all locations of the array CONSTS to contain the value 2.5.

The information literals, or data values d_i, may be any of the following types of information:

1. Real or integer constants.
2. Alphameric characters. These are written in the form nH——, where—— indicates the alphameric literal, and n is the number of characters in the literal. Alphameric characters are stored six to the computer word. If the literal does not fill out a word, the information is stored packed left with the remaining spaces filled by blanks. Thus, in a machine with 6 character words, the statement

DATA SEX(1), SEX(2) /4HMALE, 6HFEMALE/

would store the characters "MALEbb" as SEX(1) and "FEMALE" as SEX(2), where "b" indicates a blank. The information contained in the two variables could then be printed by the program, using the alphameric conversion character A.
3. Logical constants written as .TRUE., .FALSE., T, or F.

SOFT COPY I/O

The full ramifications of the concept of soft copy are discussed in more detail in Chapter 12. However, some of the more straightforward uses are discussed here.

Imagine processing a very large amount of data. If the data and the program will fit into the memory of the computer at one time, nothing is gained by storing the data on a tape or disc preparatory to its use. However, if the program is quite large and the data occupy a very large part of the internal storage of the machine, it may be impossible to store the data completely along with the program at any one time. The programmer has two options, either to process the data as they are read into the computer, or to store the data on a tape or disc as they are read into the computer and then to read the data off that tape or disc as they are needed. The first method is preferable if the data are needed but once in the processing. However, if the data are needed twice, the temporary storage method is preferable, since otherwise the data would have to be read from cards twice or more.

The information written on a soft copy I/O device (tape, disc, etc.) need not be data input to the computer. Any information the programmer wishes to store during the execution of the program in order to have it out of the way but available can be stored in this way. The terms "noncentral storage" and "peripheral storage" refer to this use of soft copy I/O. An I/O file used in this way is often referred to as a scratch file.

Two forms of soft copy have been introduced, BCD and binary. In the general case of temporary storage (a scratch file), the binary mode is used. However, if it is desired to use the output of a program as the BCD input of another program, i.e., as data, or to have the contents of the soft copy tape printed or punched as hard copy, at a later date, the soft copy tape must be written in BCD. For example, if the programmer wants to print the output of a program now, and then again later (perhaps, for a class he teaches periodically), he could produce a soft copy version of the BCD output (using a tape other than the system output tape), save the physical tape, and have the contents printed at demand. If the soft copy were in binary, this later conversion to hard copy would have to be mediated by a program to read the binary soft copy and then to output the hard copy or a BCD soft copy tape. These details are handled differently on the various computer systems and a programming advisor should be consulted before trying to use tape storage methods for permanent storage of data.

In using soft copy techniques the programmer must be able to manipulate the peripheral I/O devices and know how to select the devices to use. These two subjects are dealt with in the paragraphs that follow.

MANIPULATION OF SOFT COPY TAPES

When a programmer utilizes the soft copy facilities of Fortran, he must be able to position the physical tape in such a way as to write on and read from appropriate portions of the tape. To understand these manipulations, it is necessary to understand the physical form of the information as it is written on the tape. The information is written in a linear fashion, word after word. The first word written occurs before the second on the tape, the third after the second, etc. In order to start from the beginning of a tape, either to write on it or to read from it, the tape must be rewound on the tape reel. The command

```
REWIND i
```

causes the tape drive, device i, to rewind the tape reel mounted. With the execution of a WRITE command the list of elements is written on the tape as a "record" the length of which is determined by the number of elements in the list, and by the FORMAT if the WRITE is a BCD write. Records are separated by a space of "blank" tape called a "record gap." The tape is automatically ready to be written on unless the program encounters another tape manipulation statement.

Imagine that the program has caused three records of information to be written on a tape unit with device number i. The programmer at that point wishes to recover the second record of information. In order to position the tape so that it is at the first word of the second record, the programmer may backspace the tape to the desired record. In the example, there is one record between the position of the tape and the record desired. Hence, the programmer would write into the program:

```
BACKSPACE i
BACKSPACE i
```

each BACKSPACE causing a backspacing on the tape by one record. If the number of backspaces necessary is calculated in the execution of the program the BACKSPACE could be buried in a DO with the limit of the number of iterations, e.g., ITER, determined by the calculation.

```
      DO 111 K = 1, ITER
      BACKSPACE i
  111 CONTINUE
```

Another way of positioning the tape is by using the REWIND statement followed by READ statements with blank lists. The tape can then be spaced forward over as many records as desired by executing a READ(*i*) with no list as many times as records to be skipped.

```
      DO 222 K = 1, ITER
      READ(i)
  222 CONTINUE
```

In order to signal the end of the set of records written by a program the statement

END FILE *i*

is used. The end of file mark cannot be read past, and errors in tape reading and writing will be found by reading into an end of file.

A few important comments on tape manipulation are called for here. The system input and output tapes should never be addressed with tape manipulative statements. Before using a tape unit for soft copy I/O the tape should always be rewound. Failure to start writing at the beginning of a tape may not be accounted for in subsequent reading unless the reading follows backspace commands only. In addition, rewind after writing without an initial rewind may give an error. Finally, if the number of elements in the list is not the same as the number of elements in the record an error will occur when reading.

AN ILLUSTRATIVE PROGRAM: VERBAL

Behavioral scientists frequently have verbal or other nonnumerical data that they wish to process. The computer can easily be programmed to manipulate symbolic data, such as lists of names of subjects, lists of words emitted in a free association test, or verbal text. Contrary to general belief, these sorts of programs can be written entirely in Fortran and with as much precision as one wishes. A recent book on Fortran programming aimed at behavioral scientists encumbers the presentation of the analysis of verbal data with discussions of internal representation of Fortran characters, the internal storage of characters in binary, and a general pessimism about doing the job with precision. None of these encumbrances need be involved, and Fortran will do completely.

The way that characters, as punched on a punch card, are stored when they are read in BCD form by an A field specification varies with the computer. Consequently, if the programmer tries to manipulate the BCD characters he must know the code. However, we can use the computer to recode the BCD input into a form that we specify. The recoding is based on the fact that a character read by an A1 field specification is stored exactly as the same character stored by a 1H in a DATA statement. If we compile the character set of Fortran into an array in the program with a DATA statement and read the verbal data with a repeated A1 field specification we can compare each character in the verbal data with the contents of the array and substitute the array index for the character. This code (the index) now is a simple numerical code that we can interpret directly. The internal representation is quite irrelevant—we have simply substituted known index values for the BCD code. The Fortran character set is composed of the alphabetic characters A through Z, blank, the numeric characters 0 through 9, and the special characters, ()+−/'$.,*, a total of 47 characters. They can be compiled into a program by the statements shown at the bottom of page 181.
The continuation cards in the DATA statement are set up for convenience in writing the statement on a coding form. The specific ordering of the characters was selected because of the convenience it gives in alphabetizing by ordering the

magnitude of the recoded verbal material.

To input verbal data to the recoding process, they are read from punched cards, each verbal unit (word) separated from the adjacent unit by a space. If other verbal or textual units are important to the analysis, they can be indicated in the punching by using a code such as an asterisk for a paragraph beginning, a double space for a page change in the text, etc. In the example program developed here we assume only that there are a number of words of text and that the task is simply to list the words, each on a separate line. The reader should be able easily to construct more complex analyses of the verbal data, using the general principles illustrated in this example program.

The program VERBAL, Figure IX.2, first sets up some parameters, zeros the array WORD, and reads the data card with an 80A1 field specification. The result is that the array CARD contains the BCD characters in a form equivalent to the corresponding characters as stored by the DATA statement in the array ALPHA. In order to recode the character in the *i*th element of CARD, all that we must do is to sort through the array ALPHA until there is a match between the contents of CARD(I) and the *j*th element in ALPHA. When the match is found the index value J replaces the contents of CARD(I). This replacement is accomplished by a simple replacement statement, which is one of the reasons for declaring the array CARD an integer array.

Next, the program proceeds to gather the recoded characters into computer words to represent verbal words. The program makes the assumption that the verbal words are no more than 20 letters long, exclusive of punctuation and nonalphabetic characters. The computer words into which the verbal words are packed make up an array called WORD in the program. The array WORD is dimensioned 100 by 4 on the presumption that the example data will contain no more than 100 "words." The row elements of WORD stand for the verbal words: the first column for the first five letters of the verbal word, the second column for the second five letters, etc. When three consecutive periods are encountered on a given card the program stops processing the cards. (The last two elements of CARD are dummy elements to permit easy expression of the IF testing for the three periods.) The program assumes that the computer word has 36 bits. Since each character code is less than 48, 6 bits will contain every code ($2^6 = 64$). Only five of the 6-bit parts of the word are used because the sixth part would involve the "sign bit" of the word, which is treated by most computers differently than the other bits of the word. In the CDC 6400, with 60-bit words, 9 recoded characters can be packed to each computer word.

The method of packing the characters into the array WORD is not complicated but a graphical illustration is helpful in presenting it. Figure IX.3 illustrates the successive stages of packing the first column of WORD for a given verbal word. The first character is multiplied by a constant to place it toward the left end of CARD(I). It is then added to WORD. The next character is in CARD(I+1). It is multiplied by a value slightly smaller than that used in CARD(I); placing the

```
      DIMENSION ALPHA(47)
      INTEGER ALPHA
      DATA (ALPHA(I), I = 1, 47)
    1 /1H, 1HA, 1HB, 1HC, 1HD, 1HE, 1HF, 1HG, 1HH, 1HI, 1HJ, 1HK, 1HL,
    2 1HM, 1HN, 1HO, 1HP, 1HQ, 1HR, 1HS, 1HT, 1HU, 1HV, 1HW, 1HX, 1HY,
    3 1HZ, 1HO, 1H1, 1H2, 1H3, 1H4, 1H5, 1H6, 1H7, 1H8, 1H9, 1H(, 1H),
    4 1H+, 1H-, 1H/, 1H', 1H$, 1H., 1H,, 1H* /
```

```
CVERBAL
      DIMENSION ALPHA(47), CARD(82), WORD(100,4)
      INTEGER ALPHA, CARD, WORD
      DATA(ALPHA(I),I=1,47)
     1 /1H , 1HA, 1HB, 1HC, 1HD, 1HE, 1HF, 1HG, 1HH, 1HI, 1HJ, 1HK, 1HL,
     2  1HM, 1HN, 1HO, 1HP, 1HQ, 1HR, 1HS, 1HT, 1HU, 1HV, 1HW, 1HX, 1HY,
     3  1HZ, 1H0, 1H1, 1H2, 1H3, 1H4, 1H5, 1H6, 1H7, 1H8, 1H9, 1H(, 1H),
     4  1H+, 1H-, 1H/, 1H', 1H$, 1H., 1H,, 1H*  /
C READ CARDS AND PACK WORD WITH RE-CODED ALPHABETIC MATERIAL
C INITIALIZE INDEX VALUES FOR WORD, IWR FOR ROW, IWC FOR COLUMN, ICHAR
C FOR CHARACTER PACKED INTO WORD ELEMENT
      ICHAR = 1
      IWC = 1
      IWR = 1
      CARD(81) = 0
      CARD(82) = 0
      DO 15 I=1,100
      DO 15 J=1,4
   15 WORD(I,J) = 0
      WRITE (6,11)
   11 FORMAT(1H1)
C READ ONE CARD AT A TIME
    1 READ(5,10) (CARD(I),I=1,80)
   10 FORMAT(80A1)
C REPLACE A-FORMAT BCD CODE WITH INDEX VALUES OF CORRESPONDING CHARACTERS
C AS STORED IN ARRAY ALPHA
      DO 30 I =1,80
      DO 20 J =1,47
      IF(ALPHA(J).NE.CARD(I))GO TO 20
      CARD(I) = J
      GO TO 30
   20 CONTINUE
   30 CONTINUE
C PACK THE FIRST K.LE.5 CHARACTERS INTO THE FIRST COLUMN OF THE IWR ROW
C OF WORD, THE SECOND K.LE.5 INTO THE  SECOND COLUMN OF THE IWR ROW, ETC.
C WHEN A NON-ALPHABETIC IS ENCOUNTERED IWR = IWR+1, IRC = 1, ICHAR =1 AND
C A NEW WORD IS BEGUN. THE PATTERN ... ON A CARD SIGNALS THE END OF
C THF DATA
      DO 40 I = 1,80
      IF((CARD(I).EQ.45).AND.(CARD(I+1).EQ.45).AND.(CARD(I+2).EQ.45))
     1GO TO 200
      IF((CARD(I).EQ.1).OR.(CARD(I).GT.27)) GO TO 90
      WORD(IWR,IWC) = WORD(IWR,IWC) + CARD(I)*(100**(5-ICHAR))
      IF(ICHAR.EQ.5) GO TO 50
      ICHAR = ICHAR + 1
      GO TO 80
```

value in CARD(I+1) not quite so far to the left in CARD(I+1). CARD(I+1) is then added to WORD. This is repeated for all five characters going into WORD, using a smaller multiplier for each successive character in CARD. If a character is blank or not an alphabetic (having a recoded value greater than 27) the next verbal word is initiated. If the number of characters exceeds five, the next column of WORD is used to pack the next character, etc. When a verbal word exceeds 20 characters, the program substitutes blanks for the excessive characters. This causes extra lines in the output because each such inserted blank is interpreted as an additional verbal word by the algorithm of the program. (The same is true for nonblank, nonalphabetic characters in CARD occuring in conjunction with blanks and for multiple blanks in successive columns.)

The method of packing is reversed to unpack the characters, one verbal word at a time. The output generated by the program is shown in Figure IX.4, along with the three cards of input text used in the illustration.

The techniques used in VERBAL are not appropriate for all analyses of verbal materials. If the programmer is interested in separating the characters into verbal units to store on a peripheral file for later use, it is not necessary to use four

```
   50 IWC = IWC + 1
      ICHAR = 1
      IF(IWC.LE.4) GO TO 80
      DO 60 II = I,80
      IF(CARD(II).EQ.1) GO TO 80
      CARD(II) = 1
   60 CONTINUE
   90 IWR = IWR + 1
      IP = IWR-1
      IF(IWR.GT.100) GO TO 200
      ICHAR = 1
      IWC = 1
   80 CONTINUE
   40 CONTINUE
      GO TO 1
C UNPACK THE IWR VERBAL WORDS INTO CARD(I),I=1,20 AND PRINT WITH 20A1
  200 N = IWR
      DO 201 I = 1,20
  201 CARD(I) = 1
      IWORD = 1
      DO 210 IWR = 1,N
      IF(WORD(IWR,1).EQ.0) GO TO 250
      DO 220 IWC = 1,4
      IF(WORD(IWR,IWC).EQ.0) GO TO 270
      DO 230 ICHAR = 1,5
      J = ICHAR + (IWC-1)*5
      K = 100**(5-ICHAR)
      INDEX = WORD(IWR,IWC)/K
      CARD(J) = ALPHA(INDEX)
      WORD(IWR,IWC) = WORD(IWR,IWC) - INDEX*K
      IF (WORD(IWR,IWC).EQ. 0)  GO TO 220
  230 CONTINUE
  220 CONTINUE
  270 WRITE(6,240) IWORD, (CARD(L), L = 1, J)
  240 FORMAT( 5H WORD , I5, 5X, 20A1, /)
      IWORD = IWORD + 1
      GO TO 210
  250 WRITE(6,260) ALPHA(41),ALPHA(41),ALPHA(41)
  260 FORMAT(3X,A1,5X,A1,5X,A1)
  210 CONTINUE
      STOP
      END
```

Figure IX.2 Listing of the program VERBAL.

computer words for each verbal unit. The verbal units can be packed into computer words in a single-dimensioned array, using elements of the array to separate the verbal units. The arrangement in VERBAL facilitates alphabetizing by making each verbal unit correspond to a row in WORD. Other types of analyses of the verbal data may be facilitated by other types of storage for them.

An alphabetical ordering of WORD, after the packing is completed, can be obtained by sorting WORD into numerical order, beginning with the first column and re-sorting on the second column for those elements having the same value in column one, etc. Since the recoded characters have small values for letters early in the alphabet, the small-valued words will be high in the alphabet. The recoded value for ABCDE is 0203040506, and for VWXYZ the value is 2324252627. The fact that the verbal words are packed from left to right in the packed computer word permits verbal words of different lengths to be ordered correctly: A is 0200000000 while AB is 0203000000, and AA is 0202000000.

COMMON ERRORS IN I/O

Errors in I/O programming usually arise from either (or both) of two sources: syntax errors, and failure to understand what is actually being done in the execution of an I/O instruction.

Many I/O syntax errors are trivial in

Contents of Computer Word	Operation, or interpretation of computer word
00 00 00 00 00 00	WORD(IWR,IWC)
	ICHAR = 1
00 00 00 00 00 23	re-coded character in CARD(I), the letter V
00 23 00 00 00 00	CARD(I)*(100**(5 - ICHAR))
00 23 00 00 00 00	WORD(IWR,IWC) + CARD(I)*(100**(5 -ICHAR))
	ICHAR = ICHAR + 1
00 00 00 00 00 06	re-coded character in CARD(I+1), the letter E
00 00 06 00 00 00	CARD(I+1)*(100**(5 - ICHAR))
00 23 06 00 00 00	WORD(IWR,IWC) + CARD(I+1)*(100**(5 -ICHAR))
	ICHAR = ICHAR + 1
00 00 00 00 00 19	re-coded character in CARD(I+2), the letter R
00 00 00 19 00 00	CARD(I+2)*(100**(5 -ICHAR))
00 23 06 19 00 00	WORD(IWR,IWC) + CARD(I+2)*(100**(5 -ICHAR))
	ICHAR = ICHAR + 1
00 00 00 00 00 03	re-coded character in CARD(I+3), the letter B
00000 00 00 03 00	CARD(I+3)*(100**(5 -ICHAR))
00 23 06 19 03 00	WORD(IWR,IWC) + CARD(I+3)*(100**(5 -ICHAR))
	ICHAR = ICHAR + 1
00 00 00 00 00 01	re-coded character in CARD(I+4), a blank
	End of the verbal word; blank encountered.

Figure IX.3 Illustration of the procedure of packing recoded characters into a computer word.

that they are readily detected by the compiler and appropriate messages produced.

Table IX.2 lists some frequent error messages. Some other kinds of syntax errors, especially in FORMAT statements, are not detected until the output appears in a form different from that expected. Some of these errors, associated with insufficient field width have been discussed in Chapter 6. The H specification can cause problems that have not been discussed. For example, the statement

```
1 FORMAT (1Hb, F2.0, 10HMEANbOFbXb=b, F7.2)
```

contains an error. The string of alphameric characters following 10H is too long. This error may not be detected, depending upon the compiler. If not, the printed line might appear as

```
5.MEANbOFbXb   9.77
```

since the characters not counted in the H specification might simply be omitted.

```
MAN MAY FISH WITH THE WORM THAT HATH EAT OF A KING, AND EAT OF THE FISH THAT H
H FED OF THAT WORM, WHICH MEANS NOTHING BUT TO SHOW YOU HOW A KING MAY GO A PR
RESS THROUGH THE GUTS OF A BEGGAR...
```

WORD	1	A
WORD	2	MAN
WORD	3	MAY
WORD	4	FISH
WORD	5	WITH
WORD	6	THE
WORD	7	WORM
WORD	8	THAT
WORD	9	HATH
WORD	10	EAT
WORD	11	OF
WORD	12	A
WORD	13	KING
-	-	-
WORD	14	AND
WORD	15	EAT
WORD	16	OF
WORD	17	THE
WORD	18	FISH
WORD	19	THAT
WORD	20	HATH
WORD	21	FED
WORD	22	OF
WORD	23	THAT
WORD	24	WORM
-	-	-
WORD	25	WHICH
WORD	26	MEANS
WORD	27	NOTHING
WORD	28	BUT
WORD	29	TO
WORD	30	SHOW
WORD	31	YOU
WORD	32	HOW
WORD	33	A
WORD	34	KING
WORD	35	MAY
WORD	36	GO
WORD	37	A
WORD	38	PROGRESS
WORD	39	THROUGH
WORD	40	THE
WORD	41	GUTS
WORD	42	OF
WORD	43	A
WORD	44	BEGGAR

Figure IX.4 Input and output for VERBAL example.

Another kind of error with the H specification can be illustrated as

```
9 FORMAT (1H1, 12HXBARb=bF5.2,5X,I8)
```

In this case, the F5.2 field description would not even be entered as a part of the FORMAT, since it would be interpreted as a part of the H field. This FORMAT is completely correct syntactically; most compilers do not require a comma after an H field. The commas in FORMAT statements serve only to delimit

Table IX.2

Common error messages for I/O

Message	Cause
216* (IBM)	An attempt has been made to read from a device that can be used for output only.
219 (IBM)	An end of file has been read on an input device.
...SHOULD NOT FOLLOW AN I, E, F, OR A IN A FORMAT (UNIVAC)	Some illegal character was located in a FORMAT statement where a field description was expected.
THE STATEMENT ENDED BEFORE THE HOLLERITH FIELD ENDED (UNIVAC)	Bad Hollerith count—the closing parenthesis was included as a part of the H field.
THE . IS NOT PRECEDED BY F OR E (UNIVAC)	Self-explanatory, probably due to punching , for .
THERE IS AN ILLEGAL DATA LITERAL (UNIVAC)	An illegal character appears in a H field in a DATA statement; may be due to a bad H count.
THE FORM OF NH OR NX IS BAD (UNIVAC)	The count, or syntax, of an H field or a skip field, is incorrect.
THERE IS AN EXTRA COMMA AT THE END OF THE LIST (UNIVAC)	Self-explanatory.

*For certain kinds of errors (usually those that occur during execution), the IBM system supplies only a number code—it is then the task of the programmer to locate the meaning in a table of numbered messages.

the field descriptions – since the H field has indication of its length, the comma is not needed.

A great deal of confusion about the nature of I/O can be eliminated by stating matters simply. An executable I/O statement instructs the computer to transmit the value of certain variables to some peripheral device. The variables are named in the list. Once the values have been received by the device, something must be done with them. Say they are printed, thus requiring a description of how they are to appear in printed form. This description is the function of the FORMAT statement. There must, therefore, be one field description for each number transmitted, and that field must be appropriate for the value being transmitted.

Confusion can result when an A specification is used to transmit data. The data to be printed with an A field description must have originally been stored by reading with an A field, or by an H field in a DATA statement. Such information is stored as alphameric or "literal" data. If it is printed with some specification other than A, output will usually be obtained but it will not be recognizable. The string of binary information in core representing the literal information will be treated as if it represented a number; but the internal storage of numbers is quite different from that of alphameric information.

EXERCISES

1. You have a 100×40 array called CORR in storage. Write the Fortran statements necessary to accomplish each of the following:
   (a) Print the array in E fields (caution—don't forget how wide a printed page is).
   (b) Write the array in BCD on scratch file number 4.
   (c) Read the array from scratch file number 4 as written in problem 1*b*.
   (d) Write the array in binary on scratch file number 3. Arrange the writing so that each *row* of CORR is a separate logical file record.
   (e) Read the seventeenth row of CORR that was stored in problem 1*d*. Do this in two ways—by repeated BACKSPACE commands, and by a REWIND followed by a series of READ statements.
2. Rewrite and execute the program TRUTH2 (Chapter 8) so that all headings are produced as illustrated in Figure 8.6.
3. Write a program to read a set of data cards for a group of subjects. The format of the data cards is arbitrary, but somewhere on the card there must be 18 columns for the subject's name, and scores on 10 variables. Compute the mean and standard deviation of the 10 scores for each subject and print them, properly labeled, together with his name. Write the program as generally as possible—arrange to have the FORMAT statement for the data read at execution time.
4. Modify the program written for problem 3 so that a heading is produced to identify the output. Read and print the heading using an H field.
5. Modify the program written for Problem 3 so that the output is in the alphabetical order of the subjects' names.
6. In writing general programs, it is often useful to have provision for input of data from some file other than the system input unit (e.g., from a tape prepared by another program). To do this, the first card read by such a program usually specifies whether data are to be read from cards or from tape. In either case, the first data record read must contain the variable FORMAT statement, and the following records contain the actual data according to the format. Write the Fortran statements necessary to determine the location of the data, and read the data. The data are to be stored as an 150×17 array called X.
7. Write the statements necessary to write the FORMAT expression and the array X on a BCD scratch tape to be read by the statements written in Problem 6.
8. Write a program that will handle up to 100,000 verbal words of text and do the following analysis. Alphabetize the verbal words. Count the frequencies of the words in the vocabulary. Order the words having the same frequency by the number of letters in the word. Print out the words in this double-ordered way, by word length within frequency. *Note:* Use a binary file; a BCD file of 100,000 words is very large (see Chapter 12).

CHAPTER 10 FORTRAN IV: SUBROUTINES AND FUNCTIONS

Most experienced programmers prefer to divide a long program into several discrete segments or subsections. These sections are called by various names such as subprograms, functions, or subroutines.

At least three important advantages may be gained by writing programs as separate segments. The first is the conservation of computer time. Compiling and debugging a program is generally costly of computer time. In debugging, an entire sequence of Fortran statements must be compiled and executed, frequently finding only a single error with each compilation. When the number of Fortran statements is large, compilation during debugging can be expensive. If the program has been written as a series of discrete packages, they may be debugged individually, thus avoiding the necessity of recompiling already perfected statements.

The second advantage is a saving in programmer effort. If a certain procedure is executed several times in a program, it need be coded only once. For example, if the sums of squares of elements of several arrays are needed during the execution of the program, a single subprogram can be called upon to perform the calculation each time. Thus, rather than having to code the statements computing the sums of squares at each point where required, the programmer writes only a single statement that calls upon a subprogram. Repetition of coding is to be avoided for three reasons. In the first place it is simply an unpleasant, boring task to copy code or recode already written algorithms. Second, each statement in a program adds to the length of the program making it more unwieldy to handle and taking up more space in the computer. Third, the likelihood of an error is an increasing function of the number of lines of code. The judicious use of subprograms helps to avoid these problems.

The third advantage to be gained from the use of subprograms is a saving in storage space. Not infrequently, in behavioral science applications a program will become so large that the program and the data together exceed the storage capacity of the computer. While the data storage problem may be alleviated by the use of soft copy storage, the amount of program can often be reduced by employing subprograms.

THE GENERAL NATURE OF SUBPROGRAMS

It is convenient to think of subprograms as a sort of higher-order programming. When a subprogram is written by the programmer, or is available in the computer system library, its use is essentially the same as the use of the arithmetic or replacement statement. That is, a subprogram acts to determine the value of a variable much like the statement

```
X = A + B
```

computes the sum of A and B and stores it as X.

In the earlier chapters of this book, we use several subprograms provided by the

Fortran library of subprograms without specifically recognizing the fact. The statement

SD = SQRT(VAR)

computes the square root of the quantity VAR and stores the square root as the value of SD. The statement calls upon a subprogram named SQRT to calculate the square root.

In order to conceptualize the basic substance of a subprogram we need to distinguish it from the so-called "main program." A main program is a program from which a subprogram is called. This is an arbitrary definition because subprograms may be written in such a way that they use other subprograms in execution. The primary or main segment of a program is the coding that contains the first executable statements. The main program may be a small part of the total program and the subprograms may actually do all of the computational work. A more meaningful distinction is between a subprogram that is "called" by another program (or subprogram) and a "calling" program. The distinction is therefore between the called subprogram and the calling program.

When the calling program calls the subprogram, that call is some form of reference to the subprogram. The reference occurs in the calling program at the point where the values determined by the subprogram are needed. The form of this reference in the calling program differs with the different forms of subprograms. Calling a subprogram involves naming the subprogram and the specification of values, or of the names of variables that are the "arguments" of the subprogram.

When the subprogram returns control to the calling program, it generally provides values that may be used by the calling program, or by another subprogram called by the calling program. Depending on the type of subprogram, the data returned by the subprogram to the calling program may be single values or arrays of values or any combination of values and arrays. In some instances, a subprogram may not return any values; for example where the subprogram is used for output only.

In concluding this section the concepts of internal and external routines are introduced. Subprograms can be broken approximately into two groups, designated as internal and external. An internal subprogram is completely contained within the calling program. It therefore has access to all of the variables used in the calling program. An external subprogram, on the other hand, does not in general have access to the variables used in the calling program. The same variable *names* may appear in the calling program and in the external subprogram, but these will not usually refer to the same *storage locations.*

KINDS OF SUBPROGRAMS

Fortran divides subprograms into four categories—arithmetic statement functions, built-in functions, FUNCTION subprograms, and SUBROUTINE subprograms. The first three kinds of subprograms may be grouped together, since they are similar in the way they are used. They are referred to collectively as "functions," and differ from SUBROUTINE subprograms in that (1) functions are single valued, i.e., they return only a single value to the calling program; (2) functions are referenced implicitly within an arithmetic statement, while the SUBROUTINE is referenced explicitly with a CALL statement; and (3) the SUBROUTINE is external to the calling program. The meaning of these distinctions becomes clear with additional discussion of the functions.

The three varieties of function are distinguished from one another in several ways. The arithmetic statement function is defined by a single coding statement, which has the same general appearance as the arithmetic or substitution statement. The FUNCTION subprogram, on the other hand, may involve any number of individual Fortran statements. The built-in functions are not written by the programmer but are supplied by the Fortran operating system (i.e., SQRT).

Naming Subprograms. Subprograms of the four classes of subprograms are named. The names conform to the same general rules as variables—i.e., the name of a subprogram consists of from one to six letters or numerals, the first of which must be a letter.

The type of a function is important in that it determines the type of the single result returned by the function. In the case of the arithmetic statement function and the FUNCTION subprogram, the type may be declared implicitly by the name of the function, the code following the same pattern used for declaring the type of variables. If the type of a function is to be other than real or integer, the type must be declared explicitly.

The type of an arithmetic statement function may be declared explicitly by placing the name in a type statement. For example, if the arithmetic statement function YESNO is LOGICAL, the statement

```
LOGICAL YESNO
```

declares the type of the function.

FUNCTION subprograms, on the other hand, are assigned their type (if different from that implied by the first letter) by preceding the FUNCTION statement (see below) with the type of the function. Thus the following FUNCTION statements might be used to declare the types of functions named MEAN, TEST, WORKER, and SORT:

```
REAL FUNCTION MEAN
LOGICAL FUNCTION TEST
REAL FUNCTION WORKER
INTEGER FUNCTION SORT
```

Note that the statement REAL FUNCTION WORKER contains redundant information—it could have been written as

```
FUNCTION WORKER
```

since the first letter of the function name implies its type. The type of a built-in function need not be declared, since it is defined by the compiler.

The type of a SUBROUTINE subprogram need not be defined as it is irrelevant—the type of the result(s) returned by a SUBROUTINE is determined solely by the type of the variable in the calling reference.

REFERENCING THE FUNCTIONS

A function is called by a statement in the calling program. For the three varieties of function, the calling statement in the calling program is an arithmetic or replacement statement. The replacement statement calls on the function by giving the name followed by parentheses containing the argument(s) for the function. As a familiar example, the statement

```
SD = SQRT (VAR)
```

calls on the built-in function SQRT. The function finds the square root of the variable VAR and stores the value in the location called SD. The value SQRT(VAR) replaces the contents of the location SD as in the ordinary arithmetic statement. The value of the variable VAR is "passed" to the function as an argument; the single value of the square root of VAR is "returned" by the function.

A function may have multiple arguments. For example, Fortran has a built-in function for finding the largest value obtained by a set of numbers. Suppose that it is desired that the largest of the set of variables X(1), X(2), X(3), and CRIT be stored as the variable called BIG. The statement

```
BIG = AMAX1 (X(1),X(2),X(3), CRIT)
```

calls the built-in function AMAX1 with four arguments. The function searches the arguments, and returns the single largest value, which is stored as the variable BIG.

All of the functions, built-in, arithmetic statement, and FUNCTION subprogram, are referenced in this same way; they are called on from within an arithmetic statement.

A single arithmetic statement may

refer to any number of functions. For example, the statement

A = B * SQRT(ABS(G/LOG(X)))

calculates

$$A = B\sqrt{\left|\frac{G}{\log X}\right|}$$

To summarize, the arguments to any of the function subprograms may be any of the following, depending upon the nature and requirements of the function:

1. A constant of any type.
2. A variable name of any type, which may or may not be subscripted.
3. Any arithmetic or logical expression.
4. The name of another FUNCTION or subroutine.

THE BUILT-IN FUNCTION

The built-in, or library functions that are available in Fortran are various, depending upon the computer system and the particular installation. Table X.1 lists some of the most commonly available built-in functions.

All of the built-in functions are referenced as indicated previously. For example, to find the largest of the INTEGER values I, J, and K, the function reference

IBIG = MAX0 (I, J, K)

defines IBIG as equal to the largest value obtained by the three integer variables. To find the largest value of a set of REAL numbers, on the other hand, the REAL function AMAX1 is used:

BIG = AMAX1 (X, Y, Z)

ARITHMETIC STATEMENT FUNCTIONS

The arithmetic statement function allows the programmer to define his own functions for use throughout his program. For example, suppose that a calculation of the quantity

$$\text{ALPHA} = \frac{\text{A} - \text{B}}{\text{SQRT(C)/SQRT(XN}-1)}$$

were required at one point in the program. At another point, the value of

$$\text{BETA} = \frac{\text{X} - \text{Y}}{\text{SQRT(D)/SQRT(XM}-1)}$$

was needed. Note that the calculation is the same, but different variables are involved. A single function can be written to perform the calculation, but with different variables used each time the function is referenced. The function may be defined with the statement

CALC(Q,R,S,T)=(Q−R)/(SQRT(S)/SQRT(T−1))

The two program statements calling upon the function CALC would be

```
      .
      .
      .
      ALPHA = CALC(A,B,C,XN)
      .
      .
      .
      BETA = CALC(X,Y,Z,XM)
      .
      .
      .
```

General Form of Arithmetic Statement Functions. The general form for this kind of function is

NAME $(a_1, a_2, \ldots, a_n) = e$

where *name* is the name of the function, the a_i are the arguments, and *e* is an expression of the same type as the function (REAL, INTEGER, etc.). The a_i are dummy variable names (see below) and must be enclosed in parentheses. The dummy variable names are discrete, nonsubscripted variable names separated by commas. There may be as many variables in the dummy variable list as desired, and as many of these as desired may appear in the expression *e*.

The expression *e* in the function definition may be arithmetic or logical. If it is logical, the function itself must be defined as a logical function by a type statement. The following are valid function definitions.

Table X.1

Some commonly available built-in functions

Function	Definition	Number of Arguments	Name	Type of Argument	Type of Function
Absolute value	|Arg|	1	ABS	Real	Real
			IABS	Integer	Integer
Choosing largest value	$Max(Arg_1, Arg_2, \ldots)$	≥ 2	AMAX0	Integer	Real
			AMAX1	Real	Real
			MAX0	Integer	Integer
			MAX1	Real	Integer
Choosing smallest value	$Min(Arg_1, Arg_2, \ldots)$	≥ 2	AMIN0	Integer	Real
			AMIN1	Real	Real
			MIN0	Integer	Integer
			MIN1	Real	Integer
Float	Conversion from integer to real	1	FLOAT	Integer	Real
Fix	Conversion from real to integer	1	IFIX	Real	Integer
Exponential	e^{Arg}	1	EXP	Real	Real
Natural logarithm	$\log_e(Arg)$	1	ALOG	Real	Real
Common logarithm	$\log_{10}(Arg)$	1	ALOG10	Real	Real
Arctangent	arctan(Arg)	1	ATAN	Real	Real
Trigonometric sine	sin (Arg)	1	SIN	Real	Real
Trigonometric cosine	cos (Arg)	1	COS	Real	Real
Hyperbolic tangent	tanh (Arg)	1	TANH	Real	Real
Square root	$(Arg)^{1/2}$	1	SQRT	Real	Real
Remaindering	Remainder after division of Arg1 by Arg2	2	AMOD	Real	Real
			MOD	Integer	Integer

```
CALC(Q,R,S,T) = (Q-R)/(SQRT(S)/SQRT(T-1))
SQR(A,B,C) = A*A + B*B + C*C
TEST (L1,L2,L3) = (L1.AND.L2).OR.L3
```

The function TEST is logical, and it, along with the three logical variables L1, L2, and L3 must have their type declared by the statement

```
LOGICAL TEST, L1, L2, L3
```

Dummy and Program Variables in Functions. As indicated earlier, the arithmetic statement function is internal with respect to the calling program and has access to all variables in the calling program. Any variable that appears in the expression e in the definition of the function and *does not* appear in the dummy argument list is regarded as a variable from the calling program.

A variable a_i appearing in the argument list in the arithmetic function definition is regarded as a dummy variable, and does not refer to a variable in the calling program. This is true even if the variable names happen to be the same. When a dummy variable appears in the expression e, its value is taken not from the calling program, but from the value of the corresponding variable in the function reference. For example, suppose that we define the function CUBE as

```
CUBE (A) = A*A*A
```

Once this function is defined we can write the statement

```
SUMCUB = CUBE(X)+CUBE(Y)+CUBE(Z)
```

and obtain the value of the expression

$$X^3 + Y^3 + Z^3$$

The variable A in the function definition is a dummy variable. Each time the function CUBE is executed, the value of A is assigned the value of the variable mentioned in the reference to the function, namely X, Y, and Z. It is immaterial whether or not there is a variable called A in the calling program.

To illustrate the use of both dummy and program variables in the same function, consider the following function definition.

```
SQRB(X) = X**2 + B**2
```

In this case, X is a dummy variable within the function, but B, since it is not mentioned in the argument list, must be a variable from the calling program. A reference to the function SQRB might be

```
C = A/SQRB(G)
```

This function reference computes

$$C = \frac{A}{G^2 + B^2}$$

The value of B, at the time the function is executed, is obtained, together with the value of G which is transmitted to the function by the argument in the reference.

As another example, if the reference to a function named SUM were of the form

```
TOTAL = SUM (X,Y,Z,Q)
```

the function might be defined as

```
SUM(A,B,C,D) = A+B+C+D
```

In this case, the dummy variables are A, B, C, and D. When the function reference is executed, these dummy variables take on the values of the variables named in the reference, so that the following pairing is obtained:

Actual: X,Y,Z,Q
Dummy: A,B,C,D

However, the reference could be

```
TOTAL = SUM(X,Y,Z,A)
```

In this case, one of the arguments in the reference has the same variable name as one of the dummy names in the function definition. The pairing of actual argument (the argument in the reference) with the dummy takes place in the following manner:

Actual: X,Y,Z,A
Dummy: A,B,C,D

Note that the pairing is left-to-right by ordinal position, not by variable name. The fact that two of the variables have the same name is immaterial—they do not refer to the same storage location. The fact that the actual and dummy variables have the same name may be coincidental.

The definition of arithmetic statement functions excluded subscripted variables in the dummy argument list. This restriction does not apply to references to the function. When the function is referenced the actual arguments may be elements from arrays, and hence subscripted. For example the function SUM may be referenced by:

```
TOTAL(I)=SUM(X(I),X(I+1),X(I+2),X(I+3))
```

Using this function and this reference to it in the context of a DO yields an array containing the sums of four adjacent values of the array X up to the last four elements of X. Presuming X has N elements, an array TOTAL may be calculated by

```
     LOOP = N-4
     DO 1234 I = 1, LOOP
     TOTAL (I) = SUM (X(I), X(I+1), X(I+2), X(I+3))
1234 CONTINUE
```

The same progressive series of sum calculations could be formed by the statements

```
TOTAL (1) = X(1) + X(2) + X(3) +X(4)
TOTAL (2) = X(2) + X(3) + X(4) + X(5)
.
.
.
TOTAL (N-4) = ...
```

Location of Functions in the Source Program. Arithmetic statement functions must be defined before the first executable statement in the program. As a general rule, definitions of arithmetic statement functions should be at the very beginning of the program, immediately following the declarative statements. The typical program that uses arithmetic statement functions might have the following kinds of statements, in this order, at the beginning of the program:

Kind of statement	*Purpose*
Comments	Identification of program
Type statements	Define the types of the variables and functions in the program
COMMON statements	Allocate storage
DIMENSION statements	Allocate storage
Arithmetic statement function definitions	Define functions
Executable statements	Computation

The arithmetic statement functions follow the declarations, since the types of variables used in the functions and the types of functions must be defined before the functions themselves are defined.

The definition of an arithmetic statement function may itself contain a reference to another function. The only restriction is that the function that appears in the definition must have been previously defined. For example, the following two definitions appear in the correct order.

```
CUBE (A) = A*A*A
SUMCB (X, Y, Z) = CUBE(X) + CUBE(Y) + CUBE(Z)
```

Since the function CUBE is used in defining SUMCB, it must have been defined first. Interchanging the order of these two definitions would lead to an error indication from the compiler.

FUNCTION SUBPROGRAMS

The FUNCTION subprogram permits defining functions of such complexity that they cannot be defined by single Fortran statements. Like the arithmetic statement function, the FUNCTION subprogram is single valued, and is referenced from within an arithmetic statement in the calling program. Unlike the arithmetic statement function, the FUNCTION subprogram does not have access to the variables used in the calling program. Thus, any variable names that appear in the body of the subprogram are interpreted as being variables in the FUNCTION program, unless they are defined as dummy variables by their appearance in the argument list of the FUNCTION subprogram.

General Form of FUNCTION Subprograms. The first statement in a FUNCTION must have the general form

FUNCTION *name* $(a_1, a_2, \ldots, a_n)$

where *name* is the name of the FUNCTION and $a_1, \ldots, a_n$ are the dummy variables in the argument list. The complete general form of a FUNCTION might be indicated as

```
FUNCTION name (a1,a2,...,an)
.....
Program statements
.....
Name = expression
.....
RETURN
END
```

since all of the items indicated must appear in the FUNCTION. In particular, the name of the FUNCTION must appear somewhere in the function program on the left side of a replacement statement, or in the list for an input statement. Thus, somewhere in the FUNCTION subprogram BETA there must appear a statement of the form

```
BETA = expression
```

or of the form

```
READ (5,10) BETA
```

The reason for this rule is simple—since the function is to return a single value, that value must be stored at some location. The location where the value is stored is that location symbolized by the name of the FUNCTION subprogram. There are only two ways of placing a value at a location—reading into the location, or storing with the arithmetic statement.

As indicated previously, the type of the function may be stated explicitly preceding the word FUNCTION. Thus the following are valid first statements in defining FUNCTION subprograms:

```
REAL FUNCTION ALPHA (X,Y)
FUNCTION BETA (Q,R1,R2)
INTEGER FUNCTION WHAT (I)
LOGICAL FUNCTION WHATIF (L1,L2)
```

As is the case with variables, the type of the function need not be explicitly stated if the first-letter code correctly implies the type.

A FUNCTION subprogram may contain any valid Fortran statement, *except* SUBROUTINE (see below) or another FUNCTION statement. Thus a FUNCTION subprogram may not contain another FUNCTION subprogram definition within it.

Variables in the Dummy List. Several rules pertain to the list $a_1, \ldots, a_n$ in the FUNCTION statement. First, the variables a_i must correspond in number, order, and type to the variables used in the reference to the FUNCTION. For example, if the function FN is referenced by

```
A = FN(X, Y, I, L1)
```

where X and Y are REAL, I is INTEGER, and L1 is LOGICAL, the dummy argument list in FN must contain four variables' names, the first two corresponding to X and Y (and therefore REAL variables), the third INTEGER and corresponding to I, and the fourth must be LOGICAL.

There may be any number of variables in the dummy list, subject to the restriction above. There must, however, be at least one variable in the dummy list. This contrasts with the SUBROUTINE, which does not have to have any arguments.

None of the dummy variable names used within the FUNCTION may be mentioned in an EQUIVALENCE statement within the FUNCTION subprogram. However, the actual arguments to the FUNCTION (i.e., in the reference to the function) may be used in an EQUIVALENCE statement.

When an argument(s) to the FUNCTION subprogram is the name of an array in the main program, the corresponding dummy variable(s) must be dimensioned in the subprogram. For example, suppose that a FUNCTION subprogram is written to calculate the mean of a one-dimensional array. If the name of the FUNCTION is MEAN, it might be referenced in the calling program with the statement

```
AVER = MEAN(X,N)
```

where X is the name of the one-dimensional array and N is the number of elements in the array. This implies that the calling program contains a statement of the form

```
DIMENSION X(150)
```

The FUNCTION subprogram might be written as follows:

```
   REAL FUNCTION MEAN (ARRAY,NN)
   DIMENSION ARRAY (150)
   SUM = 0.0
 8 DO 10 I = 1, NN
   SUM = SUM + ARRAY (I)
10 CONTINUE
   FN = NN
   MEAN = SUM/FN
   RETURN
   END
```

Note that it was necessary to state the type of the FUNCTION explicitly, since the first-letter code would imply an integer function when a real value for the mean was desired. Note also the RETURN and END statements, which are discussed below.

Terminating a FUNCTION. The FUNCTION subprogram must be logically terminated with a RETURN statement. This statement, when executed, returns control to the calling program that completes the replacement statement where the FUNCTION reference is executed. In the FUNCTION MEAN illustrated above, the RETURN occurred immediately after the replacement statement defining MEAN. The END statement marks the physical end of the FUNCTION.

In some cases, there may be more than one RETURN in a FUNCTION. For example, it might be desired to take three alternative courses of action depending upon the value of one of the arguments to the FUNCTION. The following FUNCTION subprogram FN returns one of three values, depending upon the value of the dummy argument ALPHA.

```
   FUNCTION FN (ALPHA)
   IF(ALPHA - 100.) 10, 20, 30
10 FN = ALPHA/525.0
   RETURN
20 FN = ALPHA
   RETURN
30 FN = 1.0/ALPHA
   RETURN
   END
```

Note that after each of the three possible courses of action, the FUNCTION returns to the calling program. The END simply signals the end of the coding of the subprogram. There may be any number of RETURN statements in a FUNCTION, but there is only one END, and it is physically the last card in the FUNCTION.

As an example of a FUNCTION that might be found useful, consider calculating factorials of numbers. It would be convenient to have available a FUNCTION that would compute factorials. Two such FUNCTIONs are listed in Figures X.1 and X.2, one returning an integer value, and the other returning a real value. The integer FUNCTION FACT1 may be used to find factorials of numbers up to 13. Any value larger than 13!, computed as an integer, exceeds the largest allowable value for an integer variable on the IBM 7044 for which the programs were written. An error indication is printed, and the program terminates if FACT1 is called with an argument greater than 13. (See below for discussion of the statement CALL EXIT.) Both FACT1 and FACT2 require integer arguments.

FACT2 makes use of two algorithms for computing the REAL factorial of an INTEGER number. If N is less than or equal to 20, the factorial is obtained directly by successive multiplications. If N is greater than 20, an approximate factorial is obtained by the use of Stirling's formula. This formula may yield a fractional part that is truncated.

SUBROUTINE SUBPROGRAMS

The functions have three points in common, they are all single-valued, all are

```
CCALLF1
      K=5
      N = FACT1(K)
      WRITE (6,1) N
    1 FORMAT (I10 )
      STOP
      END

      FUNCTION FACT1(N)
C   GENERAL FACTORIAL FUNCTION.
C   CALCULATES INTEGER FACTORIALS OF ARGUMENTS UP TO 13.
      IF(N.GT.13) GO TO 10
      K=1
      DO 2 I = 1,N
      J=I
      K=K*J
    2 WRITE (6,1)K
      FACT1=K
    1 FORMAT ( I10 )
      RETURN
   10 WRITE (6,101) N
  101 FORMAT (1H1, 29HILLEGAL ENTRY TO FACT1. N =     ,I4)
      CALL EXIT
      RETURN
      END
```

Figure X.1 The FUNCTION FACT1.

referenced from within an arithmetic statement, and all are internal with respect to the calling program. SUBROUTINE subprograms on the other hand may be multivalued, are external to the calling program, and are referenced differently.

Referencing the SUBROUTINE Subprograms. The explicit statement

CALL *name* $(a_1, a_2, \ldots, a_n)$

is used to reference a SUBROUTINE subprogram: *name* is the name of the

```
CCALLF2
      DO 100 I = 1, 25
      N = I
      FACT=FACT2(N)
      WRITE(6,1) FACT
  100 CONTINUE
    1 FORMAT (E16.8)
      STOP
      END

      FUNCTION FACT2(N)
C   FACT2--GENERAL FACTORIAL FUNCTION.
C        IF THE ARGUMENT IS .GT.20, STIRLINGS FORMULA IS USED.
C        OTHERWISE THE FACTORIAL IS OBTAINED DIRECTLY.
      IF (N.GT. 20) GO TO 10
      A=1.0
      DO 1 I = 1, N
      F = I
      A=A*F
    1 CONTINUE
      FACT2=A
      RETURN
   10 FN = N
      E=2.7183
      FACT2 = 2.5068 * SQRT(FN) * (FN**N) * (1.0/(E**N))
      RETURN
      END
```

Figure X.2 The FUNCTION FACT2.

SUBROUTINE being referenced, and $a_1,\ldots,a_n$ are the arguments.

In the completed program for Project 3 given in Appendix B, the statement

```
CALL TEST (SCORE, SUM, I, J)
```

is used to call the subroutine that tests for the presence or absence of a particular disease.

A SUBROUTINE, in contrast with a FUNCTION, does not have to have any arguments. For example, the program for Project 1 in Appendix B uses the statement

```
CALL STAT
```

to call the subroutine that calculates means and variances. No arguments are needed, since all of the data used by STAT are stored in the COMMON section of memory and are thus available to the SUBROUTINE. A later section of this chapter discusses the use of COMMON.

General Form of SUBROUTINE Subprograms. The first statement of the SUBROUTINE has the general form

SUBROUTINE *name* ($a_1, \ldots, a_n$)

where *name* is the name of the SUBROUTINE, and $a_1, \ldots, a_n$ are the dummy arguments. The complete general form of a SUBROUTINE is

```
SUBROUTINE name (a1,...,an)
          ...
          Program statements
          ...
RETURN
END
```

The statements in the body of the SUBROUTINE may be any Fortran statements except SUBROUTINE or FUNCTION.

Variables in the Dummy List. The names in the dummy variable list may be nonsubscripted variables, or the dummy names of other SUBROUTINE or FUNCTION subprograms. There may be any number of arguments in the dummy list, or there may be no list at all. The names in the dummy variable argument list must correspond in number, order, and type to the actual variables named in the corresponding CALL statement.

A SUBROUTINE subprogram does not necessarily have access to the variables used in the main program. The same variable names may be used in both the main program and the subroutine, but those names *will not* refer to the same storage locations unless they are declared in COMMON statements in the calling program and the subroutine.

One or more of the arguments to the SUBROUTINE subprogram may be used to return output to the calling program. If any dummy variable is so used, it must appear, within the SUBROUTINE, on the left side of an arithmetic statement, or in the list of an input statement.

As an example of the use of an argument to return a value to the calling program, consider the use of the SUBROUTINE TEST in Project 3 (Appendix B). TEST is called with the statement

```
CALL TEST (SCORE, SUM, I, J)
```

The SUBROUTINE begins with the statement

```
SUBROUTINE TEST (X, SUM, I, K)
```

The dummy name X corresponds to the array SCORE in the main program that contains the scores made by the patient on four diagnostic tests. SUM has the same name in both the calling program and the SUBROUTINE, but this need not be the case. SUM is the sum of the four scores in SCORE. I is an indicator of the disease that is to be tested. The argument J (K in TEST) has one of three values, and these are determined by TEST. If the disease I is present, K is set to 1, if the disease is not present K = 2, and if the patient cannot be classified, K = 3. Upon return from TEST, J has one of the three values and is used for several purposes. In this way, the dummy variable K is used to return a value to the calling program.

When a dummy variable in a SUBROUTINE subprogram is an array, the dimension declaration for that variable must be present within the SUBROUTINE in either a DIMENSION or a COMMON statement. Additionally, the actual argument appearing in the CALL statement must have its dimension declaration in the calling program.

Variables named in the dummy argument list in the SUBROUTINE subprogram may not appear in an EQUIVALENCE statement within the SUBROUTINE.

Terminating a SUBROUTINE. As in FUNCTION subprograms, the SUBROUTINE must be terminated logically with a RETURN statement. There may be more than one RETURN within a SUBROUTINE. SUBROUTINEs must be terminated physically with an END statement.

As an example of a SUBROUTINE subprogram, consider the SUBROUTINE SIZER. SIZER scans an array of numbers, and returns the largest and smallest values to the calling program. For simplicity, assume that the array being scanned is one-dimensional, and may have as many as 1000 elements. The actual number of values contained in the array is communicated to SIZER by an argument. The program statements below constitute the SUBROUTINE subprogram SIZER.

```
      SUBROUTINE SIZER (A,N,BIG,WEE)
      DIMENSION A(1000)
      BIG = A(1)
      WEE = A(1)
      DO 10 I = 2,N
      IF (A(I) .GT. BIG) BIG = A(I)
      IF (A(I) .LT. WEE) WEE = A(I)
   10 CONTINUE
      RETURN
      END
```

Subroutine SIZER could be called upon with the following program segment. Assume that the array SCORES has already been dimensioned, and that K is an integer variable equal to the number of elements in SCORES. The program segment calls SIZER to find the largest and smallest values in SCORES. When these have been returned by SIZER, the range is computed.

```
      .
      .
      .
      CALL SIZER(SCORES,K,BIGSCR,WEESCR)
      RANGE = BIGSCR - WEESCR
      .
      .
      .
```

The two values BIGSCR and WEESCR are returned from SIZER to the calling program *via* the argument list. Once returned, they may be used in calculation.

THE USE OF COMMON

At several points in this chapter, reference has been made to the fact that a SUBROUTINE does not have access to variables in the calling program—the SUBROUTINE is external to the calling program. Each variable name used in a SUBROUTINE refers to a different storage location than the same variable name used in the calling program. At times, this causes difficulty in communication between the calling program and the subroutine, especially when both use a great many of the same variables. Until this point, the only way we have introduced for communication between calling program and SUBROUTINE is by means of the argument list. When the number of variables is large, the argument lists are ungainly, and the probability of a clerical error increases greatly. The use of COMMON alleviates these problems to a great extent.

In order to understand the COMMON declaration, the reader must know the basic facts about how the Fortran compiler assigns storage locations to variables. Variables and arrays are ordinarily stored more or less in the middle of the storage area of the computer. (Imagine a computer with 32,768 words of storage; the words will have addresses from

00,001 to 32,768.) The locations having the lowest addresses are what is known as "low memory" and contain some of the executive programs, accounting operations, etc. and are not usually available to the programmer. The highest locations in memory are likewise given a special name ("common") but they are available to the programmer for special purposes.

Ordinarily, variables, arrays, constants, etc., are stored in the "middle" area between low memory and common. Different subroutines or program segments do not have access to variables and arrays that are stored in the central portion of memory. Thus, any array or variable that is needed by several subroutines must be stored in a separate section, called common storage. The variables that are to be stored in common are declared by the declaration

COMMON $v_1, v_2, \ldots, v_k$

where v_i is the name of a variable to be stored in the COMMON area of memory.

The COMMON statement may also be used to convey dimensioning information. Thus, an array Q55 can be dimensioned and placed in common with the single statement

```
COMMON Q55(10,20,15)
```

assuming that Q55 is a $10 \times 20 \times 15$ array variable. Care must be taken that the variable is not dimensioned in two places. If dimensioning information is given for Q55 by

```
DIMENSION Q55(10,20,15)
```

the COMMON statement must be simply

```
COMMON Q55
```

As with DIMENSION, any number of variables may be listed in a COMMON statement. Thus,

```
COMMON A, B, C, Y, N, J
```

assigns 6 variables, which may be either subscripted or not, to common.

In the example of SIZER given above, the array SCORES and the number of elements K could be placed in COMMON. If this were done, those two variables would not have to be passed as arguments:

```
   SUBROUTINE SIZER (BIG,WEE)
   COMMON SCORES, K
   DIMENSION SCORES(1000)
   BIG = SCORES(1)
   WEE = SCORES(1)
   DO 10 I = 2,K
   IF(SCORES(I).GT.BIG) BIG = SCORES(I)
10 IF(SCORES(I).LT.WEE) WEE = SCORES(I)
   RETURN
   END
```

This implies that the calling program contains the statements

```
DIMENSION SCORES(1000)
COMMON SCORES, K
.
.
.
CALL SIZER (BIGSCR,WEESCR)
RANGE = BIGSCR-WEESCR
.
.
.
```

When there are several subroutines for use with a calling program, and a large number of variables are stored in COMMON, it is frequently convenient to break the COMMON area up into smaller units or blocks, each with a unique name.

Common Blocks. The common area of memory may be divided into any number of separate regions, or *blocks*. Each block may be given a name, and may contain one or more variables.

Block names consist of from one to six alphameric characters, the first of which must be a letter. The name must not be the same as that of any subroutine that is a part of the same job. A block, together with the variables in it, is defined in the COMMON statement. Suppose, for example, that the data arrays A and Y are to be assigned to a block called DATA. The statements

```
COMMON /DATA/ A, Y
DIMENSION A(50,50), Y(50,50)
```

define a block of common storage called DATA that contains two 50×50 arrays, A and Y. Note that the block name, DATA, is flanked by slashes (/) and precedes the listing of the variables in the block. Since a COMMON statement may contain dimensioning information, the two statements could be combined:

```
COMMON /DATA/ A(50,50), Y(50,50)
```

Variables named in a COMMON statement are assigned to consecutive locations in the order named in the statement, starting with the first location of the block. Thus, A and Y in the example would be arranged as

A(1,1) A(2,1) ... A(50,50) Y(1,1) Y(2,1) ... Y(50,50)

The common storage area may contain any number of common blocks. The blocks may be of two general types, *blank* and *labeled.* The simplest form of the COMMON statement

```
COMMON Q55
```

assigns the variable Q55 to a blank or nonlabeled section in common. Blank and labeled common may be assigned with the same COMMON statement, with blank and labeled regions intermixed in any desired order. For example,

```
COMMON X, Q55 /DATA/ A, Y / / N,M
```

assigns two blocks of common storage; a blank area containing X, Q55, N, and M, and a block named DATA which contains A and Y. Blank common is either defined immediately following the word COMMON, or separated from labeled common by two consecutive slashes (//), and variables assigned to it are done so cumulatively. The end of the list of variables making up a common block is signified by either another block name, the end of the statement, or beginning of a blank block.

The most useful application of COMMON blocks occurs in the writing of very long, complex programs. Such a program usually consists of a set of subroutines or functions, all called upon from some calling or main program. The process of debugging such a program can become very complex since a change in the storage assignment in one subroutine can change the storage pattern for the entire program, necessitating recompiling each routine whenever one routine is changed. For this reason, labeled common blocks are frequently employed.

Suppose that a large program was being written that required a main program and five subroutines. Some of the variables are needed by all routines, others by some combination of routines, and yet other variables by only one subroutine. Table X.2 indicates the variables used by more than one subprogram.

From the table, it is clear that all routines must have access to variables A, B, and J, while variables C through I are used only by some routines. The simplest solution to the problem is to place all of the variables in the common area. This is not difficult, since the COMMON statement may be punched once, produced five times using a reproducing punch, and a copy placed in each routine.

This solution becomes less satisfactory when the COMMON statement is more complex, when there are more routines, or when (as is frequently the case) there are several programmers working on the final product. When a number of persons are working on the problem, the difficulty increases greatly. The problems imposed by debugging are multiplied when the revised COMMON statements must be distributed to a number of people.

The way around these difficulties is the use of labeled common areas. All of the variables that are used by all routines can be placed in the blank area of common, and the remainder of common may be divided into labeled regions. The statement

Table X.2

Hypothetical use of variables by a main program and 5 subroutines

Variable	Routine					
	MAIN	SUB1	SUB2	SUB3	SUB4	SUB5
A	X	X	X	X	X	X
B	X	X	X	X	X	X
C		X	X			
D				X	X	
E	X					X
F	X					X
G		X	X			
H				X	X	
I				X	X	
J	X	X	X	X	X	X

Note: An "X" indicates that a particular variable is used by the routine indicated by the column.

```
COMMON A, B, J
```

assigns the three variables to be shared by all routines to the blank area. Three more common areas may then be defined, each shared by two routines. The area shared by SUB1 and SUB2 could be called BLK12, that shared by routines SUB3 and SUB4 called BLK 34, and that shared by the main program and routine SUB5 could be called BLKM5. The following statement defines these common blocks, and assigns the variables to them.

```
COMMON/BLK12/C, G/BLK34/D, H, I/BLKM5/E, F
```

It is recommended, however, that each block of common be defined by a separate COMMON statement. This will allow the programmer working on, say, routines SUB1 and SUB2 to proceed more or less independently of the other programmers, and then finally enable all programmers to put their separate parts together with a minimum of confusion. The following statements define the blank common area and the three labeled blocks.

```
COMMON A, B, J
COMMON /BLK12/C,G
COMMON / BLK34/D, H, I
COMMON /BLKM5/E,F
```

The same block names may be used by different subroutines, containing different variables in the different routines. Thus, the same common region may be used to store different variables. In addition, the available storage locations within a labeled common block may be allocated differently by different subroutines. The only restriction on the use of different variables within the same common block is that the block must be the same length in all cases (not required by some implementations of Fortran). Blank common does not have to be of the same length for all subroutines in a job, while labeled common must.

COMMON statements are cumulative throughout a given program or subroutine (subprogram). For example, the two statements

```
COMMON A, B/BLOCK/I, J
COMMON N /BLOCK/ X
```

have the same effect as the single statement

```
COMMON A, B, N /BLOCK/ I, J, X
```

If the labeled block name used in the main program is repeated in a subroutine the block can be split up differently. For example, if the main program has a common block defined by

```
COMMON /BIGONE/ X, Y, Z
DIMENSION X(10), Y(30), Z(50)
```

and we wished to use the 40 locations of X and Y in a subroutine at a later point in the program for an array W, the subroutine would include the statements

```
COMMON /BIGONE/ W,Z
DIMENSION W(40), Z(50)
```

Where block length must remain constant throughout the job, using the example above

```
COMMON /BIGONE/ W,Z
DIMENSION W(30), Z(50)
```

leads to an error in referencing Z in the subroutine. Dummy arrays and elements may be used to fill out labeled blocks. The corrected example is

```
COMMON /BIGONE/ W, D, Z
DIMENSION W(30), D(10), Z(50)
```

where D is a dummy array filling up locations so that Z begins at the right place in the subroutine. In some systems the compiler will indicate that D is never referenced in the program; this is of no consequence because execution is generally allowed to proceed.

Two variables in common may not be made equivalent (see below) to each other. In addition, the EQUIVALENCE statement may increase the size of a common block by bringing in additional variables. Common blocks may be extended by making some other variable equivalent to a member of the block. Thus the statements

```
COMMON /BLOCK/ A, X, Y
DIMENSION Q(4)
EQUIVALENCE (X, Q(1))
```

cause the following storage allocation:

```
A   X     Y
    Q(1)  Q(2)  Q(3)  Q(4)
```

This manner of storage has increased the size of the common area called BLOCK by two locations. Notice that Q(2) and Y also refer to the same location.

In making an array equivalent to certain portions of a common block, care must be taken that the extension does not increase the size of the block backwards, exceeding the first location of the block. Thus,

```
COMMON /BLOCK/ A, X, Y
DIMENSION Q(4)
EQUIVALENCE (X, Q(3))
```

is illegal since it would force the storage to be

```
            A     X     Y
Q(1)  Q(2)  Q(3)  Q(4)
```

which extends backwards past the beginning of the common area BLOCK.

BLOCK DATA Subprograms. In Chapter 9, the DATA statement was introduced for placing values at specific locations at the time of execution of the program. The DATA statement cannot be used to compile data into the common area. For that purpose, a special subprogram must be written—the BLOCK DATA subprogram. It can be used to compile data into a labeled common area by use of the DATA statement.

The BLOCK DATA subprogram may contain only DATA, COMMON, DIMENSION, and type statements and must begin with the statement

```
BLOCK DATA
```

As an example of the use of the BLOCK DATA subprogram, suppose in the example above that variable C is a 10 × 5 array which should be preset to the value 15.63 in all locations, and that E is a five-element logical vector that is to be preset with all elements except the first equal to .TRUE.. All other variables are nonsubscripted variables. The following BLOCK DATA subprogram compiles the required values into the arrays.

```
BLOCK DATA
COMMON / BLK12/C,G
COMMON / BLKM5/E,F
DIMENSION C(10,5)
DIMENSION E(5)
LOGICAL E
DATA C, E, /50*15.63, .FALSE., 4*.TRUE./
END
```

Note that all common blocks are not listed. Only those blocks which have data compiled into them need appear in the BLOCK DATA subprogram, but all variables in those blocks must be listed, even if the variables never appear in the DATA statement. Note also that a single BLOCK DATA subprogram may be used to compile data into more than one common block. A BLOCK DATA subprogram may not contain any executable statements, only those specific declarations listed above. Project 3 (Appendix B) illustrates a BLOCK DATA subprogram that compiles alphameric data.

ADJUSTABLE DIMENSIONS

In writing programs for general use, it is often convenient to write the program such that the sizes of arrays may actually vary from one execution to the next. For example, suppose that a matrix transposition subroutine were available. It could be called upon from any calling program when the transpose of a matrix was needed. It would be most convenient if the user did not have to worry about the size of the array to be transposed, except in the calling program. If the subroutine were written, for example, with the matrix to be transposed conveyed as an argument, and the dummy array were dimensioned within the subroutine, the first statements of the routine might look like

```
      SUBROUTINE TRANS (X)
C-----X IS THE DUMMY NAME OF THE ARRAY TO BE TRANSPOSED
      DIMENSION X(50,50)
      .
      .
      .
```

If the subroutine were written in this way, the calling program could work only with a 50×50 array, or the subroutine DIMENSION statement would have to be changed and the routine recompiled.

In SUBROUTINE or FUNCTION subprograms, but never main or calling programs, the actual size of arrays may be communicated by arguments and variables used in the DIMENSION statements within the subprogram. Figure X.3 gives a matrix transposition subroutine that makes use of adjustable dimensioned arrays.

There are four arguments in the dummy list. The first is the name of the array to be transposed. The second is the dummy name of the transposed matrix. The third and fourth arguments give the number of rows and columns, respectively, in the array X. The DIMENSION statement for the two dummy

```
      SUBROUTINE TRANS (X, Y, R, C)
C-----X IS THE ARRAY TO BE TRANSPOSED.  IT HAS R ROWS
C------AND C COLUMNS.
C-----Y IS THE TRANSPOSED MATRIX.  IT HAS C ROWS
C------AND R COLUMNS
      DIMENSION X(R, C), Y(C, R)
      INTEGER R, C
      DO 10 I = 1, R
      DO 10 J = 1, C
   10 Y(J, I) = X(I, J)
      RETURN
      END
```

Figure X.3 Transposition subroutine.

arrays makes use of the dummy integer variables R and C. These variables will have actual values when the subroutine is executed, and these values will indicate the size of the two arrays X and Y.

The subroutine TRANS can be called from a calling program which contains the following statements.

```
C-----MAIN PROGRAM--CALLS ON TRANS.
      DIMENSION MAT(30,40), MATTRN(40,30)
      .
      .
      .
      CALL TRANS (MAT, MATTRN, 30, 40)
      .
      .
      .
      STOP
      END
```

Note that the calling program dimensions the two matrices using actual values corresponding to the size of the matrices in this particular program. Another program could call on TRANS with the statements

```
DIMENSION A(10,12), ATRAN(12,10)
.
.
.
CALL TRANS (A, ATRAN, 10,12)
```

In this second example, there would be no change in TRANS, only a change in the DIMENSION and CALL statements.

NONSTANDARD RETURNS FROM SUBROUTINES

The statement

```
RETURN
```

in a subroutine or function returns control to the calling program. The next statement executed following the RETURN is the statement immediately following the CALL statement. For example, the calling program might contain the statements

```
      .
      .
      .
      CALL SUB2 (X,N)
      MEAN = X/FN
      .
      .
      .
```

and the subroutine the statements

```
      SUBROUTINE SUB2 (Y, I)
      .
      .
      .
      RETURN
      END
```

when these statements are executed, the statement MEAN = X/FN is the operation following the return from SUB2.

Fortran provides the facility for defining variable returns from subroutines (not allowed in some Fortran implementations). That is, the computer can be instructed to return to any other executable numbered statement, instead of that immediately following the CALL statement.

As an example, a subroutine may be written to test for a specific disease in Project 3. The subroutine sets an indicator IDIAG to 1 if the disease is present, to 2 if it is not, and to 3 if the patient is not classifiable. When the subroutine returns the diagnosis, the calling program branches to one of three points depending upon the value of IDIAG. If X is the array of scores that represent the individual's data from the diagnostic examination, then the following statement would call upon the subroutine to test for Fisher's F disease

```
      CALL FTEST(X, IDIAG)
```

This could be followed by a branching operation to send the program to one of three points depending upon IDIAG returned by FTEST. The CALL and branching statements could be written as

```
      CALL FTEST ( X, IDIAG)
      GO TO (23, 17, 99), IDIAG
      .
      .
      .
23    ---------   Statements executed when disease is present
      ---------
17    ---------   Statements executed when disease is not
      ---------      present
99    ---------   Statements executed when patient is not
      ---------      classifiable
      .
      .
      .
```

Using nonstandard returns from FTEST, the subroutine may return directly to any of the three points, rather than having to use the branching operation in the calling program. This eliminates the need for returning the value of IDIAG to the main program, and one argument can be eliminated. However, the three statement numbers must be transmitted to the subroutine. This is done by using an argument to the subroutine which has the general form

*n*S

where *n* is the statement number for a nonstandard return and S is the character S. Thus, the CALL statement might be written as

```
      CALL FTEST (X, 23S, 17S, 99S)
```

Several changes must be made in the subroutine to allow the nonstandard return. In the first place, the argument list in the subroutine will have the appearance

```
SUBROUTINE FTEST (Y, *, *, *)
```

where Y is the dummy array corresponding to X in the calling program. The characters "*" in the argument list inform the subroutine that the arguments conveyed from the calling program at those positions are statement numbers for nonstandard returns, and are *not* the values of variables.

Suppose that the variable I serves as the indicator for diagnosis in the subroutine corresponding to IDIAG in the calling program. Once the diagnostic steps have been completed, the subroutine could then contain the statements

```
       .
       .
       .
       IF (I-2) 10, 11, 12
    10 RETURN 1
    11 RETURN 2
    12 RETURN 3
       END
```

Here a test is made on the value of the indicator I. If it is 1, then the disease is present, and the statement RETURN 1 is executed. This form of the RETURN statement specifies that instead of standard return to the statement following the CALL, return should be made to the first listed nonstandard statement number, namely, statement 23. The same reasoning holds for RETURN 2 and RETURN 3.

The return from the subroutine can be accomplished even more simply by replacing the above five statements with the statements

```
       RETURN I
       END
```

This may be done since the variable I has been assigned a value of 1, 2, or 3 according to the diagnostic rules programmed into FTEST.

The most general form of the variable RETURN statement is

RETURN *i*

where *i* is either an unsigned integer constant, or an unsigned integer variable. In either case, it indicates a nonstandard return from the subroutine to the *i*th-listed statement number conveyed to the subroutine by the CALL statement. If *i* is missing, the return is standard to the statement following the CALL.

MULTIPLE ENTRIES TO SUBROUTINES.

It is possible to enter a subroutine or function at points other than the first statement following the SUBROUTINE or FUNCTION statement (not defined in some implementations of Fortran). That is, a subroutine or function may have multiple entry points. This feature is illustrated with an example, again making use of Project 3.

Suppose that all of the tests for the five illnesses are written as one subroutine with multiple entry points. The first time that the subroutine is called, the array of scores for the patient being considered may be transmitted. Once these are available to the subroutine, additional CALLs need not include the array X in the argument list. This is a useful application of the multiple entry point feature of Fortran. When a variety of information is to be transmitted to a subroutine by arguments, and this same information is needed several times by several subroutines, it is more conservative of computer time to "initialize" the subroutine by calling on it once with a transmission of the argument list, and then to call on other entry points to do the actual work. If this were done, the calling program would have the appearance shown in Figure X.4. The program first reads the number of patients to be processed and enters a loop that reads a patient's name, scores on X, etc., and then calls on subroutine TEST that has the function of transmitting the array of scores X and the nonstandard return statement numbers to the subroutine. All of the other CALL statements are to alternate entries to TEST. These CALLs only start the subroutine working and do not involve the transmission of information, since the routine has been initialized by the first call to TEST which transmitted the array X and the alternate entry points. The return from each of the entries in TEST are as discussed previously.

Figure X.5 presents the essential statements in the subroutine TEST. Note that the first statement is the standard SUBROUTINE statement, complete with argument list and indication of three nonstandard return points. Following this entry, the subroutine returns. The remaining statements in the subroutine are those that define the other entry points and the nonstandard returns. Since the subroutine has already been initialized, each entry point has all of the information that is required—the values of Y and the nonstandard return statement numbers.

```
      READ (5,1000) N
 1000 FORMAT (I6)
      DO 500 NN = 1, N
      READ (5, 1001) NAME1, NAME2, (X(I), I=1,4)
 1001 FORMAT (2A6, 5F2.0)
      CALL TEST (X, 23S, 17S, 99S)
      DO 10 I = 1, 5
      GO TO (1, 2, 3, 4, 5), I
    1 CALL SRBTST
    2 CALL MHLTST
    3 CALL FTEST
    4 CALL NPTEST
    5 CALL SSTEST
      .
   23 .         statements executed if patient has disease
      .
      GO TO 10
      .
   17 .         statements executed if patient does not have disease
      .
      GO TO 10
      .
   99 .         statements executed if patient is not classifiable
      .
   10 CONTINUE
  500 CONTINUE
      .
      .
      .
```

Figure X.4 Calling program for Project 3 (declarations omitted).

```
SUBROUTINE TEST (Y,*,*,*)

RETURN

ENTRY SRBTST
  .
  .             statements testing for Sarbin Syndrome
  .
RETURN I

ENTRY MHLTST
  .
  .             statements testing for Meehl Complex
  .
RETURN I

ENTRY FTEST
  .
  .             statements testing for Fisher's F
  .
RETURN I

ENTRY NPTEST
  .
  .             statements testing for Neyman-Pearson Lemma
  .
RETURN I

ENTRY SSTEST
  .
  .             statements testing for Symbol Shock
  .
RETURN I

END
```

Figure X.5 Subroutine TEST, illustrating the use of multiple entries.

The entry points for multiple entries have the general form

ENTRY *name* $(a_1, a_2, ...)$

where *name* is the name of the entry point and a_i is an argument. The argument list may have no elements, and hence, not be present in the statement.

TRANSFORMATION OF VARIABLES, EXAMPLE PROGRAMS

In order to illustrate the use of subroutines and arithmetic functions in the context of realistic problems two programs are developed here. The first program finds the Fisher r to Z_r transformation of the correlation coefficient r. The second program transforms the limits of a variable from the observed minimum and maximum in a sample to input-specified limits.

Fisher Transformation. It is known from general statistical theory that the correlation coefficient in a sample is not distributed normally when sample size is not very large. However, R. A. Fisher has shown that the transformation

$$Z_r = .5 \log_e \frac{1 + r}{1 - r}$$

is approximately normally distributed with expectation Z_ρ and standard deviation $N - 3$ where ρ is the population correlation. Two programs are shown in Figure X.6, the first illustrating an arithmetic function approach to the transformation, and the second illustrating a subroutine approach. Both of these illustrative programs give the same nu-

```
CCORR
C
C READ A 5 BY 5 MATRIX TO SIMULATE CALCULATING A CORRELATION MATRIX
C
      DIMENSION CORR(5,5)
      READ (5,100)((CORR(I,J),I=1,5),J=1,5)
  100 FORMAT (5F3.3)
      WRITE (6,300)((CORR(I,J),I=1,5),J=1,5)
  300 FORMAT(1H1,/,(5F10.3))
      N=5
      CALL RTOZ (CORR,N)
      WRITE (6,200) ((CORR(I,J),I=1,5),J=1,5)
  200 FORMAT(1H1,/,(5E12.3))
      STOP
      END
      SUBROUTINE RTOZ(ARRAY,M)
      DIMENSION ARRAY(M,M)
      DO 1 I=1,M
      K = I + 1
      DO 1 J = K,M
      ARRAY(I,J) = .5*ALOG((1.0+ARRAY(I,J))/(1.0-ARRAY(I,J)))
      ARRAY(J,I) = ARRAY(I,J)
    1 CONTINUE
      RETURN
      END
```

```
CCORR
C READ A 5 BY 5 MATRIX TO SIMULATE CALCULATING A CORRELATION MATRIX
      DIMENSION CORR(5,5)
      Z(R) = .5 * ALOG((1.0+R)/(1.0-R))
      READ(5,100) ((CORR(I,J),I=1,5),J=1,5)
  100 FORMAT (5F3.3)
      WRITE (6,200) ((CORR(I,J),I=1,5),J=1,5)
      M = 5
      DO 1 I = 1,M
      K = I + 1
      DO 1 J = K,M
      CORR(I,J) = Z(CORR(I,J))
      CORR(J,I) = CORR(I,J)
    1 CONTINUE
      WRITE(6,200) ((CORR(I,J), I=1,5),J=1,5)
  200 FORMAT(1H1,/,(5E12.3))
      STOP
      END
```

Figure X.6 Program listing for Fisher's transformation.

merical results. The data matrices output for the programs are shown in Figure X.7.

Transformation of Range. The adjustment of a set of scores to conform to the specifications of minimum and maximum value is a common transformation. Observed scores may range from WEE to BIG but we may desire that they be adjusted to range from A to B. The program XRANGE illustrated in Figure X.8 determines the observed range of a set of scores, X, and transforms the observed set to correspondingly spaced values between A and B. The values of A and B are read by the program. The program reads the number of values, the actual set of values, and then the desired limits of the transformed values. The program illustrates nested subroutine procedures. The main program calls the subroutine RANGE, which calls the subroutine SIZER. The main program simply reads the data, calls the subroutine, and prints the output data. The basic problem is to determine the point at which an observed value X(I) stands between the observed maximum and minimum BIG and WEE. This point is expressed as a proportion of the distance from BIG to

1.000E+00	7.070E-01	1.470E-01	2.000E-03	2.530E-01
7.070E-01	1.000E+00	5.310E-01	1.400E-02	1.660E-01
1.470E-01	5.310E-01	1.000E+00	2.220E-01	4.690E-01
2.000E-03	1.400E-02	2.220E-01	1.000E+00	8.540E-01
2.530E-01	1.660E-01	4.690E-01	8.540E-01	1.000E+00

1.000E+00	8.812E-01	1.481E-01	2.000E-03	2.586E-01
8.812E-01	1.000E+00	5.915E-01	1.400E-02	1.676E-01
1.481E-01	5.915E-01	1.000E+00	2.258E-01	5.088E-01
2.000E-03	1.400E-02	2.258E-01	1.000E+00	1.271E+00
2.586E-01	1.676E-01	5.088E-01	1.271E+00	1.000E+00

Figure X.7 Output from program illustrated in Figure X.6.

WEE on the observed continuum. The proportion is then used to determine the value corresponding to X(I) but in the interval specified by A and B. Call the rescaled value V(I). Then

$$V(I) = B - \left[\frac{BIG - X(I)}{BIG - WEE}\right](B - A)$$

COMMON ERRORS
IN THE USE OF SUBPROGRAMS

Errors in subprogram use, more than with any other feature of Fortran, are often related to pecularities in the specific operating system under which the job is run. Since these systems vary from installation to installation, it is difficult to give much exact information.

Executive systems that process Fortran compilations differ in their requirements for placement of subroutine decks. In some systems, the subroutine must be treated as a completely separate job, with all job control cards repeated. In others, subroutines simply follow the main program. There may or may not be system control cards required preceding the subroutine. The reader would do well to consult an advisor at his computing center and to follow his instructions on deck make-up exactly.

The situation is usually different with functions. Arithmetic statement functions are always included as a part of the main program—preceding the first executable statement. Function subprograms are usually placed following the END card of the main program, but again the rules vary according to local convention.

A frequent subprogram error is in the use of dummy variables. Such errors can usually be traced to an incorrect under-

```
CRANGE
      DIMENSION X(1000)
      READ (5,10) N
   10 FORMAT(I4)
      READ (5,20) (X(I),I=1,N)
   20 FORMAT(10F8.2)
      READ (5,30) A, B
   30 FORMAT(2F8.4)
      WRITE (6,35) A,B,N,(X(I),I=1,N)
   35 FORMAT(1H1,5H A = ,F8.4,5H B = ,F8.4,5H N = ,I4,///,(8F16.4))
C THE DATA AND NEW MAX AND MIN ARE ALL AVAILABLE--CALL THE SUBROUTINE
      CALL RANGE (X, N, A, B)
C THE TRANSFORMATION IS FINISHED, PRINT THE TRANSFORMED DATA
      WRITE (6,40) (X(I), I=1,N)
   40 FORMAT(1H1,(8F16.4))
      STOP
      END


      SUBROUTINE RANGE(X, M, WEE, BIG)
      DIMENSION X(1000)
      CALL SIZER (X, M, A   , B)
      DO 999 I = 1,M
      X(I) = WEE + ((X(I)-A)/(B-A)) * (BIG-WEE)
  999 CONTINUE
      RETURN
      END


      SUBROUTINE SIZER (V, NUM, ITSY, JUMBO)
      DIMENSION V(1000)
      REAL ITSY, JUMBO
      ITSY = V(1)
      JUMBO = V(1)
      DO 888 K = 2,NUM
      IF(V(K).GT.JUMBO) JUMBO = V(K)
      IF(V(K).LT.ITSY) ITSY = V(K)
  888 CONTINUE
      RETURN
      END
```

Figure X.8 Listing of program XRANGE.

standing of the nature of arguments and dummy arguments. Careful study of the sections of this chapter discussing this material will help to minimize these kinds of errors. Similar statements can be made about the use of COMMON storage for variables. Unless it is clearly understood what COMMON is, errors due to simple misunderstanding can easily be made.

In debugging segmented programs, it is useful to write simple testing routines to test each subroutine. These programs are usually different from those which will ultimately use the subroutine. Using testing programs allows subroutines to be checked out individually without having to compile a large main program, or a number of subroutines for each error to be found. Figures X.1 and X.2 illustrate the use of such simple main programs for testing functions. In most cases, the reference to one of the functions would be from within a much larger main program, doing work other than simply calling the function.

EXERCISES

1. Write arithmetic statement functions to accomplish each of the following:
   (a) Suppress the fractional part of the product of three REAL arguments.
   (b) Find the mean of 10 REAL arguments.
   (c) Calculate the value of

$$\sqrt{a^2 * b^2 * c^2} - 2abc$$

2. Write a FUNCTION subprogram that returns the mean of an array of 500 elements.
3. Write a FUNCTION subprogram that finds the mean of an array having a variable number of elements.
4. Using the coding scheme for random number generation given in Project 8 of Chapter 3, write a FUNCTION subprogram that returns a random number between 0 and 1 each time it is referenced.
5. Write an arithmetic statement function that calls the function written for problem 4 and scales the random number obtained into the range of integer numbers 1 to 100.
6. A job to be run consists of a main program and four subroutines. All subroutines must have access to variables ALPHA, BETA, GAMMA, and DELTA. ALPHA and BETA are integer arrays of dimension 90 by 105. GAMMA and DELTA are 5 by 5 logical variables. Subroutines SUB1, SUB2, and SUB3 must share XYZ1(100) and XYZ2(100). Subroutines SUB2 and SUB4 require access to JIM, JOHN, ISAAC, JONNY, and SAM. Each of these is a 4 by 10 array and they are never used at the same time XYZ1 and XYZ2 are needed. The main program and subroutines SUB1 and SUB3 share LAMBDA, PSY, and CHI which are real arrays 10 by 90, 90 by 10, and 50 by 50, respectively. Write all necessary declarations for all sections of the program to arrange storage in the most efficient manner.
7. In the set of routines for problem 6, write BLOCK DATA subprograms to do the following: set all values of GAMMA to .TRUE. and all values of DELTA to .FALSE.; and set the first 50 values of XYZ1 equal to the first 50 positive integers, respectively.
8. A subroutine INVERT is to work with a two-dimensional array whose actual dimensions will vary, with the actual size being conveyed by arguments. In addition, the routine, due to its logical structure, can only accomodate an array whose largest dimension does not exceed 50. Write the statements for both the calling program and the subroutine to establish the array. In the subroutine, test the size of the array, print an appropriate message, and terminate if the array is too large.
9. A subroutine is to examine an array SCORES(10,95) and return one of 5 possible values of an indicator variable called TEST. The values are 10, 20, 30, 40, and 50. If the value returned is 10, the main program immediately branches to statement 1005, if TEST is either 20 or 40, the branch is to statement 1009, and to 1000 if TEST is equal to 30. If TEST equals 50, branch to statement 9999. Write the necessary code to accomplish the CALL and branch. Write the program in two ways—using the computed GO TO, and the variable return feature.

PART III

TOPICS IN COMPUTING

CHAPTER 11 BASIC SIMULATION TECHNIQUES

This chapter outlines the basic nature of simulation in the behavioral sciences and presents the methods of random number generation necessary to simulate random processes.

Simulation is an important tool in research when models of the phenomena being studied are either too complex to express mathematically or when the phenomena are understood as a process but without a clear mathematical specification. When a model of a phenomenon or a process is expressed as a computer program and the program is executed on a computer, the running of the program is a simulation of the phenomenon or process, as stated in the model. For example, imagine a psychologist who believes he knows what the process of problem solving is—a process of identification of certain characteristics of the problem, a search of all of the identifiable "solutions" for a match between the problem characteristics, the discontinuance of the search when the match is above a certain level of excellence, etc.; the selection of the characteristics of the problem, the identification of the characteristics of the solution, the level of excellence demanded, etc., are determined by the problems and "solutions" and by the properties of the subject in a way that involves random components. The psychologist may have little success in attempts to express his process theory as a mathematical model. However, he may be able easily to express the entire process as a computer program that procedes from one step to the next in an orderly and controlled way.

Behavioral scientists have been active in fashioning models of behavior in terms of computer programs since the early days of the computer. These models are diverse, including models of problem solving, neural networks, personality, social structure, and attitude and opinion change. In general, a model is formulated as a logical process, an algorithm, and the computer puts the model into practice, reporting the results of the operation of the model. The usefulness of this sort of modeling is largely that it provides clear, and often copious, evidence of the detailed consequences of the model for behavior. If the results of operating the model are consistent with actual behavior, the implication is that the model is possibly an accurate theoretical statement of the natural process. On the other hand, if the results of the simulation turn out to be in conflict with what is known about the phenomenon, it is clear that the model is incorrect (if the simulation expresses the model correctly), at least in some aspect, if not totally. The modification of a simulation program, to study the effects of the modification on the simulation, can lead to an understanding of the property of the model that makes it unrealistic or erroneous as a model of empirical phenomena.

In general terms, there are four basic reasons why a behavioral scientist would approach a problem with a computer simulation. First, it might be too costly, or impossible, to observe the process in the real world under experimental conditions without first justifying the practicability and desirability of doing the experiment. Simulation will provide some information on the processes involved and on the character of the results that will be observed. This situation might arise in socially or biologically dangerous experiments. A model of the experiment and of the subjects of the study is built on the basis of the knowledge that is available about the processes involved. The model is expressed as a program and a simulation executed. Untoward or undesired results may be detected by the simulation, and the experiment can be modified to rectify the objectional parts of it before it is actually run. Second, a model or theory may be too complex to permit formal mathematical expression, or the mathematical tools needed may not exist. In such circumstances, a clearly stated theory or a detailed model may be expressible in terms of a computer program, which in turn is used to simulate the model of theory. Third, although mathematical methods may actually exist it may be more practical for the researcher to write a simulation program than to do the mathematical work involved. The practicality of the simulation must be weighed against the greater precision and rigor of the mathematical results. Finally, where a number of alternatives to action exist and there is no way to determine the appropriate alternative to achieve a desired goal, simulations of the alternative actions can give the needed information to choose the action taken.

A model and its simulation program are composed of three kinds of entities: input variables, output variables, and status variables and operations. Input variables in a simulation generally are the base data with which we begin, such as the number of conditions under which a simulated experiment is to be run, the specific experimental conditions, and information regarding the phenomenon being simulated. Output variables are the "behavioral" consequences of operating the simulation, such as the frequency of certain events in the simulation, the condition of the process at certain stages in the simulation, and the simulated dependent variable observed. The output variables are the consequences of the simulated system with the specific input given to the program. Status variables and operations include such things as the parameters built into the program, operating functions and relationships defined between the input and the output variables, and feedback systems that change the status of functions and relationships of values of the operating functions as a consequence of operation of the model. Status variables and functions are the parts of simulation models that we focus on in this chapter. For the sake of economy of space and time we present a very simple mock-up of a simulation model and then develop the specific technology of Monte Carlo methods used in simulation.

THE GENERAL MODEL

A rather general view of natural phenomena, particularly in the behavioral sciences, is that illustrated in Figure XI.1. Input, or independent, variables have an effect (possibly) on the process (organism, society, neural system, economic system, etc.) that is reflected (possibly) on the output, or dependent, variables. The center section of the figure is conceived of as a "black box" about which certain information may or may not be known. If the scientist knew the entire story on the operation of the black box there would be no need to simulate the phenomenon, but we assume that we are interested in areas of some uncertainty. However, if enough is known about the process embodied in the black box a model can be built, expressing unknown elements and functions in the black box as manipulable parameters and hypothesized processes, and the relationship between the input and the output segments of the phenomenon studied. In a simulation, the input and output, as well as the processes, are expressed in symbolic terms, whereas in empirical study of the phenomenon the actual input and output variables would be involved. Figure XI.2 illustrates a conceptualization of simulation of a phenomenon. The input is the same as that in the natural phenomenon. The output is a consequence of the input and the specific characteristics of the simulation program. The scientist is interested in comparing the relationship of input and output in the natural phenomenon with the simulation of the phenomenon. If the relationships are highly similar he knows that he is not too badly off in his conceptualization of the function of the black box. If the relationships are extremely divergent he knows that his model is not a model of the natural phenomenon, in at least one way that is important to the phenomenon.

Projects 13, 14, and 18 are good exam-

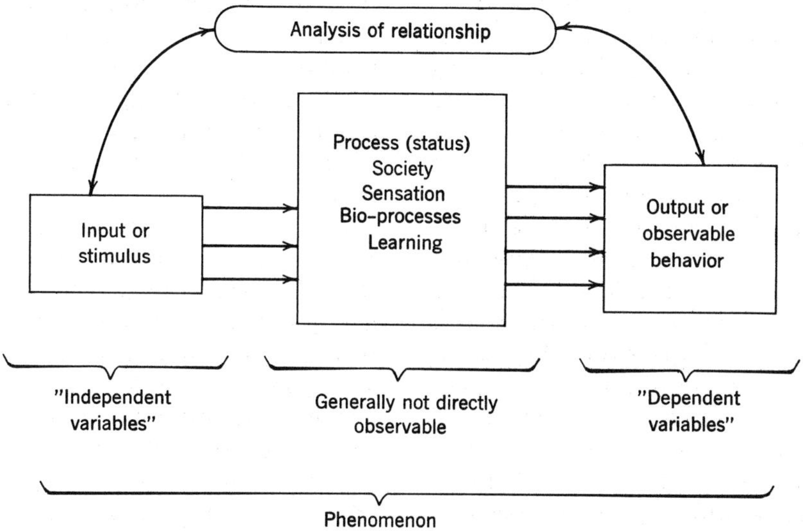

Figure XI.1 A conceptualization of natural phenomena.

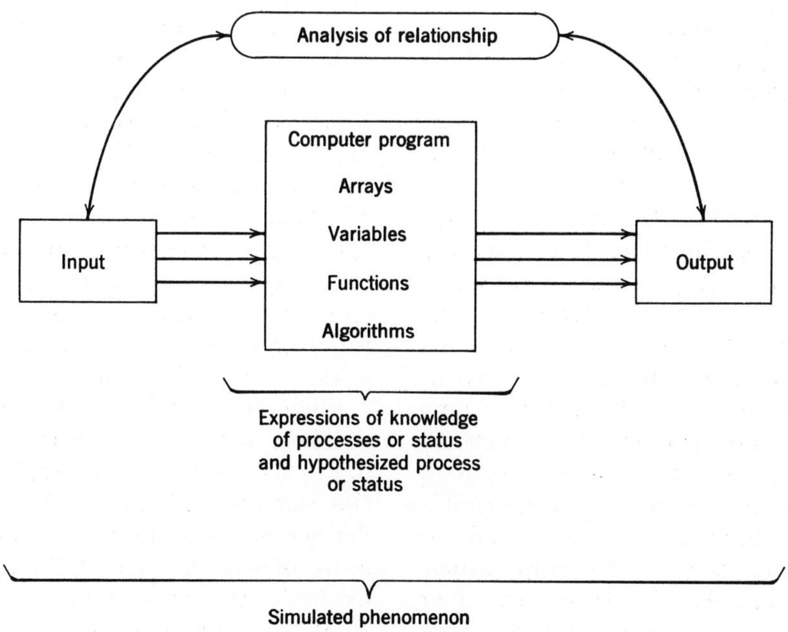

Figure XI.2 A conceptualization of simulation.

ples of the sorts of processes amenable to study by simulation. The descriptions of these projects should be reread at this point. Project 16, Nerve Network Simulation, is a different type of simulation problem. In Project 16 the actual operation of the system described is deterministic—i.e., it does not depend on random functions or "black" boxes at all. The complexity of the model, however, makes the simulation interesting. On the other hand, a random element could be introduced easily and realistically by varying in a random way the number of impulses needed to fire a second level element, or varying the intensity of simulation needed to fire a first level element.

Two types of models are of general interest to behavioral scientists, the first more so than the second. The first type is a stochastic model in which the status variables and perhaps even the status functions are determined in a "random" way. The word random here means not helter-skelter, or without rhyme or reason, but according to some probability rule assigning different likelihoods to possible values of the status variables. The second type is a deterministic model in which the values or states of status variables occur inexorably in a fixed sequence, changing according to a fixed rule or function with each step in the operation of the model. We are not concerned with the second type of model in this chapter.

The fundamental character of a stochastic model is the transition from one step to the next step in the operation of the model by way of a random process. The specific values of status variables and operating functions at each step in the operation of the model are functions of the previous values and functions and/or a random component. Figure XI.3 illustrates a random process in a graphical manner. Imagine a status event or variable A that has four different values, A_1, A_2, A_3, and A_4. The status event or variable B is a function of the status event A at a particular stage in the simulation. The function might be a simple mathematical function (such as the square or a trigonometric function) or it might be partially determined on a random basis. Imagine that it is partially random but that the specific value of A is also important in determining the specific value of B, B_1, B_2, B_3, B_4, or B_5. For $A = A_i$ one or another of the values of B, say B_j, will characterize the simulation at the given step in the simulation. The specific value B_j depends on A_i and a random device. Suppose that the random device is logically equivalent to a spinner like that used in certain games. The edge of the spinner is divided into segments that denote the various values of B. The value of B is determined by flicking the spinner arrow and letting it spin to a stop. The segment pointed to by the arrow determines the specific value $B = B_j$. In the figure there are as many spinners as there are values of A—each spinner having different sized segments for the values of B. On some of the spinners, e.g., the spinner for A_2, there are no segments associated with some of the values of B—in these instances those values of B (B_3, B_4, B_5) are not possible states. The relative area in the segment for a B value is the same as the probability of that value at the time a B status event is generated in the model. For example, B_1, B_2, B_3, and B_4 all have equal probabilities given A_1. Figure 11.3 is intended to suggest the entire random process starting with a value A_i, selecting a spinner and spinning it, and finally determining the value of status event B, B_i. In computer simulation programs the "spinners" are replaced by routines that calculate (generate) "random" numbers.

Each spinner in Figure XI.3 can be marked with values from the interval (0,1.), as shown in Figure XI.4. Each of the regions defined for B events can be defined as a subinterval on the numerical scale of the spinner of Figure XI.4. For example, the spinner for A_1 would select B_1 if the number on the spinner was in the interval from 0 up to (but not in-

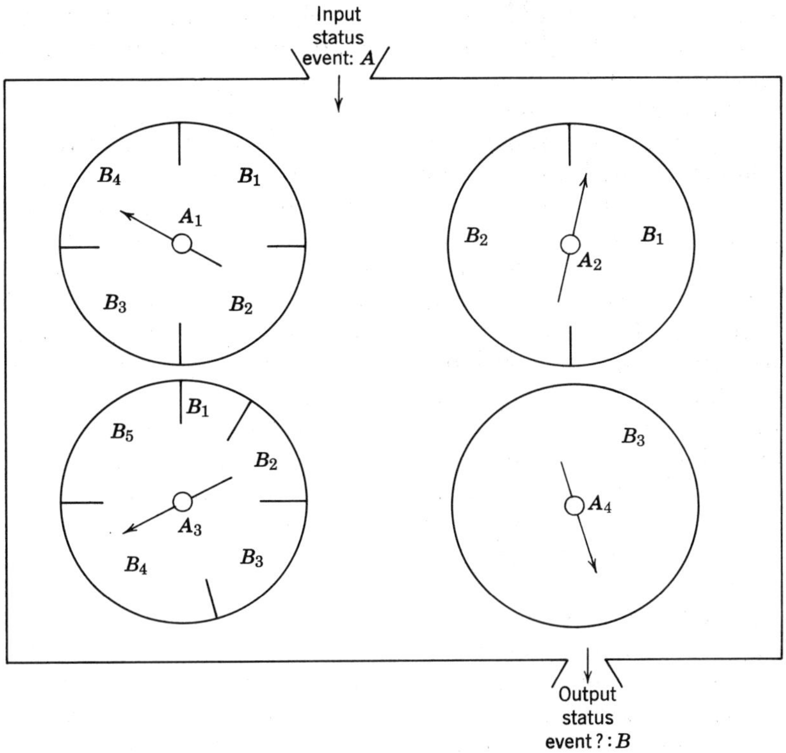

Figure XI.3 A random process relating two variables or conditions.

cluding) .25, B_2 if the number was from .25 up to .5, B_3 from .50 up to .75, B_4 from .75 up to 1.0. Thus, a mechanism that produces numbers from 0 up to 1.0 so that each possible number has the same likelihood of occurring (just as the spinner is equally likely to stop at one point as another on the circle) can be substituted for the physical device of the spinner. In probability theory such a mechanism is called a random variable with a uniform distribution on the unit interval. Other random variables and probability distributions are also important in the theory and practice of simulation but the uniformly distributed variable plays a key role. In the sections to follow it is shown how a number of random variables with nonuniform distributions, such as the normal, binomial, or geometric, can be obtained from uniformly distributed random variables.

In computer simulation a truly random device is not available. However, it is possible to generate a sequence of numbers that have all of the desirable properties of a series of observations on a uniformly distributed random variable. The computer program that generates the

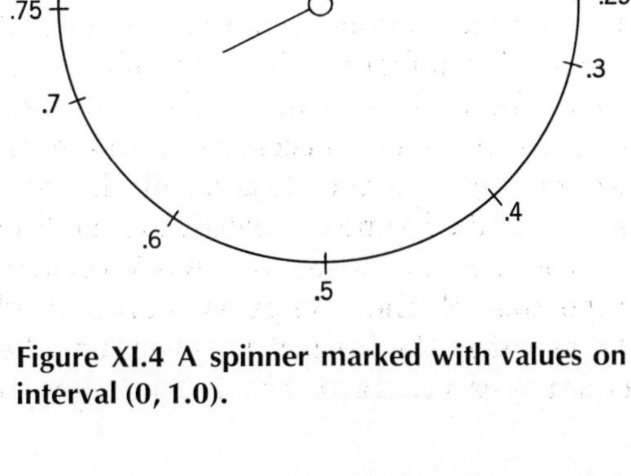

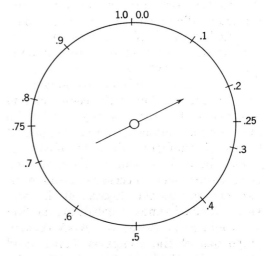

Figure XI.4 A spinner marked with values on interval (0, 1.0).

series of numbers is called a pseudorandom number generator. The pseudorandom number generator that is presented in this chapter is "pseudo" because once the sequence is begun, each number in the sequence is determined precisely by the preceding number, and once a number is regenerated it must, of course, be followed by the number that followed it on the previous cycle. However, since the relative frequency of the numbers generated this way will, in certain circumstances, be like that from a sequence of samples from a uniformly distributed random number, the generator simulates the random variable. Also, the independence of successive samples from a random variable is simulated by the pseudorandom number generator if a sequence of generated numbers is used in evaluating the independence—the pseudorandom numbers generated are "stochastically" independent although they are a deterministic sequence. The reader is referred to the reading list at the end of Chapter 1 for references to additional discussion of pseudorandom number theory, particularly to Naylor et al.

A RANDOM NUMBER GENERATOR

For the sake of simplicity we use the term random number generators rather than the term pseudorandom number generators, although we always mean the latter. The technique presented here is called the multiplicative congruential method of generating random numbers. The method produces numbers in a sequence that is completely dependent on the starting number of the sequence and a constant. The basic theory behind the congruential method is the mathematical theory of numbers, which we shall not discuss here. The essence of the method is to define each successive number in the sequence as the product of the previous number times a constant, modulo m, where m is chosen to satisfy certain properties of the computer being used and specifies the largest number that the sequence can contain. The $i+1$ number in the series is defined by the congruence relationship in number theory:

$$n_{i+1} \equiv an_i (\text{modulo } m)$$

If this relation is used to produce the sequence $n_0, n_1, \ldots, n_i, n_{i+1}, \ldots, n_k$ each of the numbers will be nonnegative and smaller than m. Also, if the interval 0.0 to m is divided into equal subintervals, the frequency with which the numbers will fall into those intervals will not depart seriously from the uniform frequency distribution.

In order to obtain each of the successive numbers in the sequence, an initial number n_0, the constant a, and the modulus m must be chosen. A number of mathematical and empirical studies have been reported on choosing these values. Several criteria are used in selecting the proper values: the number of values in the sequence before a repeat (causing the sequence to cycle through the same values again); the goodness of the uniformity of the frequency distribution; the degree to which the successive values are uncorrelated, etc. General principles are that the modulus should be as large a number as can be represented in the computer being used. If the number of bits in a product is $2b$, the modulus most appropriate is 2^b. The constant a is probably best close to 2^d+3, where d is the integer smaller than or equal to $b/2$. The constant a *must* be an odd number. The initial value in the sequences, n_0, can be any odd number less than the modulus, m. To compute n_1 the product of a and n_0 is taken in integer arithmetic, which gives $2b$ bits for the product, the lower-order ("rightmost") b bits of which define the value of an_0 modulo 2^b as desired. In many Fortran implementations the multiplication of a and n_0 in integer arithmetic automatically discards the b upper-order bits leaving the b lower-order bits. However, some Fortran implementations do not operate that way (e.g., the CDC 6600 and 6400 computers do not have an integer multiply, and a and n_0 are first floated and then multiplied, the higher order bits being preserved) and another mechanism must be used. Where necessary the library function MOD(an_i,m) can be evaluated to get the floating point congruence relationship for floating point values of the constant, modulus, and number in the sequence. When the number n_i is obtained, it is rescaled to the unit interval by dividing by the modulus, m. The number n_i and the modulus m are floated, and n_i/m is calculated to find the random number in the unit interval. Two Fortran programs that generate sequences of random numbers in the unit interval, with uniform distributions are given here. Both of these will give a long cycle of nonrepeated numbers, with an acceptable degree of uniformity of distribution, and with a high degree of sequential independence for this type of generator. The integer arithmetic generator is preferred where it will work on the computer being used.

Integer Generator. Where two integer numbers ranging up to 2^b bits in length are multiplied to leave the lower b bits of the product, the following subroutine and function will generate one random number in the sequence. The number will be in the unit interval. M1 is the current number in the congruence sequence, M2 is the multiplicative constant, XMOD is the modulus. Early in the calling program the values of M1, M2, and XMOD should be set to their initial values:

```
M2=(initial value close to 2^(b/2)+3, and odd)
M1 = 2*(2**(K-1) -2) + 1
XMOD = 2.0**K
```

where K is the number of bits of integer accuracy in the integer word (the number of bits in the word less the sign bit if the computer word is a "sign-magnitude" type of word). Where the integer word is 36 bits long, with 35 bits of accuracy and one bit for a sign, the following statements set up the random number generator in an "optimal" way:

```
M1 = 2*(2**34-2)+1
M2 = 2**17+3
XMOD = 2.0**35
```

M1, M2, and XMOD should not appear on the left of a replacement sign anywhere else in the program except the subroutine RAN. When a random number in the unit interval is needed it is obtained by calling the subroutine RAN(M1, M2, XMOD, X):

```
SUBROUTINE RAN(M1, M2, XMOD, X)
M1 = M1*M2
X = M1
X = X/XMOD
RETURN
END
```

When RAN is called the next time M1 is the number just calculated in M1 = M1*M2. If we wish to generate several random numbers and store them in an array Z, a call to the following subroutine, ZRAN, would place N random numbers in Z(1), ..., Z(N). The calling program must have dimensioned Z large enough to store all N values.

```
  SUBROUTINE  ZRAN(M1,M2,XMOD,Z,N)
  DIMENSION Z(N)
  DO 1 I = 1, N
  M1 = M1*M2
  X = M1
1 Z(I) = X/XMOD
  RETURN
  END
```

When the subroutines are called the second time, or any successive time, they begin generating numbers in sequence from the previously generated number, unless M1 is changed between calls to the subroutine.

Floating Point Generator. The floating point version of the generator is less satisfactory than the integer version because of the smaller number of values in the cycle—the number of bits of precision in fixed point representation generally is larger than in floating point representation. However, the generator will work on any computer with a Fortran IV compiler with a floating point modulus function, AMOD(X_1,X_2). X_1 and X_2 are the arguments of the function. The value of the function is defined by

$$X_1 - (X_1/X_2)X_2$$

where the parenthetic term is the largest integer the magnitude of which does not exceed the magnitude of the ratio in the parentheses, and the sign of which is the same as the ratio. The argument X_2 is the modulus of the function. Imagine the modulus is 1000 and $X_1 = 5467$. Then $(5467/1000) = 5$ and

$$\text{AMOD}(5467, 1000) = 5467 - (5)1000 = 467$$

If this is applied again to the number just obtained, multiplied by the constant 497 in a random number generator, i.e.,

$$n_2 = an_1 \text{ (modulo 1000)}$$

we get

$$\begin{aligned} n_2 &= (497)(467) \text{ (modulo 1000)} \\ &= \text{AMOD}(232099, 1000) = 232099 - (232)1000 = 099 \end{aligned}$$

Repeating this to get the third and fourth number in the sequence gives

$$\begin{aligned} n_3 &= (497)(099) \text{ (modulo 1000)} \\ &= \text{AMOD}(49203, 1000) = 49203 - (49)1000 = 203 \\ n_4 &= (497)(203) \text{ (modulo 1000)} \\ &= \text{AMOD}(100891, 1000) = 100891 - (100)1000 = 891 \end{aligned}$$

This sequence of numbers n_1, n_2, n_3, and n_4 was generated by applying the same algorithm to each successive value when $n_0 = 11$. The sequence is equivalent, in general form but not in values, to the sequence obtained by the integer generator programmed in the previous section. When the numbers n_1, n_2, n_3, and n_4 are divided by the modulus, the random numbers obtained are .467, .099, .203, and .891, a pseudorandom number sequence on the unit interval. It should be clear that if the modulus is as small as 1000, as in the example, the sequence must begin to repeat before the 999th number generated (all of the numbers possible have occurred by then). When a number is generated that has already occurred in the sequence (it must be the number n_0) the cycle starts over. Selecting an appropriate initial value, n_0, constant a, and modulus will optimize the desired characteristics of the generator. In general, the properties of a floating point generator is a function of the maximum number of bits of floating point accuracy available on the computer. The accuracy varies with machine. For example, on the IBM 7090 the accuracy is equivalent to 28 bits while on the CDC 6400 the accuracy is equivalent to 48 bits. The general rule is that the product of the constant and the number n_i in the sequence of random numbers must not exceed the accuracy of the floating point number. Since the coefficient a should be in the range of $2^{b/2}$ the 48 bits of accuracy can be divided into two parts, one for the modulus and one for the constant: Modulus $= 2^{24} - 1$ and $a = 2^{24} - 3$.

Early in the calling program the values of XM1, XM2, and XMOD should be set to their initial values, perhaps with the following explicit statements:

```
XM1  = (any odd number less than XMOD)
XM2  = 2.0**24 - 3.
XMOD = 2.0**24 - 1.
```

When a random number in the unit interval is needed it is obtained by calling the subroutine XRAN(XM1, XM2, XMOD, X):

```
SUBROUTINE XRAN(XM1, XM2, XMOD, X)
XM1 = XM1*XM2
X = AMOD(XM1, XMOD)/XMOD
RETURN
END
```

If we wish to generate several random numbers and store them in an array Y, a call to the following subroutine would place N random numbers in Y(1), ..., Y(N). The calling program must have dimensioned Y large enough to store all N values.

```
  SUBROUTINE YRAN(XM1,SM2,XMOD,Y,N)
  DIMENSION Y(N)
  DO 1 I = 1, N
  XM1 = AMOD(XM1*XM2, XMOD)
1 Y(I) = XM1/XMOD
  RETURN
  END
```

The coding of the floating point generators is a bit simpler than that of the integer generators. However, the cost in computing is greater because of the need to evaluate the AMOD function.

Library Generators. Almost all computing centers have random number generators in their program libraries. We should investigate these generators and consider them as serious contenders for use in any simulation. Most often the generator in the program library will be coded in machine language to give the fastest possible execution with the largest possible number of unique random numbers. However, the user should carefully check the method used if there is any question. Also, it is important that the user be able to select his own n_0 for a sequence of numbers: you don't want the same n_0 for every simulation; you may want to run two simulations with the same n_0 (identical sequences but some change in models, perhaps) in the same computer run.

STATISTICAL TESTS OF RANDOM NUMBERS

When a sequence of random numbers is generated, the purpose is to simulate a uniformly distributed random variable on the unit interval. In an application, the random variable is really desired, not the simulation of the random variable, but we must take the simulation in place of a real random variable. Consequently, we would like to know if our random variable simulation leads to a suspicion that the numbers that are produced by the generator could not have come from an unbiased, independent trial, sampling from a random variable with the desired properties. The method of discovering "bad" sequences of random numbers is to apply standard tests of statistical hypotheses to the obtained sequences. In all cases we assume the null hypothesis of uniformity of distribution, independence of successive samples (numbers in the sequence), etc. The property that is tested depends on how the numbers are to be used in the model. For example, if events in the model are to be selected in a sequential way, in a fixed sequence, the independence of the numbers from the generator, as related to the event sequence, should be tested, as well as the uniformity of distribution. These tests are not discussed here in detail because they generally are familiar to behavioral scientists.

Uniformity Test. The unit interval is divided into subintervals, the random number frequencies for each of the subintervals is determined by counting, and the chi square test for departure from uniformity (equal frequency) is performed. If the test gives a very small significance probability the sample is rejected and a new sample of random numbers is calculated. The sample of numbers inspected in this test should be that sample for which uniformity is required. Two samples when pooled may indicate a departure from uniformity even though each sample separately would not give that result. If the samples are used separately in the model, the pooled sample result is not relevant to the information needed.

Dependency Test. If events are to be selected at various points in a simulation model such that they are independent, the random numbers used to simulate the selection of events must not seriously depart from independence. There are a number of tests that can be used to reject samples of random numbers on the grounds that they probably did not come from independent trials. If successive numbers are involved, the test involves the use of a chi square test of independence of observations on jointly distributed random variables with multiple values (subintervals in the unit interval). If there is a need to guard against correlation over whole subsequences in the random generator, the test to use is the lagged product test involving the product of numbers from corresponding trials in the subsequences. These two tests are described, in sufficient detail to perform them, by Naylor et al.

Other tests related to other properties of the random number sequence are available. For details of these, and a discussion of their use, see Naylor et al.

GENERATION OF RANDOM VARIATES

There are two general uses of random numbers in simulation models: (1) the introduction of a random component in variables, both status and output; and (2) the selection of elements from lists, populations, events, etc. In this section we discuss the use of random numbers generated by the generators presented above to generate random variates that have a certain frequency function. The selection of elements is discussed in the following section.

It is possible to devise methods for simulating random variables of many distribution forms. We present the information necessary to simulate six such random variables. These are: (1) uniformly distributed between arbitrary limits, (2) exponentially distributed, (3) normally distributed, (4) multivariate normally distributed, (5) geometric distributed, and (6) bionomially distributed. In all of the following we presume RAN and ZRAN are available as subroutines in the library or program deck.

Uniform. The special case of the uniformly distributed random variate given by the programs above can be generalized. First, it should be noted that the numbers generated are at most $2^b - 1$, and consequently, the random variate x is at most $(2^b - 1)/2^b$. Also, since N_0 and a are odd, x will be at least one bit greater than zero, and $0 < x < 1$. If we want to modify the range of the variate to $A < x < B$, the simple transformation

$$x = x(B - A) + A$$

rescales x to the desired limits. The uniformity is preserved. If $A = 10$ and $B = 25$, in the rescaling the following lines of code in the calling program produce the desired variates:

```
A = 10
B = 25
...
...
CALL RAN(M1,M2,XMOD,X)
X = X*(B-A) + A
...
...
```

Frequently we wish to generate an array index in a way to permit selection of elements from the array with an equal probability rule. The generator RAN provides the basis for these values. Imagine N elements in the array—i.e., indices are 1, 2, 3, ..., N. First rescale x to $0 \leq x < N$ by the method just cited. Now let all values $0 \leq x < 1$ be transformed to 1, all values $1 \leq x < 2$ be transformed to 2, ..., all values $N - 1 \leq x < N$ be transformed to N. Since each of the intervals so transformed have equal probability so do the index values. The transformation uses the truncation feature of Fortran. First add 1.0 to the rescaled x and then truncate. The result is the integer just larger than x, even if x is an integer:

```
XN = N
CALL RAN(M1,M2,XMOD,X)
I = X*XN + 1.0
PICK = ARRAY(I)
```

PICK is a randomly selected element in ARRAY where all elements have equal chances of being selected over many such selections.

Exponential. The exponential distribution is found in situations where the time between events is a random variable. In particular, examples such as the number of time units between successive automobiles passing a given point, the number of units of time between pecks by a pigeon at a key in a Skinner-box, the number of units of time between encounters of rumor carriers, etc. If we assume that (1) the probability of an event is a constant function of the time units, but (2) independent of the number of elapsed units, then as the time units are taken to be very small the probability of an event in any given unit becomes very small, and the time, t, between the preceding event and the next event is a random variable with

$$f(t) = pe^{-pt}$$

and

$$F(t) = \int_0^t pe^{-pt}\,dt = 1 - e^{-pt}$$

where p is the probability of an event in any time interval, and $e = 2.71828$. It can be shown that

$$E(t) = 1/p$$
$$var(t) = 1/p^2 = [E(t)]^2$$

For a process with waiting time $E(t)$ the parameter $p = 1/E(t)$. Generally a model will specify $E(t)$, giving a way of generating values of t as a random variable.

The method used is to let $F(t)$ be simulated by a uniform random variate X on the unit interval. Then for a given p the equality

$$X = 1-F(t) = e^{-pt}$$

This leads to

$$t = -\frac{1}{p}\log X$$
$$= -E(t)\log X$$

Thus, for each uniform random variate X an exponentially distributed random variate may be generated by

```
ET = (the desired value)
CALL RAN (M1,M2,XMOD,X)
T = -ET*ALOG(X)
```

Normal. The normal distribution is widely known to behavioral scientists. Consequently, we present without further discussion methods of generating normally distributed random variates. The basic problem is to generate X with a normal distribution and variance of 1.0 and expectation of 0.0. Two methods are used, the first based on the central limit theorem, the second on a trigonometric transformation of a uniformly distributed variate on the unit interval.

The central limit theorem states that the sum of identically distributed independent random variables $X_1, X_2, \ldots, X_k$ has approximately a normal distribution with expectation $kE(X_i)$ and variance $kvar(X_i)$. If X is uniformly distributed on the unit interval it has an expectation of .5 and variance of 1/12. Thus, $Y = X_1 + X_2 + \ldots + X_k$ is approximately normal with $E(Y) = .5k$ and $\mathrm{var}(Y) = k/12$. Consequently,

$$Z = \frac{Y - .5k}{\sqrt{k/12}}$$

is approximately normal with $E(Z) = 0$ and $var(Z) = 1$.

The random variable Z can be evaluated by generating k uniformly distributed random variates by the generators given above. The central limit theorem implies that the approximation is better if k is larger. The degree of goodness of approximation needed depends on the use to which the variates are put. The value $k = 12$ is large enough to give a reasonably good approximation and insures a particularly fast calculation. For $k = 12$ the denominator term of Z is 1.0 and consequently does not appear in the equation. The equation simplifies to

$$Z = Y-6$$

If k is a multiple of 12 where $k/12$ is a perfect square, e.g., 12, 48, 108, etc., Z is also very simple. If $k = 48$

$$Z = .5(Y-k/2) = .5(Y-24)$$

The following code produces one variate

from a normally distributed random variable with zero expectation and variance of 1.0.

```
   SUM = 0.
   CALL ZRAN (M1, M2, XMOD, X, 12)
   DO 1 I = 1, 12
 1 SUM = SUM + X(I)
   Z = SUM - 6.
```

Two trigonometric transformations of two independent uniformly distributed random variates on the unit interval give two approximately unit standard normal variates. Let X_1 and X_2 be the uniform variates, then

$$Z_1 = (-2 \log_e X_1)^{1/2} \cos(2\pi X_1)$$
$$Z_2 = (-2 \log_e X_1)^{1/2} \sin(2\pi X_2)$$

are unit standard normal deviates. The approximation is quite good and the speed of calculation is better than the central limit method if k is very large. In general it is a good idea to take X_1 and X_2 from separate generators, but successive numbers from a single generator will give reasonably satisfactory results for most purposes.

Normal variates with expectation EZ and variance VZ can be generated by first generating a unit standard Z and applying the transformation

$$ZT = VZ*Z + EZ$$

ZT will be a variate from a normally distributed variable with expectation EZ and variance VZ.

Certain functions of samples of normally distributed random variables are of special interest to behavioral scientists. The chi square distribution, the F distribution, and Student's t all may be simulated by generating samples of variates with unit standard normal distribution. For example, for m variates

$$X = \sum_{i=1}^{m} Z_i^2$$

is distributed as chi square with m degrees of freedom.

The F distribution is simulated by taking the ratio of two chi square variates divided by their respective degrees of freedom. Where X_n or X_m are chi square distributed with n and m degrees of freedom, respectively,

$$Y = \frac{X_n/n}{X_m/m}$$

is F distributed with denominator and numerator degrees of freedom m and n, respectively.

The t distribution is simulated by

$$W = Z/\sqrt{X_n/n}$$

where Z is unit standard normal and X_n is chi square with n degrees of freedom.

Bivariate Normal. Many behavioral science research designs involve two or more jointly distributed variables, input, output or status. When simulation methods are involved in such research it is often useful to simulate the jointly distributed variables. If the variables X and Y are jointly distributed, each simulated variate will be a pair of values, say (x, y). Two special cases are considered here: (1) when x is known, y is determinable as a function of x, e.g., y is uniform in interval $bx\text{-}c \leq y \leq bx+c$ (b is a regression constant), or y is normal and variance of 1.0 and expectation $E_y = a + y^2$; (2) when (X,Y) are bivariate normal with σ_y, σ_x, μ_y, μ_x, $\rho_{x,y}$ as parameters.

In the first cited problem the "dependent" variate is generated by the appropriate procedure, e.g., by RAN if X is uniform on the unit interval or by one of the normal variate generators if X is normally distributed. Once a value of X is generated, x, the function is applied to x in order to get y. The procedure is dependent on the specification of the conditional distribution of Y. Essentially the procedure is to evaluate a random function with a parameter x.

For bivariate normal variates the problem can be addressed in a more general way. The two values (x,y) are dependent on σ_x, σ_y, μ_y, μ_x, and ρ_{xy}. Two independent standard normal variates Z_1 and Z_2 are generated and used in

$$x = \sigma_x Z_1 + \mu_x$$

$$y = \sigma_y(\rho_{xy} Z_1 + Z_2\sqrt{1-\rho_{xy}^2}) + \mu_y$$

Geometric. In phenomena where a sequence of trials or events are observed, each trial being a "success" or "failure," the number of success trials before the first failure often is a random variable with a geometric distribution. The $n+1$ trial is a success if the nth trial is the last failure. The probability of a string of n failures on independent trials each with probability q of failure ($p = 1\text{-}q$ is probability of success) is q^n. Hence the $n+1$ trial sequence has probability pq^n. The random variable x, the number of failures before the first successful trial, is distributed as

$$f(y) = pq^y \qquad y = 0, 1, 2, \ldots$$

The distribution function is

$$F(y) = \sum_{n=0}^{y} pq^n$$

Note that $1-F(y) = P(Y>y)$ and $P(Y>0) = q$. Consequently

$$1-F(y) = q^{x+1}$$

Since $y \geq 0$ the largest that $1-F(y)$ can be is $q^{0+1} = q$. Thus

$$1 - F(y)/q = q^{x+1}/q = q^x$$

is bounded on the unit interval. Generating a uniform variate x on the unit interval is equivalent to selecting a value from the value set of q^y. Let $x = q^y$ and consequently

$$y = \frac{\log x}{\log q}$$

where y is truncated, i.e., rounded to the integer just smaller than y.

An alternative to this procedure may be desirable when q is close to 0.0 or 1.0 (log 0 is infinite, log 1 is zero, and precision of the logarithm of q may not be very good). The basic sequence of trials is simulated by generating a sequence of uniform variates x_i in the unit interval. If $x_i \leq q$ the variate is said to simulate a failure. The first time $x_i > q$, $y = i$ is the value of the geometric variate.

Binomial. The geometric distributed variable describes part of a "larger" variable, the binomial distributed variable. It arises if a simple experiment or trial in a larger experiment gives rise to one or another event, say success or failure, with probability p of success. If p is constant over a sequence of n such trials the number of successes is a binomial random variable S. The simulation of S where n is relatively moderate, say $n \leq 20$, is most simply done by simulating n trials and counting the number of successes in the n trials. A trial is simulated by generating a uniform variate x on the unit interval and identifying it as "success" if $x \leq p$. The following code gives a single simulated observation on S with N trials and probability P of success.

```
  INTEGER S
  ...
  S = O
  CALL ZRAN (M1, M2, XMOD, Z, N)
  DO 1 I = 1, N
  IF(Z(I).LE.P) S = S + 1
1 CONTINUE
  ...
  ...
```

SELECTION OF EVENTS FROM LISTS

In addition to simulating random processes by the methods just outlined, the researcher using simulation models often needs to select events randomly from lists of events. The term random is used here, in the most general way, to include equal probability rules, *a priori* distributions of the probability among the events, and empirically specified probabilities. Two general procedures are used, both of which require representing each event in the list of events as one or more elements in an array, and the generation of a uniformly distributed random variate. The first procedure is defined for the equal probability event selection. The second procedure is defined for *a priori* and empirical event probabilities, i.e., any arbitrary probability distribution.

Equal Probability. The array, LIST, with M elements, contains the names or values of the events to be selected in the simulation. The contents of LIST may even be "pointers" to other lists, thus providing what is known as list-processing simulation. The program SORT2, for example, might be used as the basis of such a list-processing simulation program. The columns of array TAB in SORT2 would play the role of LIST. Selecting a column in TAB is equivalent to selecting a sublist of the elements sorted by SORT2.

In order to select an element from LIST a uniform variate x on the unit interval is generated. The value x is transformed to an integer, 1, 2, ..., M, and the integer is used in referencing LIST. The following code selects an event from LIST with each element having probability of $1/M$ of being selected:

```
XM = M
CALL RAN(M1, M2, XMOD, X)
I = X*XM + 1.0
EVENT = LIST(I)
```

Arbitrary. When the events in the list are to be selected with probabilities other than equal probabilities there are two types of procedure that can be used. The first procedure uses more storage in the computer but is very fast. Each event has a probability. If the probabilities, p, are stated in increments of 10^{-k} (10^{-1} gives .0, .1, .2, ..., 1.0; 10^{-2} gives .00, .01, .02, ..., .99, 1.00; 10^{-3} gives .000, .001, .002, ..., .999, 1.000), the event value or name is stored in $(10^k)p$ elements in LIST, which must have 10^k elements, where p is the probability of the event. When all events (names or values) have been stored in LIST an element is selected from LIST with the equal probability method.

Imagine that the list of events, from which a random selection is to be made, contains five elements, E_1, E_2, E_3, E_4, and E_5, with $P(E_1) = .1$, $P(E_2) = .2$, $P(E_3) = .2$, $P(E_4) = .3$, $P(E_5) = .2$. Since the probabilities are in tenth units the number of elements of LIST must be $10^1 = 10$. There must be $10P(E_1) = 1$ elements of LIST indicating E_1, $10P(E_2) = 2$ elements of LIST indicating E_2, $10P(E_3) = 2$ elements of LIST indicating E_3, $10P(E_4) = 3$ elements of list indicating E_4, and $10P(E_5) = 2$ elements of list indicating E_5. If an element is chosen from LIST by the equal probability method described above, the probability of selecting an event is the number of elements of LIST indicating the event divided by 10, i.e., the stated probabilities of the events.

The disadvantage of this procedure is the amount of storage that is required to match the event probabilities in an equal probability sampling from LIST. If the probabilities are stated in ten thousandths of a unit, i.e., if probabilities like .0001 and .0002 are to be distinguished in the sampling, the number of storage locations that must be allocated to LIST is 10,000. Where less precision is needed to represent the probabilities of events, this method is very fast. There is some time spent in setting up LIST from the probabilities of the events and this must be weighed against the efficiency of the second method, described below. Where the number of elements in LIST is not too restrictive and where the number of repetitions of the sampling is neither too small nor too large neither method is particularly more advantageous than the other.

The second procedure is called a binary search method. The probabilities of the events are replaced by the cumulative probabilities. For the kth element in the list the cumulative probability is

$$\sum_{i=1}^{k} P(E_i)$$

as illustrated in Figure XI.5. A uniform random variate x on the unit interval is generated. This variate is compared with the cumulative probability of the element in the middle of the array (using integer arithmetic the middle is the $k = M/2$ element). If x is smaller than the

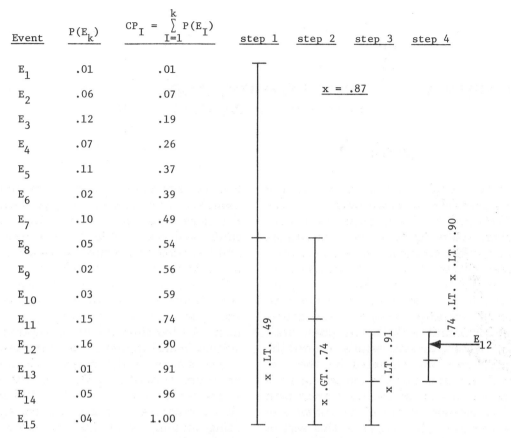

Event	$P(E_k)$	$CP_I = \sum_{I=1}^{k} P(E_I)$
E_1	.01	.01
E_2	.06	.07
E_3	.12	.19
E_4	.07	.26
E_5	.11	.37
E_6	.02	.39
E_7	.10	.49
E_8	.05	.54
E_9	.02	.56
E_{10}	.03	.59
E_{11}	.15	.74
E_{12}	.16	.90
E_{13}	.01	.91
E_{14}	.05	.96
E_{15}	.04	1.00

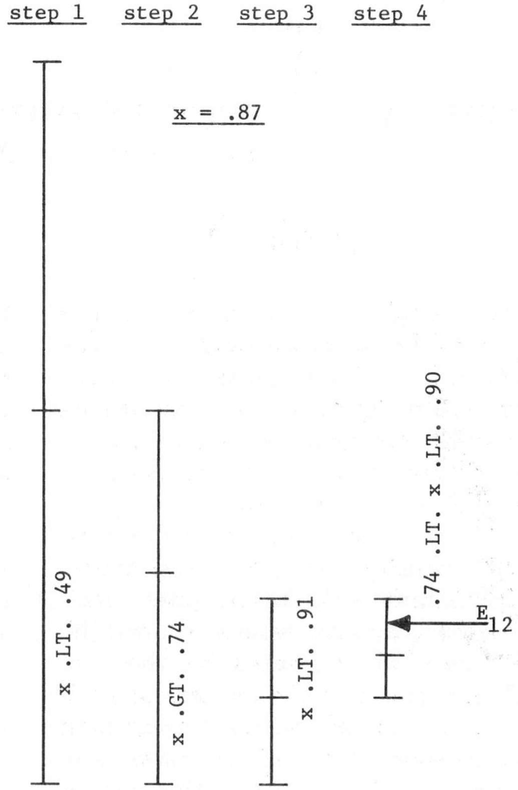

Figure XI.5 Illustration of binary search procedure.

probability, the event selected will be one of those in the first half of the array. The lower half of the array is then bisected $(M/2)/2 = k$ and the variate compared with the kth element in the array. If the variate is larger than the cumulative probability of that element it must be an element with index $(M/4) < k \leq (M/2)$. Each comparison of x with a cumulative probability results in the exclusion of approximately (one fewer or one more) one-half of the elements remaining. It can be shown that for the smallest value k such that $M \leq 2^k$, k is the largest number of steps needed to find the event selected by x.

Figure XI.5 illustrates the process of a binary search with specific data. Fifteen events are possible, each with the probability $P(E_k)$ as listed. The corresponding cumulative probabilities are shown in the column headed CP_I. A uniform random variate is generated, say $x = .87$. This is compared with CP_I where $I = 15/2 = 7$ (truncated): $CP_7 = .49 < .87$. Hence $x = .87$ refers to E_I. $I > 7$ and E_I for $I \leq 7$ are ruled out. The next value of I is $7 + 15\text{-}7/2 = 11$. CP_{11} is compared with $x = .87$: $CP_{11} = .74 < .87$. Hence $x = .87$ refers to E_I $I > 11$, and only E_I for $I > 11$ are possible. The next value of I must be midway between 15 and 12: $12 + (15\text{-}12)/2 = 13$ (ratio truncated). $CP_{13} = .91 > .87$ and I must be less than 13, which leaves only $I = 12$ so E_{12} is selected.

At each step the largest possible index and the smallest possible index are noted. As soon as the two are the same the index specifies the event selected. Also, should $x = CP_I$ the event selected is E_I.

CHAPTER 12 PROGRAMMING AND OPERATING SYSTEMS

In the early days of the computer, the programmer wrote down long lists of detailed computer instructions in octal notation, referring to specific operations and specific storage locations in the computer. When these were punched on cards they were carried by the programmer into the "machine room," whence he became operator, debugger, and generally combatant with the computer until the program ran successfully or until the programmer was defeated by the program, machine, and the computing environment in general and went away with a "postmortem" dump of the contents of the computer. No longer is this sort of game played in computing; a "beat the system" game has replaced it. The "game" goes somewhat as follows. The programmer writes his program in a less demanding language (but still a bit like an old-maid school teacher standing over the stupid student who cannot remember where the comma goes). The programmer then hands his deck to a clerk who will do one of several things to it: write a nasty note on the top card that the programmer has made a stupid error and should do such and such or take his business elsewhere; drop the deck and put it back together in some silly permutation without bothering to tell anyone; lay it aside until the programmer demands that a general alarm be set off for a search for his deck; or perhaps it is given to the operator of a card reader. The card reader operator stacks the program deck together with a group of other programs and attempts to "read" the cards onto an input file, tape, or disc, so that the computer has access to the jobs. If the cards are not mangled in the process, they go back to the clerk who waits for the paper and cards produced as output. The card deck and the output then run the same gamut on their way to the programmer.

The ghastly picture presented above is not always true, fortunately. However, the "game" seems to plague programmers. All too often the human operating system in and around a computing center is the source of the major problems a programmer must face. However, there is a greater source of potential difficulty that a programmer must face; the operating system, or monitor or executive system that is in control of the computer operation itself. These systems are sets of programs that are designed to take charge of the operation of the computer in order to relieve the programmer of the responsibility of battle with the computer—they are intended to provide a buffer between the programmer and the mechanical, logical structure of the computer not directly involved with the program being run. However, all too often, the operating system of a computer can act not like a benevolent buffer but like an impenetrable barrier between the computer and the programmer. In addition to programming in Fortran or another language, the programmer must learn to use the operating system. When the "system," including the operating program, the clerical staff, and the operations personnel, are all put together smoothly and intelligently, it can provide a fine environment in which to use the computer. However, the user who wants to transgress outside the limits of standard use of Fortran is faced with a number of obstacles and hurdles that he must learn how to handle.

OPERATING SYSTEMS

We cannot attempt here to review operating systems in detail, not even for an example computer system. The best that we are able to present is a general description of the sorts of things that systems do. An operating system, whether it is called a monitor or an executive system, is a group of programs that control the sequence of events during the operation of the computer over a period of time, including the processing of the many jobs that are submitted to the computer. Most systems schedule the jobs with respect to each other, giving a priority for certain jobs, taking them as they are submitted, etc. The system communicates with the operator of the computer, informing him of the current and past activity of the computer, the input/output units being used, the amount of time a given program may have been running, the number of jobs waiting to be run, etc.

Figure XII.1 illustrates an imaginary operating system with a block diagram. There are seven primary functions performed by the operating system:

1. Communications with the operator.
2. Input/output control and operation.
3. Schedule and execution of jobs.
4. Process programs into executable form.
5. Account for the time and activity of the computer.
6. Load programs into the computer in such a way that they will execute.
7. Monitor the actual execution of programs.

General Operation. The operating system is a collection of programs under the supervision of a program that serves as

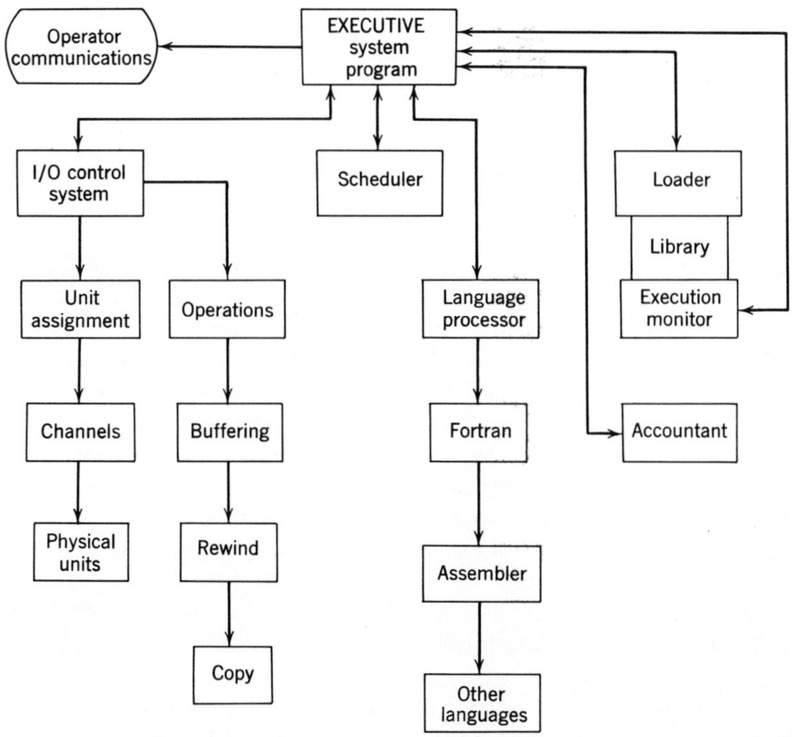

Figure XII.1 A block diagram of an operating system.

an overall executive program, called the Executive in Figure XII.1. This program actually operates the computer, causing the computer to process the stream of jobs that are submitted to it by the input devices attached to the computer, including the operator's console (typewriter, keyboard on a display screen, etc.). The program is designed to seek jobs to do from input sources and to keep the output flowing smoothly. In a very real sense the Executive is the main program of the computer and all other jobs are subprograms. The Executive is directed by Executive command statements located in job decks, or typed into the operator's console. When there are no jobs to be done the Executive is "idle," like an automobile parked with its motor running, but ready to react to signals from input units attached to the computer. When a signal is generated by pressing a button on the input unit the Executive interrogates that unit, reading commands from cards or from the keyboard, and takes appropriate action. The Executive may cause jobs to be read onto a peripheral I/0 device like a disc, where they are considered part of the job stream, to be attended to when the computer gets to them.

A job is defined as a deck of cards (or signals from some input device) that defines a unit of work for the computer. The unit of work may involve many separate parts, such as establishing communications with a given reel of tape, telling the operator to remove the tape when the job is done, compiling a Fortran program, getting subprograms from the library, or printing out results. The segments of the job deck generally are in a well defined order: job card, system command cards, a card signaling the end of the subdeck of system control cards, cards making up a program (perhaps a Fortran program together with object decks from previously compiled programs), a card signaling the end of the program deck, data cards, a card signaling the end of the data deck, system control cards, and a card signaling the end of the job deck. In some systems it is possible to stack programs together in one job deck, in which case the system control cards at the end of the program would be followed by the same sequence of subdecks as in the first program.

The conventions used to indicate the end of subdecks in a job vary from computer system to computer system. Also the system control commands that can appear on system control cards are idiosyncratic to computer systems. The more modern, complex, computers tend to have a wider variety of system control commands, which perform a wider and more complex array of tasks for the computer user. Some Executive commands are generally necessary parts of the system control subdeck, as for example, those indicating the input and the output units that are used by a program or indicating the type of processing desired (e.g., compile a Fortran program and execute it). Because of the diversity of system commands we do not refer to any particular system here but rather attempt only to communicate the general Executive system functions. The reader should consult with the computing center he is using to obtain an operating system manual or at least to obtain the basic information regarding the operating system.

Communications with the Operator. It is necessary at times to communicate with the operator of the computer when the program is being run. This cannot be done by waiting at the computer center for the program to come on. Often the operator does not know when a particular program will be run—that may be determined by the Executive. Also, as soon as the program begins, it is essentially too late to communicate with the operator unless the program itself does the communication—the program will execute in an elapsed time of a few seconds perhaps. The most frequent reason for communicating with the operator is to inform him that somewhere in the program there is a PAUSE statement that permits him time to mount a reel of tape on a tape drive; when the tape is mounted he should let the program continue. The system command language permits messages in the card deck (in the system control part of the deck, generally) to be "sent" to the operator's console when the job is begun.

In addition to programmer-operator communication the Executive keeps the operator informed of the status of the job stream. Also, if there are execution or Executive errors, or if some part of the computer is not functioning properly, the Executive can communicate with the operator, who in turn may be able to take remedial action.

The operator of the computer can enter Executive commands through his console, often by simple button pushing or by typing the commands into a keyboard on the console of the machine. These commands cause action by the Executive in the same way that Executive control commands in job decks do. In most cases the commands that are originated at the console take precedence over the program that is executing at the moment. The operator can, for example, cause a program to terminate and the Executive to proceed to select the next job in the job stream.

Input-Output Control and Operation. The input and output facilities on modern computers tend to be the most complicated part of the system. At least four parts of the I/O system of a computer are the responsibility of the operating system. Physical units within the I/O system must be assigned for specific purposes in the computer system. For example, certain segments of a disc may be used to hold the job stream, others may be usable by programmers for temporary (scratch) storage, and certain tape drives may be reserved for the accounting data, etc. The assignment of the units is monitored by the operating system, although Executive control cards can, in some instances, be used to establish assignment of physical units as particular symbolic units (see below).

In addition to assigning units, the operating system must assign communication channels to the physical units so that data can be transmitted between the computer and the physical I/O devices. In general, a channel is simply a communication line, across which signals can be transmitted. Channels in a modern computer generally are shared by a number of peripheral I/O units in the computer system. A channel handles signals in such a way that it is necessary to limit use of a channel to one peripheral device at a time. Consequently, it is necessary to control the use of the channels. Generally, users' programs have no control over channels but channels are assigned by the operating system as they are needed. Of more immediate concern to the user of the computer is the necessity of assigning specific physical units as designated symbolic units, e.g., a particular tape drive as symbolic unit 22, for which the user has some particular use. If a reel of tape, on which data have been recorded, or onto which data are to be written, is to be mounted on some physical tape drive, the program must be able to refer to that drive by the standard READ and WRITE statements using a symbolic designation, such as unit 22. Executive commands are provided to permit assigning symbolic designations to specific physical units. Together with the designation of units, communication with the operator permits the establishment of coordination between I/O requirements of a program and the physical setup of the computer I/O facilities.

In addition to establishing communication linkages for I/O, the Executive serves a number of other I/O functions. Manipulation of storage units is often possible through Executive commands. For example, tapes can be rewound, or unloaded (disengaged from the read/write heads on the tape drives). Many Executive systems permit the transmission of data from one I/O device to another without a Fortran program, by way of Executive commands alone. For example, it is possible to have data, stored on a magnetic tape, copied into a segment of a magnetic disc before a Fortran program is executed, and then to read the data from the disc in the Fortran program.

When reading or writing in a Fortran program the data being transmitted are not transmitted a variable (element) at a time to or from the I/O device. The steps necessary to establish linkages in the communication system for I/O generally are too time consuming to permit this approach to transmission of data. Rather, blocks of computer memory are set aside by the Executive to provide a buffering of the process. The blocks of memory set aside are filled by the I/O programs in the Executive and then the transmission takes place. The blocks of memory set aside for the processing of I/O data transmission are called buffers. The definition of the buffers, the locations in memory, and the connection between buffers and symbolic I/O units are established by the Executive. The size of the buffers often is adjustable by the programmer by way of Executive command cards. A Fortran WRITE transmits information to the output buffer in memory, and transmission from there to the physical device is accomplished under supervision of the Executive. Fortran READ statements cause similar activity in transmission of data from I/O devices to memory.

Scheduler. In most of the early computer systems the scheduling of jobs to be executed on the computer was done by a clerk. The clerk would sort jobs as they were submitted to the computer center in terms of the priority of the job (as indicated by the project number), the seniority of the programmer, etc. The jobs would be stacked in the card reader in the order of the priority assigned by the clerk. However, the faster computers that are in use today simply overrun the speed with which this manual task can be performed. In addition, it has become possible to store each job on a peripheral I/O unit (generally a disc) as it is submitted, allowing the Executive to select from the jobs on the unit in order of a priority determined by the Executive from information on the job card. The schedule of execution of jobs is determined in such a system by the Executive from tables it constructs as the jobs are placed on the peripheral unit. Priorities assigned to jobs may be determined by several variables, such as expected execution time, the source of the job (student, faculty, government research, commercial, etc.), the number of I/O units required, or the amount of memory required by the job, according to local policy.

Accountant. In most computing environments someone has to pay for the computer time and the materials used. In order to keep track of the use of the computer and materials connected with computer runs, an accounting program is included in the Executive. When a job is executed it will take so many seconds or minutes of time and use so many pages of output, punch so many cards, read so many cards, etc. The Executive keeps track of these functions and makes an entry into the accounting records, generally stored on a peripheral I/O device. At a later time, perhaps only once a month, at billing time, these records are tallied and each project number is charged with the total number of seconds, etc., that all of the jobs run under the project used.

An Executive ordinarily will have a table of approved or active project (account) numbers. When a job is submitted under a project number the table of numbers is consulted. If the number is not in the table the job is not permitted on the computer, it is dropped from the job stream, perhaps with a message to the person who submitted the job.

Processor. Part of the system is the Fortran compiler, which compiles Fortran statements into programs that can be executed by the computer. It is generally a very large program that resides on a peripheral unit until it is needed. The sophistication and efficiency of the program generated by the compiler from the Fortran code varies a great deal from system to system. In some computer systems, the compiler refines the compiled code several times (makes several passes at the program) until it has "optimized" execution properties of the program. Other compilers are written to compile quickly, without special concern for the efficiency or elegance of the compiled program. The trade-off appears to be one of efficiency (time) in compilation versus efficiency (time) in execution.

When a compiler has processed the Fortran program, the compiled program is not automatically executed. Rather, it is stored on some peripheral device until the Executive is ready to cause the program to be executed. There are two main reasons for this: the program may not be complete (subprograms, library function, etc. may be needed); it is often more efficient to compile a number of programs before executing any of them (to avoid having to bring the compiler program into memory for each separate compilation). The actual preparation of the compiled program for execution is done by the loader (see below) and the execution of the program is overseen by the execution monitor.

Most computer systems have a variety of programming languages available. The Fortran language is the most heavily used language in the United States but in Europe the language ALGOL (for algorithmic language) is most widely used. In addition, there are languages with special purpose applications, such as COBOL, the Common Business Oriented Language. For each language available on a computer system there must be a processor or compiler that transforms the source language program into an executable form. Consequently, part of the Executive command repertoire is a command that permits the programmer to specify the appropriate processor. Since the Executive and the processors are programs, they may be changed, and in particular new programming languages may be added to the processing capability of a system. System program modifications may cause programmers frustrating problems if they are not taken into account by the programmer. Most computer centers publish information bulletins, which contain notices about systems changes.

Loader. When a Fortran program is compiled it generally is not a complete, executable, program. It will perhaps lack certain subprograms, for example, the subprograms that are already in the system library and many of the operational subprograms that are used in I/O. In order for the program to be executed, these subprograms must be obtained from the system library and included with the program to be executed. This work is done by the system program called the loader. In addition, the loader oversees the linkage between subprograms (defines addresses of variables in argument lists), coordinates assignment of memory to arrays in COMMON, assigns memory space for data compiled into the program by DATA and BLOCK COMMON subprograms, etc. In the process of loading a program for execution, the loader generally will produce a "map" of the program as it resides in memory for execution. This map, or memory map, contains such information as the location of programs, arrays, variables, and subprograms, in the memory of the computer in terms of memory addresses. If there are subprograms defined in the Fortran program, or supposedly on the system library, but not available to the loader, a diagnostic is generated after the memory map, indicating the names of the missing routines. If the loader is unable to complete loading a program (missing routines, insufficient memory for the program, etc.) the loader (on most systems) will return to the Executive and the program will not be executed.

The memory map produced by the loader of the loaded program is invaluable in debugging programs when there are programming or system errors that cannot be found in the Fortran program. The interpretation of dumps (see below) begins with the identification of the names of locations in the computer memory.

Execution Monitor. Once the program has been loaded it can be executed. A program can get into trouble in many ways during execution, by doing illegal arithmetic (square root of a negative number), by trying to write on the input unit, by attempting to store data into locations beyond the legal confines of the program (letting an index of a variable on the right of a replacement statement get too large), etc. The executive system has components that handle such problems in the execution of the program. The executive system generally is at least partially resident in memory at all times the computer is running. Failure of a program to operate properly (according to the rules of the computer or the system) will cause the executive to "take over," producing messages to the programmer and the operator when necessary, and proceeding to the next order of business, often causing the troublesome program to be dropped, and the next program to be loaded.

There are many different kinds of frequently encountered execution errors, most of which will result in a diagnostic being printed by the Executive. Some of the errors encountered are: numerical errors, referencing I/O units not assigned to the program, mismatched mode of variables and FORMAT field specifications, improper control in indexing variables beyond array limits, improper argument to subprogram, and attempting to read beyond the data in the job deck or on a peripheral I/O unit. The interpretation of the diagnostic messages printed by the Executive when an execution error is encountered is often difficult without help from the Executive system manual or a similar document provided by the computer center.

An Example Deck. Figure XII.2 illustrates a job deck containing blocks of Executive command cards as well as a mixture of processor decks and a data deck. The job card is the first card of the deck. Following this card are four Executive command cards. The first of the Executive cards identifies the processor(s) to be used on the following program deck. The second card requests the system to assign a tape unit to the program, perhaps as a symbolic tape with the name TAPE A, or the name DATA. The third card is a message to the operator to put reel XXXXX (a number assigned by the computer center to the reel) on the unit to which the Executive has assigned the symbolic designation requested in the second card. Finally, the Executive is instructed to load the program and execute it when it is compiled. Following the Executive control block is a block end card—specifying that the next deck of cards is the program to be processed. The next block of cards is a deck of Fortran cards, a deck of subprograms that have already been compiled and are in object program deck form (see below), and an assembly language program deck (the system will have to be able to process assembly programs as part of Fortran processing if this arrangement is to work). Next in the deck is an end of block card signaling the end of the programming the processor has to process. Next is a block of data cards that are read by the program when it executes, followed by a block end card. Finally there is a block of Executive command cards causing a reel of tape to be rewound and unloaded, and a message to the operator to retrieve the reel from the tape drive. Finally there is an end of job card, specifying that the job is complete.

PERIPHERAL I/O PROCEDURES

It is often convenient to use peripheral storage devices in the process of executing a program. Problems that deal with large amounts of data, either input or generated in the process of computing,

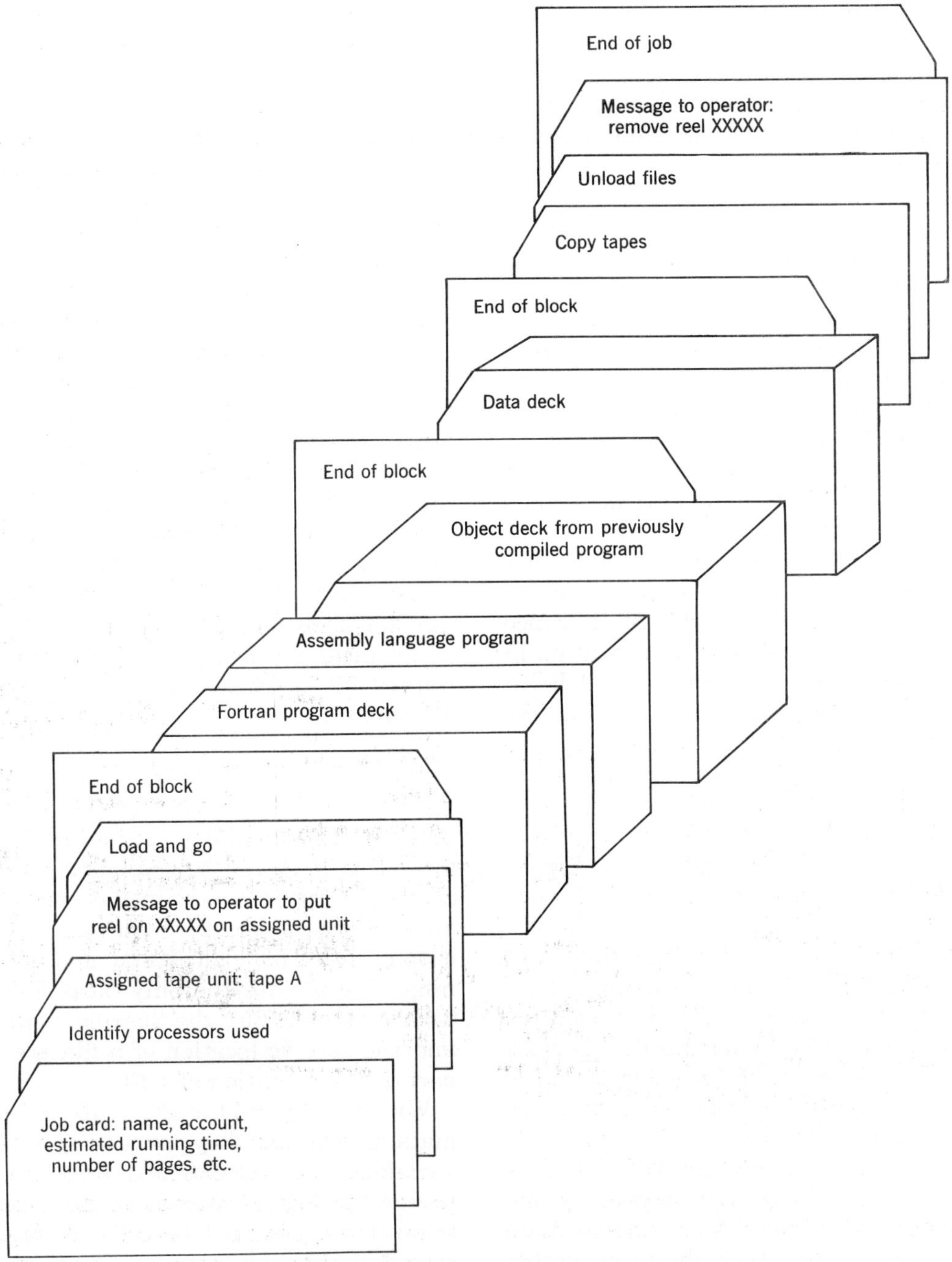

Figure XII.2 An illustrative sequence for Executive action.

require the use of peripheral equipment. Magnetic tape and disc storage generally is used in problems of these sorts, magnetic tape in particular when large amounts of data are to be kept for input over a long period of time (several uses in different programs, for example). The I/O statements discussed in Chapter 9 are used to control the reading and writing of information on the peripheral devices.

It is not possible, in a reasonable amount of space, to describe the details of storage of information on peripheral devices. Techniques and details differ from computer system to computer system. However, a discussion of the generalities here should be useful, particularly to the beginner.

Information may be recorded in binary or BCD information on tape or disc (review Figure IX.1). For efficiency of storage, both in time and space, the binary mode is recommended since the information is written on the unit exactly as it appears in memory. Reading and writing in BCD (under the control of a format statement) requires conversion of the binary information in memory to the code specified on the format statement. The BCD code internal to memory and the BCD code of tape and disc are, in general, different; usually referred to as internal BCD and external BCD. Since there is a good deal of standardization in external BCD but not in internal BCD, the use of BCD for recording data on tape is recommended if the data are to be used on machines other than the machine that generated it.

If data are to be stored temporarily in the execution of a program and then read back into memory the binary mode should be used. The list of the READ statement must correspond to the set of variables, arrays, and constants that are transmitted by the WRITE statement. A field specification is not needed because the entire contents of a memory word are transmitted to and from words that are defined in the program in the same mode for the READ as for the WRITE. This kind of use of external storage is like using scratch paper to store intermediate values in a calculation; the term scratch unit is often used to describe an I/O unit used this way.

In Chapter 6 we indicated that each peripheral unit was assigned a unit number, a symbolic designation, that was used in reading and writing. In many systems, READ and WRITE statements referring to any units except the input and the output unit will cause one of the segments of the disc to be used as the unit unless a physical tape unit has been assigned to the symbolic unit referred to in the Fortran statements (by way of the Executive command cards). When a scratch unit is needed during the execution of a program the user should use a disc unit; generally it is faster and does not have to be rewound like a tape.

The nomenclature in information processing involving peripheral I/O is variable with computer systems. However, a basic unit of organization of information is the file. Two kinds of files are referred to, a physical file and a logical file. A physical file generally is a reel of tape or a segment on a disc or a deck of cards. A physical file may contain a number of logical files, such as data matrix A in file number 1, data matrix B in file number 2, etc.

A logical file is simply a collection of related information and as such it may be stored in any way compatible with the computer system: a deck of cards, a segment on a disc, a reel of tape, or an array in memory. The input unit of the computer is the depository of the files of information input to the computer, the job decks submitted make up the input file, and the output generated makes up the output file. The logical end and beginning of a file are the only basis for the definition of a file; the specific contents and the specific location of a file are not part of the definition of a file.

Within a logical file the units of information, whether they are cards, arrays, variables, etc., are called records, and in particular logical records to distinguish them from physical records. A logical record is simply a logical subportion of a file. In the instance where the file is a single logical record the file and the record are identical. In most operating systems a logical record is that unit of information transmitted by a single READ or WRITE statement, whether it is binary or BCD. In each logical record there may be several physical records. For example, imagine an array with two subscripts having 50 rows and 20 columns. Each of the rows is transmitted separately by a READ or a WRITE statement. If the file is a card deck, and each row is contained on two cards (the first card perhaps having the first 12 columns of the row and the second card having the last 8 columns), the physical file is composed of 100 cards. The logical records consist of the 50 rows of the array, the physical records consist of the 100 cards, two cards to a logical record. The logical file consists of the 50 logical records and the 100 physical records. When this array is stored on the input file it possibly (depending on the system) will consist of physical records corresponding to the 80-column card images, 80 characters per record. If the array is read into memory the logical file may be thought of as the array. The physical file would be the set of memory words allocated to the array by the compiler and the logical records might be thought of as the separate elements of the array, the rows or the columns of the array. The physical records of the array would correspond to the memory words in which the array resides. If the array is output to a disc with a WRITE statement, the entire array may be specified in the list of the WRITE, in which case the logical record and the logical file will be the same. However, the physical records might depend on the way that the data are written by the hardware of the unit. For example the unit may write 512 words in a block on the physical file and then skip a space on the physical file (record gap) and then write 512 more words in a block, etc. The physical records would be the 512 word blocks. In general the physical records involved in I/O with peripheral units is determined by the size of the buffers assigned as well as by the hardware characteristics of the I/O units. In the example just cited the buffers would be 512 words of memory. The READ and WRITE statements in the program initiate a transfer of data into and out of the buffer and the transmission of the buffered data to the array in the program or to the peripheral unit is handled by I/O routines provided by the Executive system when the program is loaded.

OBJECT PROGRAMS

Ultimately, a program must be expressed in binary code that can be interpreted by the hardware of the computer. A program of this kind—expressed in binary notation—is called an object program. The program as expressed in some programming language, whether an assembly language or compiler language program, is known as a source program. The source program is compiled or assembled into a machine language object program by the respective processor.

There is clearly an advantage to having a program available in object form in that it can be executed without having to be compiled. In particular, if a Fortran program is more than a few statements, and if it is to be executed repeatedly, it is to the user's advantage to have the program retained in its object form. There are two general ways by which the binary or object program can be retained—on binary cards, or on a system storage device.

Binary Decks. Nearly all executive systems have provisions for punching an object program onto cards. The cards generally are called binary cards. Binary cards have a quite different appearance from other cards as can be readily seen in Figure XII.3. In the card illustrated, produced by an IBM 7044, each set of three columns contains one binary word —i.e., one instruction word from the computer's internal storage.

A deck of cards made up of an object program is called an *object deck.* The Executive system can be instructed, by means of control cards, to load the binary program contained in the deck directly into memory. Such a program is ready to be executed; it has already been translated into object form and is available on binary cards. The cards may be loaded without additional processing and the

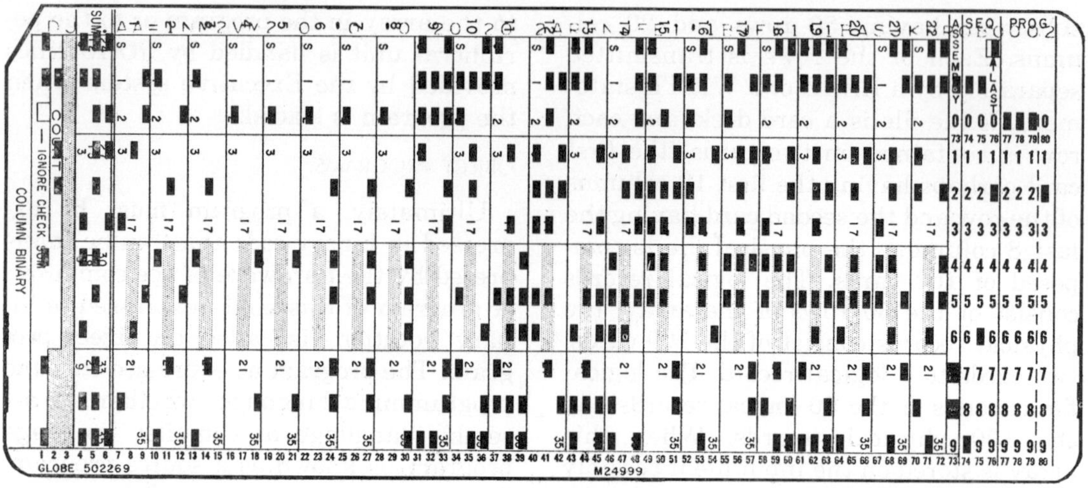

Figure XII.3 A column binary card.

program is ready for execution, when the needed subroutines and functions are loaded.

System Storage. An even more convenient means of storing the object of a program is by instructing the executive system to place the program on a peripheral storage device. This is usually accomplished by an Executive control card containing a word like SAVE or STORE following the program name. For example, the Executive control card might be

STORE CORDEM

This card, recognized by the appropriate Executive subprogram, would cause the object form of the program CORDEM, currently in memory, to be written on a peripheral device such as a disc. At some later time, the programmer might wish to execute CORDEM. To do this, an Executive control card such as

EXECUTE CORDEM

followed by the data for CORDEM would cause the object program for CORDEM to be loaded into memory and executed. The program would then process the data in exactly the same way as if the program had been compiled as part of the job.

Many computing centers maintain sizable libraries of object programs on peripheral storage devices. The use of these is usually not much more complicated than just illustrated. It is necessary, of course, to know the local rules, and also to have the data prepared in accordance with the requirements of the program.

DUMPS AND THEIR USE

One of the most valuable tools that an experienced programmer has at his disposal for locating errors in a program is the memory dump. A dump is a printed listing of the contents of memory. Often, when a program is in trouble, the Executive system can be instructed to write the contents of memory onto the output device. While such a listing is not immediately readable, with a little practice the dump may be read without a great deal of difficulty. For some kinds of errors, the use of a dump is virtually a necessity, since it allows a direct "look" inside the computer at information that is not normally available.

In order to understand and make use of a dump, some additional technical information is needed that has not, until this point, been presented.

Loading and Relocation. When a source program is compiled, the result is an object program, which is in binary form. It is possible on most Executive systems to have the object program listed after it is compiled. (Generally, the binary program is not listed, but rather an assembly language version of it, using mnemonic and octal notation.)

When the object program is loaded prior to execution, each machine language instruction is placed at a specific location in memory. Since each location in memory has an address, each machine language instruction is given an address. The loaded program need not begin at address 00000 in memory. That is, the instruction given the number 00000 in the object program might actually be loaded into location 00112 in memory. Each instruction would therefore have a new true address (00000 would become 00112, 00001 would become 00113, etc.). This characteristic of shifting the origin point of the program is called relocation. The address given in the assembly listing is a relative address—it is relative to the start of the program. Nearly all systems compile Fortran programs in relocatable form.

As a part of the information produced by the compiler, a listing of storage locations of variables is produced. When the programmer writes

```
X = Y*10.
```

he causes the product of Y and 10. to be stored at a location that he calls X. The listing of storage locations provides relocatable addresses for the variables used in the program, in the same way that the relative addresses on object program statements provide addresses for the program. This listing of locations, together with a loading map, allows the programmer to find the locations for his variables.

The map gives the actual addresses at which various parts of the program begin. For example, a job deck consisting of a main program and a subroutine might produce the following simplified loading map:

SYSTEM	*00000*
MAIN	*00235*
SUBA	*00520*

This indicates that the first 235_8 (octal—maps are nearly always in octal) locations in memory are devoted to various system routines. The first instruction in the object program is loaded at location 235_8, and the subroutine SUBA has its first instruction at location 520_8.

The loading map, along with the listing of variable storage locations, is the essential tool that a programmer needs to read a dump. He will also want to arm himself with a table giving octal-decimal equivalents such as given in Appendix D (or hexadecimal-decimal equivalents if his computer dumps in hexadecimal).

Reading a Dump. The process of reading a dump can best be illustrated by an example. Suppose that a program is not operating properly, and the programmer suspects that he may get a clue to the trouble if he can determine the value that a variable named IERR had when the program stopped.

The first step in determining the value of IERR is to arrange for a dump. This step varies according to the Executive system, and the reader is advised to consult a programming advisor. Suppose that the dump has been obtained and the value of IERR is needed. The actual storage location of IERR must first be determined. Two items are needed for this—the load map and the list of storage locations.

Assume for a moment that the storage location listing gives the following information:

I	126
IERR	127
J	128

The load map given above indicates that the main program begins at location 235. The location of IERR is given relative to the beginning of the main program; therefore, by adding the relative address for IERR to the location of the first instruction of the main program, we locate the actual address of IERR: $235_8 + 127_8 = 364_8$.

With the actual address available, we find in the dump the number stored at location 364_8. If that number were

000000000077, consulting an octal-decimal table indicates that the value of IERR is 63_{10}.

The example is simple since IERR is an INTEGER variable. If the value of a REAL variable is required, the location procedure remains the same but the determination of the value is more complex. The programming advisors must be consulted, since the storage procedures for REAL values vary considerably with computers.

Another difficulty occurs when an element of an array is needed. In this case, the listing of storage locations gives the relative address for the first location —e.g., X(1). To find some other location the value of the desired subscript must be added to the relocatable address. For example, if the value of X(65) were needed, and X were listed as beginning at 00277_8, and the program began at 235_8 when loaded, the required true address would be $65_{10} + 277_8 + 235_8 = 635_8$. In addition, if the array is greater than one dimension, the multiple subscripts must be converted to single before the address can be found. It should be noted that some computers store arrays consecutively in ascending addressed locations, and some in descending.

Uses of Dumps. The dump is usually regarded as a last resort in locating program errors. The programmer usually goes through a hierarchy of procedures in locating errors; first he corrects syntax errors diagnosed by the compiler. Then, if there are incorrect answers, he can use one of the trace methods discussed in Chapter 9. Ultimately, a dump can be requested and used.

There are usually several kinds of dumps that can be obtained, and usually in several formats. As these vary widely according to local custom, only a few general statements can be made. It is often useful to distinguish between post mortem and snap-shot dumps. A post mortem dump, as the name implies, occurs after the program is already "dead." That is, after the executive system has detected an error. A dump at this time shows the contents of memory when the error occurred. A snap-shot dump is called during execution, usually by a CALL statement in the program. Often a snap-shot CALL will specify limits for the dump—rather than dumping all of memory, only specified regions containing the variables of interest are dumped. Most dumps are restricted in their scope; rarely is all of memory dumped. For example, there are usually some system programs for accounting and so forth in memory—these are rarely dumped, and in some computer systems they cannot be dumped by a programmer.

Snap-shot dumps are valuable in tracing the values of variables as execution proceeds. A snap-shot dump might be called, for example, before a loop is entered, after every fifth time through the loop, and immediately upon exit from the loop. A technique such as this might allow the programmer to locate an error that was occuring during the looping process—perhaps the counting variable indexing the loop was being modified inside the loop in an unknown way.

As a check of data being correctly read, a WRITE may be executed immediately after reading, or a snap-shot dump called to determine whether or not the data were correctly read.

FAST FORTRAN COMPILERS

A comparatively recent development in Fortran programming has been the introduction of the fast or truncated compiler. These programs have been developed for use in teaching Fortran programming and generally require less compilation time than the compilers supplied by computer manufacturers. There is therefore a real advantage in computer time when large numbers of students are learning to program.

The fast compilers, of which WATFOR and AGIE are two examples, have two features which are of sufficient interest to merit some discussion. First, some features of the Fortran language as discussed previously are usually omitted. It may not, for example, be possible to use arrays of greater than two dimensions. As a rule, such features as tape manipulation, EQUIVALENCE, adjustable dimensions, or complex and double precision variables, are not available. In short, many of the more sophisticated features of Fortran, which are useful in advanced programming, are not available.

A second common feature is the inclusion of much more extensive diagnostic information than is normally available. Since the fast compilers have been developed for student use, it is appropriate that they give the greatest amount of helpful information to the beginning student.

REMOTE COMPUTING

One of the most recent developments in computing is the use of the remote computer—i.e., using a computer which is physically located some distance away from the user. The computer in such a case is almost always a very large system, having a great deal of storage and capable of operating very fast. Peripheral devices or terminals are connected to the central computer, usually by telephone lines. From the point of view of the user, the computer is "his" machine, even though he is sharing the computer with other users. There are two forms which remote computing usually assumes, *remote batch* computing and *demand* ("time shared") computing.

Remote Batch Computing. Implicit in nearly all of this book is an assumption that the reader will be familiar with, and have ready access to, a traditional batch processing computer system. In a batch system, the user submits his job deck to be run, and then returns at a later time to receive the results of his run.

In remote batch computing, the process is essentially the same, except that the input device which receives the user's input deck is located at some distance from the physical computer. The terminal device usually consists of a card reader and a printer. There may, depending upon the installation, be some storage associated with the remote batch terminal.

Demand Computing. In some highly sophisticated computing systems, the central computer may be able to service users as their need arises—thus the term demand computing. In such a computing environment, the user is often able to engage in a sort of dialog with the computer. It may be possible, for example, to write a program at a remote console, with the computer giving immediate diagnostic information about each program statement as it is written. There are a wide variety of consoles, the most common of which are similar to ordinary electric typewriters.

Much has been written about demand (often called time shared) computing. A great deal of time and energy on the part of system designers has been expended to offer demand computing. The advantages of such a situation are several. In the first place, there is no need to wait for an entire batch of programs to be run. The user can obtain immediate feedback on his problem. Second, ready availability of a computer tends to encourage exploration of data to a greater degree than would be possible with a batch system. Finally, the user of a demand computing terminal feels that he actually has control of the computer.

It is usually possible to initiate batch processing from a demand terminal. For example, an investigator might have a large amount of data stored internally in the computer in a storage device. From a terminal, he might perform some operations, such as finding means and standard deviations of one or more variables, or he might update his data by adding scores to replace previously missing data. Then he might instruct the computer to intercorrelate and factor analyze the variables, and print the results at some batch processing station. This operation would be essentially a batch operation in that the results would probably not be immediately available—the user might have to wait to have the results.

In most demand computing environments the user feels that he, and he alone, has control of the computer. This is not strictly true. From the point of view of the central computer, there are a number of users and each is serviced in turn. The central computer, for example, might be controlled by an Executive that is programmed to spend at most one-half a second on each user. That is, user A would have his problem worked on for at most one-half a second, then user B, and so on. Finally, user A's turn would come up again for another one-half second. The process continues in such a fashion until all of the users have completed their jobs. From the point of view of the user, the service to his terminal should appear to be continuous. The computer completes its "rounds" of the terminals so quickly that the user does not notice any delay.

Demand computing is a developing art. At the present time, there are only a few computer installations that are able to supply their customers with demand computing. The field is developing and growing very rapidly, and within a very few years demand processing will be readily available to many computer users.

PART IV

APPENDIXES

APPENDIX A SOURCES OF PROGRAMS

There are a number of ways in which a computer user can obtain programs, other than by writing them himself. While most of this book is concerned with writing programs, it is more efficient and convenient for a computer user to make use of an already available program than to write a program—if the available program does the desired job correctly and efficiently. Four sources of programs are discussed here and two rather general data handling "programs" are referenced.

One of the characteristics of computer programs is that they are difficult to understand without sufficient documentation. This extends to the use of the program as well as to the internal workings of the program. The degree of documentation accompanying a program obtained from the sources of programs discussed in this Appendix is widely variable. It is not worthwhile to try to use someone else's program when it is not documented with a user's description. It is not worthwhile to try to adapt a program to your needs unless it is documented with respect to the internal workings of the algorithm and the meaning of the various components of the program. At the lowest level of documentation supplied with a program there should be an indication of the computer configuration required at the minimum, the operating system for which the program was designed, and the special characteristics of the program requiring input/output files, etc. If you do not have the basic computer configuration, the programming language, and a comparable operating system, the modification of the program to your computer may be difficult.

The material presented in Appendix C can be used as an aid in determining the kind and extent of modification that may be required. At the simplest level, the modification may consist of changing the assignments of input and output devices. At the other extreme, some basic subroutines may not be available, the program may depend on word length of the computer in a complex way, the program may use five-dimensional arrays and you have only three defined in the Fortran implementation available, etc. In instances where the program modification is extensive and complicated the user is probably well advised to seek another program or to write his own. Not only can program modification be difficult but it may result in subtle changes in the algorithm. The changes may lead to numerical insufficiency or inaccuracy of the program, or to failure because of I/O problems.

There are four major sources of programs: user groups, program abstracts, local program libraries, and published collections.

USER GROUPS

All of the major manufacturers support groups of computer users with similar interests. For example, IBM supports the Society to Help Avoid Repetitive Effort, SHARE, a group of users of IBM machines devoted both to scientific and to industrial operations. The Control Data Corporation supports a user group named in the corporate self-image of CDC, Very Immense Machines, VIM. UNIVAC supports the UNIVAC Scientific Exchange, USE. The local computing center will have a user group representative, usually the manager or librarian of the center, and contact with the user group repertoire of programs can be made through the local representative.

The user groups maintain lists of available programs, usually with an abstract describing the program and its purposes and restrictions. Programs are usually available by writing to the programmer, or in many instances to the computing center at which the program was written, and in some groups to the group headquarters associated with the manufacturer. Programs are transmitted by card decks for small programs and by magnetic tape for large programs. It is generally up to the person requesting a program to furnish the magnetic tape for the shipment of the program. The imported program generally will be recorded as BCD card images that can be punched onto cards. The cards must then be modified to conform to local conditions, and the program compiled and debugged (yes, that stage is usually necessary). Under the circumstances that the computers involved are similar enough, it is possible sometimes to execute a program from an object deck (shipped as a binary tape) without recompiling. For example, if two computer centers had identical machines operated under identical operating systems (rare, since systems programmers seem to live happily by modifying operating systems in local centers), programs could be swapped between the centers in object-deck form and the programs run without any modification at all.

User groups as sources of programs have the advantage that usually only minor modifications are required, because members of the group involved will have (possibly) similar computer systems.

PROGRAM ABSTRACTS AND ALGORITHMS

Several journals regularly publish abstracts of programs. Of most interest to readers of this book are those appearing in *Behavioral Science*. The abstracts in this journal contain indications of the computer required, the logic of the program, the input and output, restrictions, and availability information. These programs are of general interest to behavioral scientists, and the journal is readily available.

A number of other journals list programs, or methods of solution (algorithms). Included in this category are several publications of the Society for Industrial and Applied Mathematics (SIAM) such as *SIAM Review* and *SIAM Journal on Numerical Analysis*. The Association for Computing Machinery publishes *Communications of the ACM*, which contains a section each month on algorithms. The ACM routines are often expressed as programs in Fortran or Algol.

LOCAL PROGRAM LIBRARIES

Most computing centers maintain a library of programs—it is often unnecessary to go outside your own center to find a program. The local library is built up over a period of time from programs written at the center and programs obtained from other centers.

Manufacturer-supplied programs and subroutines also fall into this general category. No major computer is supplied without any programs. As a part of the manufacturer-supplied package of programs, a set of subroutines is often supplied. Many of these programs or subroutines can be extremely useful to the programmer. In many cases it is possible to write complex programs by calling on available subroutines to do the actual work. For example, on some computers we can write a factor analysis routine (complete with rotation) by setting up a few arrays, reading data, and then calling matrix manipulation subroutines in the proper order with the proper arguments.

PUBLISHED COLLECTIONS

A large number of books present "collections" of programs. In some cases, the complete program is listed; in other cases, flow charts or other expressions of algorithms appear.

Of particular interest to behavioral scientists are two books on multivariate analysis: Cooley and Lohnes (1962), and Horst (1965). These books present the logical structure of a wide variety of multivariate procedures, and list Fortran programs. The programs can be keypunched directly from the book, or obtained from the authors on magnetic tape. In either case, it is likely that some modification will have to be done to the programs.

Under the general heading of "mathematical methods" or "numerical analysis," many books giving algorithms or listings may be found. For example, Ralston and Wilf (1960, 1967) and Pennington (1965) discuss a large number of numerical analysis problems and present both algorithms and program listings. Many of the problems discussed in such books are of little interest to most behavioral scientists, but there are some that may be of considerable value.

Of special interest to behavioral scientists is the book by Veldman (1967). The illustrative programs developed in Veldman's book are helpful and suggestive in programming for statistical analysis.

META-FORTRAN

The behavioral science programmer often finds himself using the same algorithm over and over again, particularly when he is interested primarily in statistical data analysis. This usually is because of the nature of behavioral science data—a matrix of scores, subject by variable. It seems natural to develop a package of subroutines that do the work of these algorithms in a general way. The package then serves as an addition to the basic repertoire of the Fortran language. In a sense, these subroutines are beyond Fortran in that they do not have the same characteristics as Fortran statements and expressions and that they expand the programmer's capability to get large amounts of computing done with a single line of coding (after the subroutines are ready). In the sense that the package is one step beyond Fortran we call such packages Meta-Fortran languages, perhaps somewhat whimsically.

There are two sorts of implementations of the idea of a Meta-Fortran. The first is illustrated by a subroutine package named PERSUB, developed by Joe Ward, Jr., at the USAF Personnel Research Branch at Lackland Airfield. PERSUB is a collection of subroutines designed to fit together in the analysis of statistical matrices. They must be called from within a Fortran program just as any ordinary subprogram is. This type of Meta-Fortran program has the advantage that the programmer can make use of the subprograms without losing any of the general facilities of Fortran, providing he is careful to observe the conventions of data storage in PERSUB. The second type of Meta-Fortran is illustrated by SMIS (Symbolic Matrix Interpretive System) written by E. Wilson at the University of California Computer Center (Berkeley). The SMIS program is self-contained and cannot, as it was originally written, be used as a subprogram of another Fortran program. SMIS provides a wide range of data manipulative options of interest to behavioral scientists by "interpreting" cards punched by the user as instructions. This interpretation is accomplished by comparing the alphameric data in the first field of a card with the list of matrix manipulations defined in SMIS. The subroutine that actually performs the manipulation is called by using computed GO TO to select the subroutine. One of the major advantages of SMIS over PERSUB is that the programmer does not need to keep track of the arrays, the dimensions, etc., of the data in SMIS. In PERSUB the data are manipulated by calling subroutines within a Fortran program written by the programmer. The subroutines are written so that the programmer must state the number of columns and rows of each matrix, the location of the matrix in the PERSUB storage scheme, and other such details. In SMIS, once the matrices are defined by a name, a number of rows, and a number of columns, the references to the matrices are by the name only. PERSUB has a considerable advantage over SMIS for nonstandard matrix manipulations because the programmer is able to move from Meta-Fortran to Fortran, enhancing his control over the data processing. Perhaps a compromise between the two systems could be worked out permitting the utilization of the better aspects of both systems.

References

Cooley, W. W. and Lohnes, P. R. *Multivariate Procedures for the Behavioral Sciences*, New York, Wiley, 1962.

Horst, P. *Factor Analysis of Data Matrices*, New York, Holt, Rinehart and Winston, 1965.

Pennington, R. H. *Introductory Computer Methods and Numerical Analysis*, New York, Macmillan, 1965.

Ralston, A. and Wilf, H. S. *Mathematical Methods for Digital Computers*, New York, Wiley, 1960.

Ralston, A. and Wilf, H. S. *Mathematical Methods for Digital Computers*, Vol. II, New York, Wiley, 1967.

Veldman, Donald J. *Fortran Programming for the Behavioral Sciences*, New York, Holt, Rinehart and Winston, 1967.

APPENDIX B **COMPLETED PROGRAMMING PROJECTS**

This appendix presents completed programs for four of the projects suggested in Chapter 3. Each completed project contains documentation for the program, the program listing, a listing of the data cards, and illustrations of the output from the program.

The documentation accompanying each program is in two parts. The first discusses the nature of the program in general terms and gives instructions for its use, including data card punching. The second part of the program description is intended for the person who needs to know more about the program than simply its use and presents a discussion of the technical aspects of the program, a definition of variables, a flow chart, and the program listing.

It is possible to design and write many successful programs to solve a given problem. The programs for any given task will vary along many dimensions. One of the characteristics of a program is the efficiency with which the program is written. Another is the efficiency with which it solves the problem, i.e., the computational efficiency. Other characteristics of programs could be listed. However, the reason for bringing this up here is to point out that other programs, and most certainly more efficient programs (both from the point of view of the coding and the execution) can be devised. We have tried to keep the programs free of tricks and fancy coding. To our knowledge we used no idiosyncracies of the Fortran compiler to get around shortcomings of Fortran, nor used statements in a way not specified in the definition of the statements unless we identified them in the description of the program.

PROJECT 1. LEARNING SCORES

This program is designed to score data obtained from an experiment on learning. Data for ten subjects are processed. Each subject may have up to 12 trials on which he is "correct" or "incorrect." Six variables are calculated from each subject's data as follows:

Variable 1: Total number of correct responses.

Variable 2: Total number of trials to meet criterion.

Variable 3: Number of incorrect trials before the first correct response.

Variable 4: Number of incorrect trials after the first correct response.

Variable 5: Number of correct responses between (and including) the first correct and last incorrect responses.

Variable 6: Number of runs of two consecutive correct responses.

Each subject is given a value on each of the six variables. In addition, the program calcu-

```
           col. 1↙                       col. 73↙
Input:          1101001100009                  SUB 01
                11100100009                    SUB 02
                111100009                      SUB 03
                00009                          SUB 04
                1100009                        SUB 05
                1010100009                     SUB 06
                1111000100009                  SUB 07
                100009                         SUB 08
                11010100009                    SUB 09
                1111010100009                  SUB 10
```

Figure B.1 Input data and output from Project 1.

Output:

RESULTS OF LEARNING SCORE ANALYSIS FOR 10 SUBJECTS.

	CORRECT RESPONSES	NUMBER RESPONSES	INCORRECT BEFORE FIRST CORRECT	INCORRECT AFTER FIRST CORRECT	BETWEEN FIRST CORRECT AND LAST INCORRECT	RUNS OF TWO CORRECT
SUBJECT 1	7	12	2	3	3	4
SUBJECT 2	6	10	3	1	2	4
SUBJECT 3	4	8	4	0	1	3
SUBJECT 4	4	4	0	0	1	3
SUBJECT 5	4	6	2	0	1	3
SUBJECT 6	6	9	1	2	2	3
SUBJECT 7	7	12	4	1	3	5
SUBJECT 8	4	5	1	0	1	3
SUBJECT 9	6	10	2	2	2	3
SUBJECT 10	6	12	4	2	2	3
MEANS	5.400	8.800	2.300	1.100	1.800	3.400
VARIANCES	1.440	7.960	1.810	1.090	0.560	0.440

Figure B.1 (continued)

Table B.1

Variables used in project 1

variable	meaning
COMMON	
ISCORE(10,6)	Gives the score of each of the 10 subjects on each of the 6 variables
Main Program	
I	Subject index in main loop
IDATA(10,13)	Raw data array, rows are subjects, columns are trials
IEND	Last incorrect trial
IFIRST	First correct trial indicator: = 0 if first correct has not occurred = trial number of first correct trial otherwise.
J	Trial number index in inner loop
SUBROUTINE STAT	
I	Subject index in addition loop
J	Index of variable in addition loop
SUM(6)	Sums and means of six variables
SUM2(6)	Sums of squares and variances of the six variables.
TEMP	A temporary REAL variable to contain floating point ISCORE(I,J) in addition loop

lates the mean and variance of each of the six variables for the 10 subjects.

Each subject's data, coded as error = 1, correct = 0, blank = 9, are punched on a separate card. On each card, only the first N+1 columns are used, where N is the number of trials for that subject. For example, a subject who made the sequence of responses error, error, correct, error, correct, correct, correct, correct would have his data coded as the series 110100009 in the first 9 columns of his data card. The remainder of his card can be blank, but identifying information (e.g., the subject's name or number in columns 73–80) is useful if punched there even though it is not used in the program. A total of 10 such cards make up the data deck for the program.

Output from the program consists of the scores of the 10 subjects on each of the 6 variables. Subjects are identified by number, and the variables by names. The means and variances of the 6 variables are also printed. Figure B.1 illustrates input data for the program and output produced by it.

Technical Aspects of the Program. Table B.1 defines the variables used in the program. The data are read into the 10×13 array called IDATA as INTEGER values by the FORMAT (13I1). Another array, ISCORE (10,6) represents the scores of the ten subjects on the six variables, each column corresponding to one of the six values. ISCORE is stored in COMMON and is initially set to 0. Figure B.2 is the flow chart and Figure B.3 is the program listing.

The program enters a DO loop on I over the ten subjects, I thereby indicating the subject. Within each subject, another loop, indexed on J, scans the 13 data values of the subject. Once in the scanning loop, a three-way branch on the value of the data being considered is executed. If the data value indicates a correct response, several steps are executed. First, the value of IDATA being considered is compared to the next value. If they are equal (and therefore both correct), the counter for the number of runs of two (ISCORE(I,6)) is increased by one. Second, the counter for the number of correct responses (IDATA(I,1)) is increased by one. Finally, if this is the first correct response (as indicated by the variable IFIRST), the value of IFIRST is set to J, and

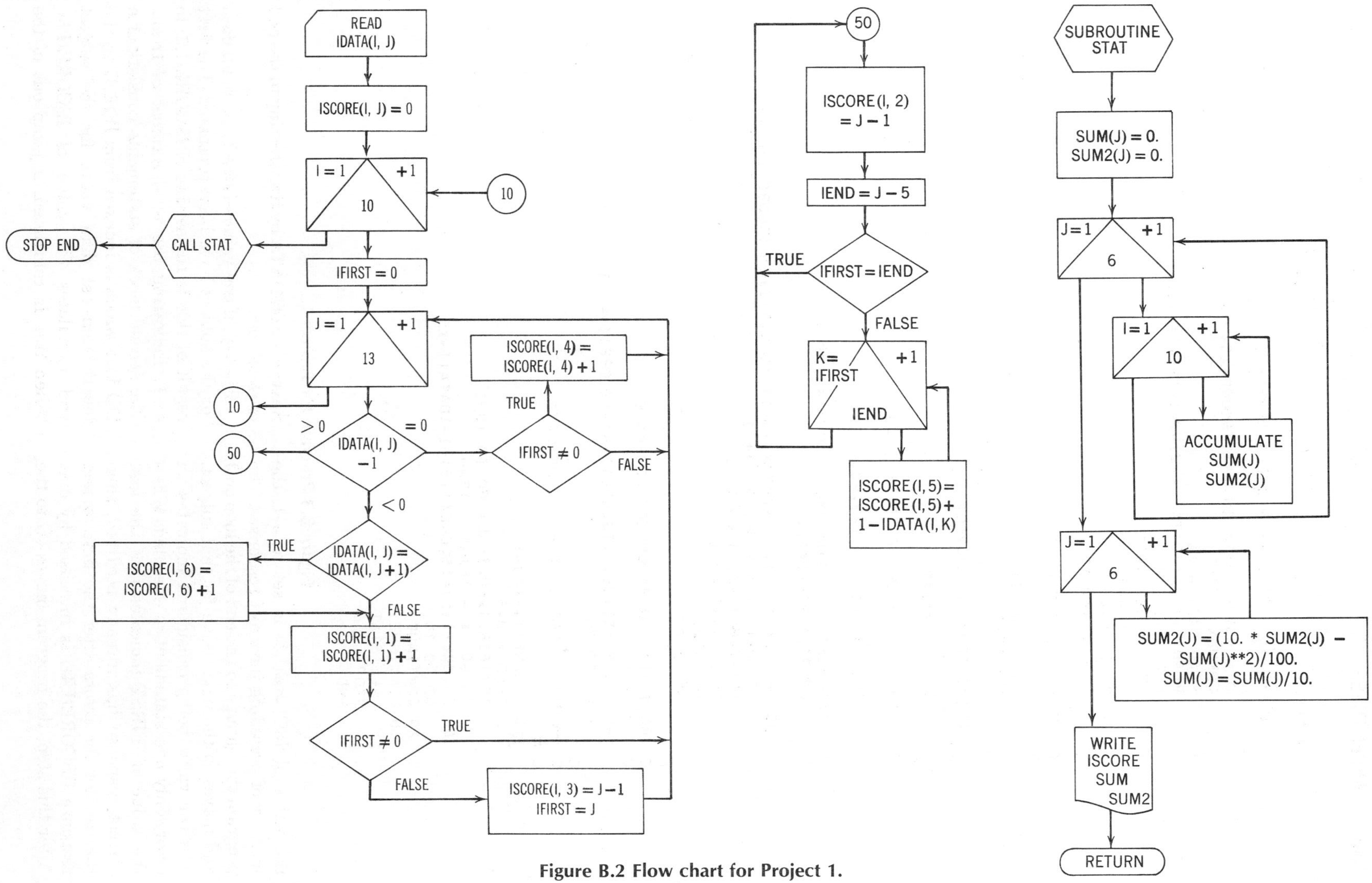

Figure B.2 Flow chart for Project 1.

```
CPROJ1
C
C  LEARNING SCORES -- PROJECT NUMBER 1.
C
      DIMENSION IDATA(10,13),ISCORE(10,6)
      COMMON ISCORE
C     READ DATA ARRAY
      READ(5,94)((IDATA (I,J),J=1,13),I=1,10)
   94 FORMAT(13I1)
C     ZERO SCORE ARRAY
      DO 1 I=1,10
      DO 1 J=1,6
    1 ISCORE(I,J)=0
C
C  START SUBJECT LOOP
C
      DO 10 I=1,10
      IFIRST=0
C
C  START SCAN OF SUBJECT I
C
      DO 20 J=1,13
C
C  BRANCH ON VALUE OF IDATA (I,J)
C
      IF(IDATA(I,J)-1)30,40,50
C
C  STATEMENT 30 BEGINS THE ROUTINES FOR A
C     CORRECT RESPONSE.
C
   30 IF(IDATA(I,J).EQ.IDATA(I,J+1))ISCORE(I,6)=ISCORE(I,6)+1
      ISCORE(I,1)=ISCORE(I,1)+ 1
      IF(IFIRST.NE.0) GO TO 20
      ISCORE(I,3)=J-1
      IFIRST=J
      GO TO 20
C
C  ROUTINES FOR INCORRECT RESPONSE
C
   40 IF(IFIRST.NE.0)ISCORE(I,4)=ISCORE(I,4)+1
      GO TO 20
C
C  ROUTINES FOR LAST PIECE OF DATA
C
   50 ISCORE(I,2)=J-1
      IEND = J-5
      IF(IFIRST.EQ.IEND) GO TO 10
      DO 60  K = IFIRST, IEND
   60 ISCORE(I,5)=ISCORE(I,5)+1-IDATA(I,K)
      GO TO 10
   20 CONTINUE
   10 CONTINUE
      CALL STAT
      STOP
      END
```

Figure B.3 Program for Project 1.

the value of ISCORE(I,3) is set to J-1, the number of preceding incorrect responses. The program then jumps to the end of the loop on J and moves to the next value for that subject.

If the value being considered indicates an error, only one statement is executed. When the value of IFIRST indicates that the first correct response has already occurred, then the counter for errors after the first correct response (ISCORE(I,4)) is increased by one. After this step, the program moves on to the next value of IDATA by transferring to the end of the J loop.

Finally, if the value of IDATA is 9, all data for the subject have been processed. The first result of this is the setting of ISCORE(I,2) to J−1, indicating the total number of trials. The second block of statements consists of a DO loop which is indexed from IFIRST to the fourth-from-last data value for the subject and calculates the value of ISCORE(I,5). When this is completed, a jump out of the range of the subject-scanning loop occurs, and the program moves to the next subject.

When all data have been processed, a subroutine STAT is called. STAT calculates the means and variances of the six variables and prints the scores of the 10 subjects on the 6 variables, together with the means and variances.

PROJECT 3. AUTOMATIC DIAGNOSIS

This program reads scores on four variables for a number of patients. On the basis of the scores, the program performs a diagnosis of the ailments of the patients. The rules by which the patients are classified are as follows:

Sarbin Syndrome. If ($X_1 > 14$, $X_2 < 10$, $X_3 = 1$, and $X_4 < 10$) or if ($6 \leq X_i < 14$ for all i), then Sarbin's Syndrome is present. Otherwise Sarbin's Syndrome is not present, unless all scores are in excess of 15 in which case the patient is not classifiable with respect to the syndrome.

The Meehl Complex. If X_1 is greater than 10, Rule I applies; otherwise Rule II applies. *Rule I*: If $X_1 + 3X_2 - 4X_3 + X_4$ is greater than X_1, then the Meehl Complex is present; otherwise it is not. *Rule II*: If $(X_1 + X_2)/(X_3 + X_4)$ is 1.0 or greater, then the Meehl Complex is present; otherwise it is not.

Fisher's F. If $1 - (X_1^2 + X_2^2)/(X_3^2 + X_4^2)$ is positive, then Fisher's F is a significant factor in the patient's disease. If it is negative the patient is not troubled by Fisher's F. If it is zero, the patient is unclassifiable.

Normal Deviation. If $\frac{1}{4}(X_1 + X_2 + X_3 + X_4) > 10$, apply Rule I; otherwise, apply Rule II. *Rule I*: If $\frac{1}{4}(3X_1 + 3X_2 + 3X_3 + 3X_4) > 30$, then normal deviation is present; otherwise it is not. *Rule II*: If $\frac{1}{4}(5X_1 + 5X_2 + 5X_3 + 5X_4) \leq 50$, then normal deviation is present; otherwise it is not.

An analysis of the problem indicates that two of the diseases, as defined by the diagnostic rules, are nondiscriminating. That is, the

```
      SUBROUTINE STAT
C
C  CALCULATES STATISTICS FROM LEARNING SCORES
C     MAIN PROGRAM
C
      DIMENSION ISCORE(10,6),SUM(6),SUM2(6)
      COMMON ISCORE
      DO 1 J=1,6
      SUM(J)=0.0
    1 SUM2(J)=0.0
C     CALCULATE SUMS AND SUMS OF SQUARES
      DO 2 J=1,6
      DO 2 I=1,10
      TEMP = ISCORE (I,J)
      SUM(J)=SUM(J)+TEMP
    2 SUM2(J)=SUM2(J)+TEMP**2
C     CALCULATE MEANS AND VARIANCES
      DO 3 J=1,6
      SUM2(J)=(10.0*SUM2(J)-SUM(J)**2)/100.0
    3 SUM(J)=SUM(J)/10.0
C     BEGIN OUTPUT
      WRITE(6,101)
  101 FORMAT(1H1,34X,51HRESULTS OF LEARNING SCORE ANALYSIS FOR 10 SUBJEC
     1TS./////21X,7HCORRECT,12X,6HNUMBER,10X,9HINCORRECT, 8X,9HINCORRECT
     2, 7X,13HBETWEEN FIRST,  5X,11HRUNS OF TWO,/20X,9HRESPONSES,10X,9HR
     3ESPONSES, 7X,12HBEFORE FIRST, 5X,11HAFTER FIRST, 7X,11HCORRECT AND
     4,  8X,7HCORRECT,/57X,7HCORRECT,10X,7HCORRECT, 8X,14HLAST INCORRECT
     5    ////)
      DO 4 I=1,10
    4 WRITE(6,102)I,(ISCORE(I,J),J=1,6)
  102 FORMAT(1H0,1X,9HSUBJECT   ,I2, 6X,6(7X,I2,8X))
      WRITE(6,103)(SUM(J),J=1,6)
  103 FORMAT(/////3X,5HMEANS, 8X,6(7X,F7.3,3X))
      WRITE(6,104)(SUM2(J),J=1,6)
  104 FORMAT(/////3X,9HVARIANCES, 3X,6(7X,F7.3,3X ))
      RETURN
      END
```

Figure B.3 (continued)

rule leads to the nonsense result that all patients are characterized by the disease, regardless of the scores. Symbol Shock is one of these two diseases. By the application of simple algebra the two equations are shown to be identical. This "dirty trick" was introduced into the problem in order to demonstrate that a little bit of mathematics is often better than a great deal of computer analysis. Behavioral scientists tend to suffer what might be called "symbol shock"—an unreadiness to make even the simplest mathematical explorations into matters of interest and concern to them.

The second nonproblem is not identified here. The program was written with the nonproblem included for two reasons. First, it is excellent practice to modify a program to do a slightly different task. Modifying the program to exclude the nonproblem will result in valuable insight into the workings of the program. Any rewriting of the program should include the input and output and all of the arrays. The second reason for leaving the nonproblem in the program is to suggest that the output of the program itself is useful in debugging the program, and the problem as well.

Input to the program consists of one card per patient. The patient's name or other identifying information should be punched in columns 1–18. This information will be used to identify the patient in the output of the program. Columns 19–26 contain the patient's scores on the four variables, each score occupying two columns. For example, if John Jones scores 19, 15, 9 and 4 on variables 1, 2, 3, and 4, respectively, his data card should be punched as

JOHNbJONESbbbbbbbb19150904

where the letter b indicates a blank column. Note that the leading zeros are punched in the case of a one-digit value (e.g., the third score, 9, is punched 09).

Any number of patients may be processed in a single execution of the program. Their data cards, punched as indicated above, are placed together in any order and form the data deck. The last card in the data deck —i.e., the card following the last patient's data—must be blank. The input deck thus consists of N+1 cards, where N is the number of patients.

Each patient may be afflicted with, not afflicted with, or unclassifiable with respect to, each of the four diseases. A given patient may have more than one disease. Output from the program consists of three items: a listing of the names of the patients together with the diseases that they have, do not have, or cannot be classified as having; a count of the number of patients in each diagnostic category; and the frequency of the pairwise incidence of the diseases (e.g., how many have both Sarbin Syndrome and Fisher's F). Input and output are pictured in Figure B.4.

Technical Aspects of the Program. The diagnosis of each patient according to the rules built into the program is fairly straightforward; the most complex aspects of the program are concerned with output. The program consists of a main program, two working subroutines, and a BLOCK DATA subprogram. The flow chart and program listing for the complete project are given in Figures B.5 and B.6, respectively. The glossary of variables is Table B.2. The main program reads the data for the patients in turn. All processing for one patient is completed before the next card is read. After some preliminary calculation, the subroutine TEST is called four times, once for each disease. Upon each return, the main program sets in-

```
Input:

          Col. 1                    Col. 19
              T. TEST                  02111117
              R. CORRELATION           05130220
              A. VARIANCE              10120801
              P. LEVEL                 16062005
              F. STATISTIC             10101010
              U. SET                   20161920
              B. REGRESSION            12080913
              R. Z. TRANSFORM          05101005
              S. DEVIATION             09161116
              blank card
```

Figure B.4 Input and output for Project 3.

Output:

AUTOMATIC DIAGNOSIS PROGRAM

	HAS	DOES NOT HAVE	IS NOT CLASSIFIABLE AS
T. TEST	FISHER NORMDV	SARBIN MEEHL	NONE
R. CORRELATION	FISHER NORMDV	SARBIN MEEHL	NONE
A. VARIANCE	MEEHL NORMDV	SARBIN FISHER	NONE
P. LEVEL	FISHER NORMDV	SARBIN MEEHL	NONE
F. STATISTIC	SARBIN MEEHL NORMDV	NONE	FISHER
U. SET	FISHER NORMDV	MEEHL	SARBIN
B. REGRESSION	SARBIN MEEHL FISHER NORMDV	NONE	NONE
R. Z. TRANSFORM	MEEHL NORMDV	SARBIN	FISHER
S. DEVIATION	FISHER NORMDV	SARBIN MEEHL	NONE

Figure B.4 (continued)

	TOTAL INCIDENCE OF DISEASES			
	SARBIN	MEEHL	FISHER	NORMDV
NUMBER OF CASES	2	4	6	9

PAIRWISE INCIDENCE OF DISEASES			
	MEEHL	FISHER	NORMDV
SARBIN	2	1	2
MEEHL		1	4
FISHER			6

Figure B.4 (continued)

dicators that define the diagnostic status of the patient.

When all testing has been completed for a subject, the main program carries out some preliminary work for output and calls PRINT to output the patient's name and diagnostic information. After the return from PRINT, the main program reads the next patient's data and the process repeats. When the end of the data is detected the main program prints the summary values of the one-way and two-way frequency classifications. The next several sections discuss the program in detail.

The Main Program. The main program begins by printing a general heading and then reads the data card for the first patient. Next follows a test to see if this is the blank card signaling the end of patient processing. This test is accomplished by comparing the first field of the card (PNAME1) with the value of BL which was entered into the /NAMES/ block of COMMON by the BLOCK DATA subprogram. If this is the blank card, the program transfers to statement 100, which marks the start of the final output from the program.

If the data card read contains valid (i.e., nonblank) data, the program begins the testing routine by calculating the sum of the four values for the patient (SUM). Next, the SUBROUTINE TEST is called four times from inside a loop. Each call to TEST results in one diagnosis; the disease to be diagnosed is communicated by the argument I. Upon return from TEST, the appropriate entry in ILLNES is set to the disease indicator returned by TEST (J), and the counter for the number of the three diagnostic possibilities (has disease, does not have, etc.) is incremented appropriately. When all diseases have been tested for, the program exits from the testing loop and increases the frequency counters ILLSUM and ILBYIL according to the diseases that were found to be present in the patient.

The next step is the output of the results for the patient being considered. The maximum list length (i.e., the greatest number of occurrences of "has disease," "does not have disease," etc.) is calculated (IR) and SUBROUTINE PRINT is called. Following the return from PRINT, the program transfers to the READ statement which reads another patient's data card. If that card is blank, the summary output from the program begins. This output consists of the arrays ILLSUM and ILBYIL, each with appropriate labels.

SUBROUTINE TEST. Immediately upon entering the subroutine, a computed GO TO is executed, branching to one of four points depending upon which disease is to be considered. Each of these blocks of Fortran coding embodies the diagnostic rules as stated in the introductory section for this program. The coding is self-evident and need not be discussed in detail. In short, whenever a condition is found that indicates presence of a disease, the statement GO TO 100 is executed. Statement 100 sets the diagnostic indicator K to 1 and returns. On the other hand, if the

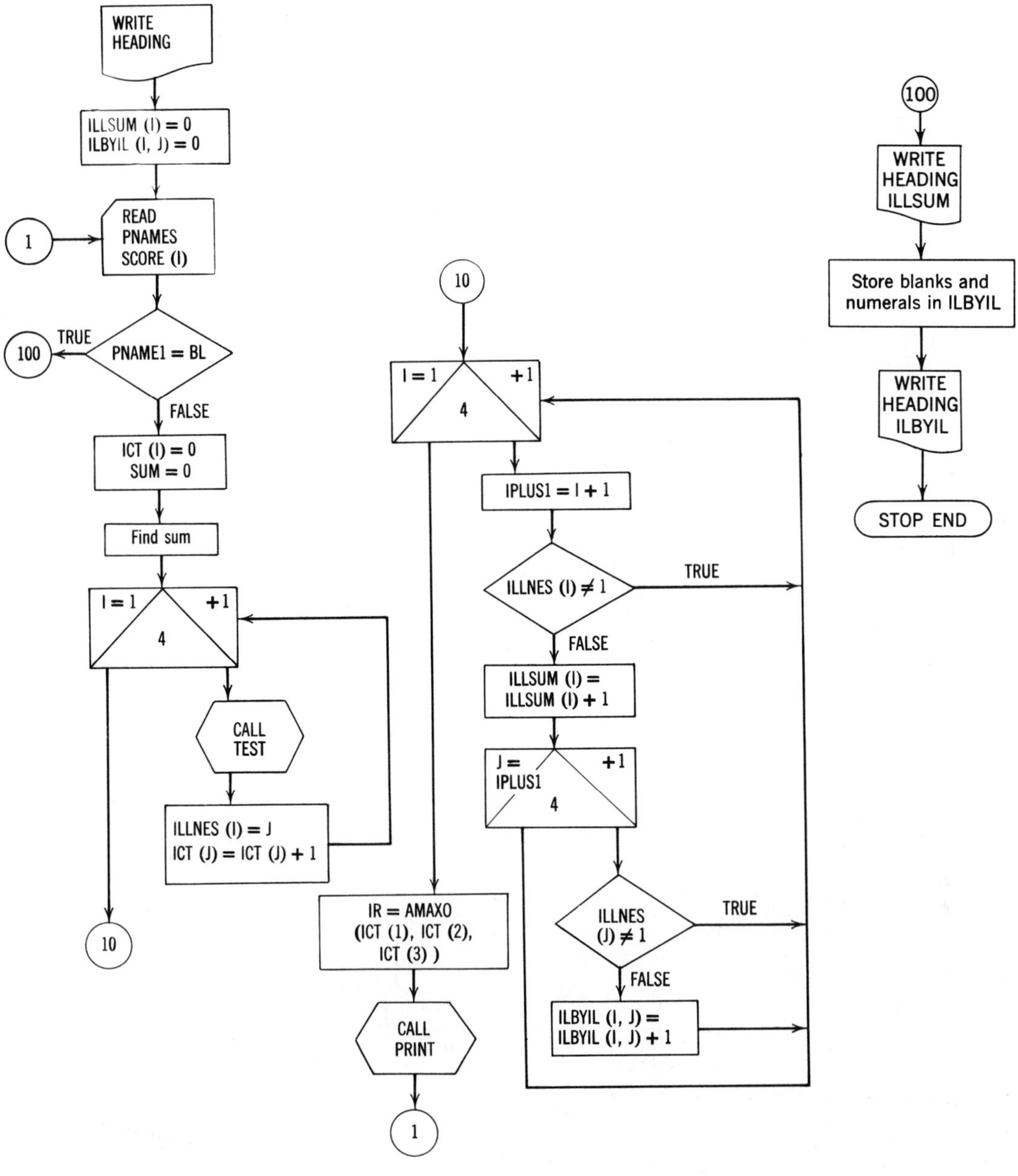

Figure B.5 Flow chart for Project 3.

disease is not indicated, the transfer is to statement 200, which sets K to 2 and returns. If the patient is not classifiable, GO TO 300 is executed, K is set to 3, and the subroutine returns.

SUBROUTINE PRINT. The subroutine is called with two arguments, IROW (IR in main program), and ISICK (ILLNES). The purpose of this SUBROUTINE is to place disease names in lists, each list corresponding to a column of TAB. The columns of TAB represent the classifications "patient has disease," "patient does not have disease," and "patient is not classifiable with respect to." The entries in TAB are the alphameric representations of

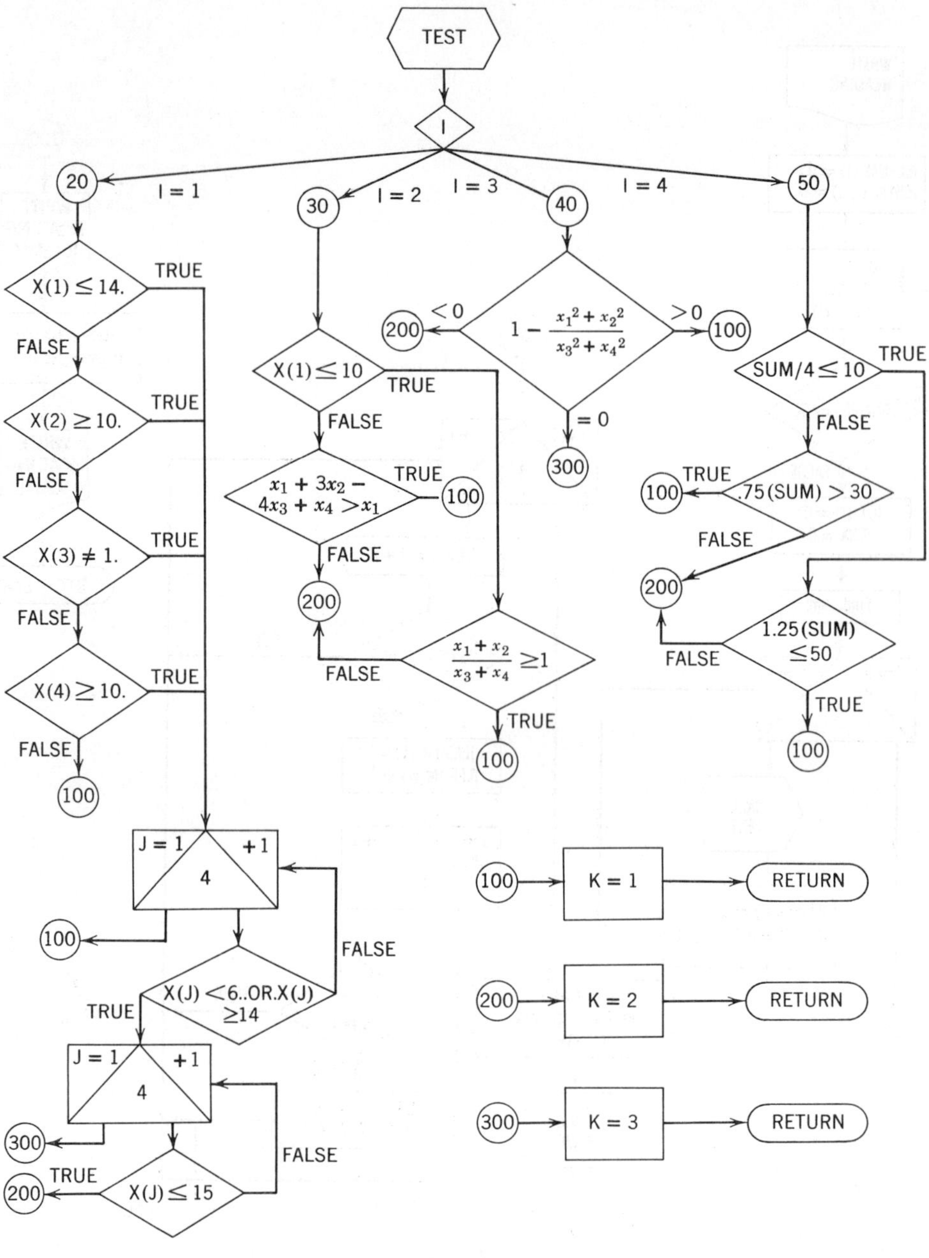

Figure B.5 (continued)

the names of diseases. These names are stored in the array NAME which is in the COMMON block /NAMES/. Suppose, for example, that patient T. Test had Sarbin Syndrome and Meehl Complex, did not have Normal Deviation, and could not be classified for Fisher's F. His output would appear as

	HAS	DOES NOT HAVE	IS NOT CLASSIFIABLE AS
T. TEST	SARBIN	NORMDV	FISHER
	MEEHL		

The entries in the table, the disease names and blanks, are entries in the array TAB.

It is possible that a patient may have all four diseases. In this case TAB must have four rows, since all of the four disease names must appear in one column. On the other hand, since there are four diseases, a patient

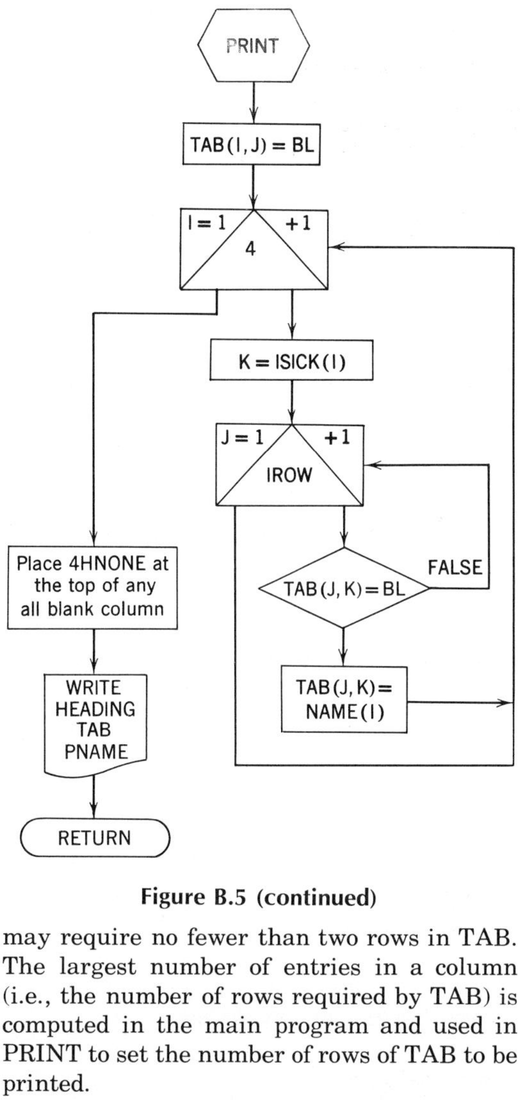

Figure B.5 (continued)

may require no fewer than two rows in TAB. The largest number of entries in a column (i.e., the number of rows required by TAB) is computed in the main program and used in PRINT to set the number of rows of TAB to be printed.

The main loop in subroutine PRINT (DO 2) scans the four entries in the array ISICK, corresponding to the array ILLNES in the main program. The entries in ISICK may be one of the values 1, 2, or 3, indicating presence, absence, or nonclassification for each of the four diseases. The first statement inside the loop sets the variable K equal to ISICK(I). This allows the use of the variable K to indicate a column in TAB since the value of ISICK(I) is the column in which the disease name is to be printed.

The array TAB was set to blanks early in PRINT. Before the first disease name is entered, therefore, all entries are blanks. The inner loop (DO 1) searches in column K to find the first blank location (i.e., the bottom of the list in that column). When this is found, control transfers to a statement that places the name of a disease at that location. The loop continues until names corresponding to each of the four diseases (entries in ISICK) have been entered into TAB. This accomplished, the subroutine checks to see if any of the columns in TAB are completely blank. If so, the word NONE is stored at the top of the list in that column. The characters representing the word NONE are stored as the variable ZERO by the BLOCK DATA subprogram.

When all of the entries in TAB have been filled properly with either a disease name, the word NONE, or blanks, the table is printed. The name of the patient whose diagnoses are being printed appears to the left of the first row of TAB. Following the printing, the subroutine returns to the main program.

BLOCK DATA Subprogram. The subprogram BLOCK DATA compiles alphameric data into the common block /NAMES/. These values are used to fill the array TAB in subroutine PRINT, and to test for the blank data card that signals the end of processing.

PROJECT 7. SCATTER PLOTTING

This program prints a scatter plot of the joint distribution of the variables X and Y. A large number of pairs of values of X and Y may be plotted. (*Hint.* analyze program to find the limits.) The value of N, the number of pairs of observations, is determined by the program and is printed as part of the output. Each pair of values is punched in a separate data card, and the last data card must be followed by a blank card. The values of X and Y are limited to the integers 1–20, inclusive. Thus, each card in the input deck is to contain two two-digit numbers, X in columns 1–2, and Y in columns 3–4.

The output from the program consists of the bivariate scatter plot of the N pairs of values. Values of Y appear as the ordinate and X forms the abscissa. The scales are appropriately labeled and the heading for the table gives the number of pairs of values. Where one pair of observed values occupies a single point, the point is plotted as the character "*." When more than one pair of observations is located at a point, the number of pairs is printed as the plotting character. Figure B.7 illustrates the data cards and output.

```
C  PROJECT NUMBER 3
      DIMENSION SCORE(4),ILLNES(4),ILBYIL(4,4),NAME(4),
     1ILLSUM(4),ICT(3), P(9)
      INTEGER BL, ZERO,PNAME1,PNAME2,PNAME3, P
      COMMON PNAME1, PNAME2, PNAME3/NAMES/BL,NAME,ZERO
      DATA (P(I),I=1,9)/1H1,1H2,1H3,1H4,1H5,1H6,1H7,1H8,1H9/
C     PRINT HEADING FOR OUTPUT
      WRITE(6,102)
  102 FORMAT(1H1,39X,27HAUTOMATIC DIAGNOSIS PROGRAM//////33X,3HHAS,11X,
     113HDOES NOT HAVE, 3X,23HIS NOT CLASSIFIABLE AS      )
C     ZERO FREQUENCY ARRAYS
      DO 9 I=1,4
      ILLSUM(I)=0
      DO 9 J=1,4
    9 ILBYIL(I,J)=0
C     READ A CARD FOR A PATIENT
    1 READ(5,101)PNAME1,PNAME2,PNAME3,(SCORE(I) ,I=1,4)
  101 FORMAT(3A6,4F2.0)
C     TEST FOR LAST CARD
      IF(PNAME1.EQ.BL) GO TO 100
C     IF NOT LAST PATIENT,CALCULATE SUM AND SET ICT(I) TO ZERO
      SUM=0.0
      DO 12 I = 1,3
   12 ICT(I) = 0
      DO 2 I=1,4
    2 SUM=SUM+SCORE(I)
C     CALL TEST ONCE FOR EACH ILLNESS
      DO 10 I=1,4
      CALL TEST (SCORE, SUM, I, J)
C     UPON RETURN, SET DISEASE INDICATOR AND INCREASE LIST LENGTH
C        FOR THE APPROPRIATE OUTPUT COLUMN
      ILLNES(I)=J
   10 ICT(J)=ICT(J)+1
C     INCREASE ONE- AND TWO-WAY FREQUENCY COUNTS
      DO 11 I = 1, 4
      IPLUS1 = I + 1
      IF(ILLNES(I).NE.1) GO TO 11
      ILLSUM(I)=ILLSUM(I)+1
      DO 11 J = IPLUS1, 4
      IF(ILLNES(J).NE.1) GO TO 11
      ILBYIL(I,J)=ILBYIL(I,J)+1
   11 CONTINUE
C     FIND LONGEST LIST LENGTH AND CALL PRINT
      IR = AMAX0(ICT(1),ICT(2),ICT(3))
      CALL PRINT (IR,ILLNES)
      GO TO 1
C     WHEN ALL PATIENTS HAVE BEEN PROCESSED, OUTPUT THE ONE- AND
C     TWO-WAY FREQUENCY DISTRIBUTIONS
  100 WRITE(6,103)
  103 FORMAT(1H1,25X,27HTOTAL INCIDENCE OF DISEASES)
      WRITE(6,104)(NAME(I),I=1,4)
  104 FORMAT (1H0,19X,4(A6,5X))
      WRITE(6,105)(ILLSUM(I),I=1,4)
  105 FORMAT(1H0,   15HNUMBER OF CASES   , 3X,4(I2, 9X))
      DO 18 I=1,4
      DO 18 J=1,4
      IF(ILBYIL(I,J).EQ.0)ILBYIL(I,J)=BL
      IF (ILBYIL(I,J).EQ.BL)GO TO 18
      K = ILBYIL(I,J)
      ILBYIL(I,J) = P(K)
   18 CONTINUE
      WRITE(6,106)
  106 FORMAT(//////24X,30HPAIRWISE INCIDENCE OF DISEASES   )
      WRITE(6,108)(NAME(I),I=2,4)
  108 FORMAT(1H0,25X,3(A6,5X))
      DO 19 I = 1,3
   19 WRITE (6,107) NAME(I),(ILBYIL(I,J),J=2,4)
  107 FORMAT (1H0,16X,A6, 6X,3(A2, 9X))
      STOP
      END
      BLOCK DATA
      DIMENSION NAME(4)
      INTEGER BL, ZERO,PNAME1,PNAME2,PNAME3
```

Figure B.6 Program for Project 3.

```
      COMMON/NAMES/BL,NAME,ZERO
      DATA BL, NAME(1),NAME(2),NAME(3),NAME(4),ZERO/1H ,6HSARBIN,
     16HMEEHL ,6HFISHER,6HNORMDV,4HNONE/
      END
      SUBROUTINE TEST (X, SUM, I, K)
      DIMENSION X(4)
C     BRANCH ON I
      GO TO (20, 30, 40, 50), I
C     TEST FOR SARBIN SYNDROME
   20 IF(X(1).LE.14.) GO TO 1
      IF(X(2).GE.10.) GO TO 1
      IF(X(3).NE.1.) GO TO 1
      IF(X(4).GE.10.) GO TO 1
      GO TO 100
    1 DO 8 J = 1, 4
    8 IF (X(J).LT.6..OR.X(J)  .GE.14.) GO TO 9
      GO TO 100
    9 DO 2 J=1,4
    2 IF(X(J).LE.15.) GO TO 200
      GO TO 300
C     TEST FOR MEEHL PARADOX
   30 IF(X(1).LE.10.) GO TO 3
C     RULE 1--MEEHL
      IF(X(1)+3.*X(2)-4.*X(3)+X(4).GT.X(1)) GO TO 100
      GO TO 200
C     RULE 2--MEEHL
    3 IF((X(1)+X(2))/(X(3)+X(4)).GE.1.) GO TO 100
      GO TO 200
C     TEST FOR FISHERS F
   40 IF(1.-(X(1)**2+X(2)**2)/(X(3)**2+X(4)**2))200,300,100
C     TEST FOR NORMAL DEVIATION
   50 IF(SUM/4..LE.10.) GO TO 7
C     RULE 1--NORMAL DEVIATION
      IF(.75*SUM.GT.30.) GO TO 100
      GO TO 200
C     RULE 2--NORMAL DEVIATION
    7 IF(1.25*SUM.LE.50.) GO TO 100
      GO TO 200
  100 K = 1
      RETURN
  200 K = 2
      RETURN
  300 K = 3
      RETURN
      END
      SUBROUTINE PRINT (IROW,ISICK)
      INTEGER BL, ZERO,PNAME1,PNAME2,PNAME3 ,TAB
      COMMON PNAME1,PNAME2,PNAME3/NAMES/BL,NAME,ZERO
      DIMENSION TAB(   5,3),ISICK(4),NAME(4)
C     SET TAB TO BLANKS
      DO 6 J = 1,3
      DO 6 I = 1,IROW
    6 TAB(I,J) = BL
C     INSERT DISEASE NAMES IN TAB
      DO 2 I = 1,4
      K = ISICK(I)
      DO 1 J = 1, IROW
      IF(TAB(J,K).EQ.BL) GO TO 3
    1 CONTINUE
    3 TAB(J,K) = NAME(I)
    2 CONTINUE
C     INSERT WORD ''NONE'' AT HEAD OF AN ALL BLANK COLUMN
      DO 4 I = 1,3
    4 IF(TAB(1,I).EQ.BL)TAB(1,I)=ZERO
C     PRINT TAB
      WRITE (6,101) PNAME1,PNAME2,PNAME3,(TAB(1,J),J=1,3)
  101 FORMAT (/////9X,3A6,4X,3(A6,14X))
      DO 5 I = 2, IROW
    5 WRITE (6,102) (TAB(I,J),J=1,3)
  102 FORMAT(1H ,30X,3(A6,14X))
      RETURN
      END
```

Figure B.6 (continued)

Table B.2

Glossary of variables in project 3

Variable	Meaning
COMMON variables	
Blank COMMON	
PNAME1	First part of subject's name—INTEGER
PNAME2	Second part of subject's name—INTEGER
PNAME3	Third part of subject's name—INTEGER
/NAMES/	
BL	Character 1Hb—compiled by BLOCK DATA
NAME(4)	Six-character alphameric words containing names of illnesses—compiled by BLOCK DATA
ZERO	Characters 4HNONE—compiled by BLOCK DATA
Main program	
I	General index—usually refers to disease I
ICT(3)	Counts the number of occurrences of diagnoses of disease present, disease absent, and patient not classifiable respectively, for a patient
ILBYIL(4,4)	Counts frequency of joint occurrence of pairs of illnesses
ILLNES(4)	Indicator for diagnoses. If ILLNES(I) = 1, disease I is present; = 2, disease is not present; = 3, patient is not classifiable for disease I.
ILLSUM(4)	Frequency of occurrence of disease I across patients
IPLUS1	Equal to I+1 in a loop which computes joint occurrence of diseases
IR	The largest of the entries in ICT. It is the longest list of diseases that are to appear in a single column in the table printed by SUBROUTINE PRINT
J	Disease indicator returned by SUBROUTINE TEST. Has same values and meanings as ILLNES.
P(9)	Contains 1H1, 1H2, etc. for alphameric printing of numbers
SCORE(4)	The four scores for a given patient
SUM	The sum of the values in SCORE for a given patient

Arguments to TEST: SCORE, SUM, I, J

Arguments to PRINT: IR, ILLNES

Technical Aspects of the Program. In comparison with the program written for Project 3, this program is written in an elementary manner. The glossary of variables for the program appears in Table B.3. The flow chart and program listing are in Figures B.8 and B.9, respectively. A 20×20 array PAGE is defined, and is later printed, forming the scatter plot. The first statements in the program set the value of N to zero and store zeros at all locations of PAGE—this is equivalent to making sure that the plotting begins with a clean sheet of paper. The logic of the program is simple. A pair of X, Y values are

Table B.2 (continued)

SUBROUTINE TEST

Dummy argument names: X, SUM, I, K

TEST does not use COMMON

I	Argument indicating which disease is to be tested
K	Disease indicator—returned to the main program as J
SUM	Same as SUM in main program
X(4)	Same as SCORE in main program

SUBROUTINE PRINT

Dummy argument names: IROW, ISICK

IROW	Maximum number of diseases to be listed in a single column of TAB—the number of rows to TAB printed. Same as IR in main program.
ISICK(4)	Disease indicators for the subject being printed—same as ILLNES in main program.
TAB(5,3)	Table of alphameric information. Each column corresponds to one of the classifications has disease, does not have, etc. Each column contains a list of alphameric information—names of diseases.

read in. If they are blank, the program terminates by printing PAGE; if not, a point is plotted by incrementing PAGE(I,J).

The testing for a blank data word deserves some additional elaboration. In Project 3, the program terminated on a blank card also, but that card had been read with an A specification, so that the "value" of a blank field is equivalent to the characters 1Hb, which can be stored with a DATA statement. In this case, however, the field was read with an I specification, and the blank is therefore stored as a "number" rather than as the literal character "b." The storage of a blank read as a numerical value differs with different computer systems, but in the IBM 700−7000 series on which this program was executed, a blank is stored as −0, while a legitimate value of zero is stored as a +0. Testing for a blank then involves checking the sign position of the data value. This may be accomplished by several means. One of the simplest methods that occurs to most programmers is the use of the arithmetic IF statement. This will not serve the purpose since the sign of a zero value is not inspected. This mechanism may work on other machines. The approach used in this program involves exchanging the sign of the data value with the value of a variable known to be positive, in this case END, which is assigned the value +99 by a DATA statement. Many Fortran systems provide a sign-exchange as the built-in function SIGN. In this example the function reference SIGN(END,X) is used. This returns the value of END, but with the sign that was attached to X. In this example program, if X has a positive value

Input:

```
Col. 1
0701
1315
0301
2019
 .
 .
 .
1010
bbbb
```

Figure B.7 Illustrative input data and output from Project 7.

Output:

```
    20                                                                               2   *   2

  SCATTER PLOT OF X AND Y  WITH   45 PAIRS OF OBSERVATIONS.                2       2   *

                                                                           *

                                                                               *

    16                                                           *   2

    15                                                   *       *   *

    14                                               *

    13

    12                                                   *

    11

    10                                       2   *

Y    9                                   *       *

     8

     7

     6                   *       *   *

     5               *       *           *

     4           *           *

     3       *       *   2   *   *

     2           *

     1   *       *   *   *       *

         1   2   3   4   5   6   7   8   9  10  11  12  13  14  15  16  17  18  19  20

                                            X
```

Figure B.7 (continued)

Table B.3

Glossary of variables for project 7

Variable	Meaning
K	Used in printing PAGE so that the graph will be printed with the top row first.
LABEL(20)	Contains the integers 1 - 20
N	Number of pairs of values of X and Y that have been plotted.
P(100)	INTEGER array containing the alphameric characters b, *, 2, 3, ..., 99
PAGE(20,20)	INTEGER array that stores the characters in the scatter plot—a piece of "graph paper."
X	INTEGER data value.
Y	INTEGER data value.

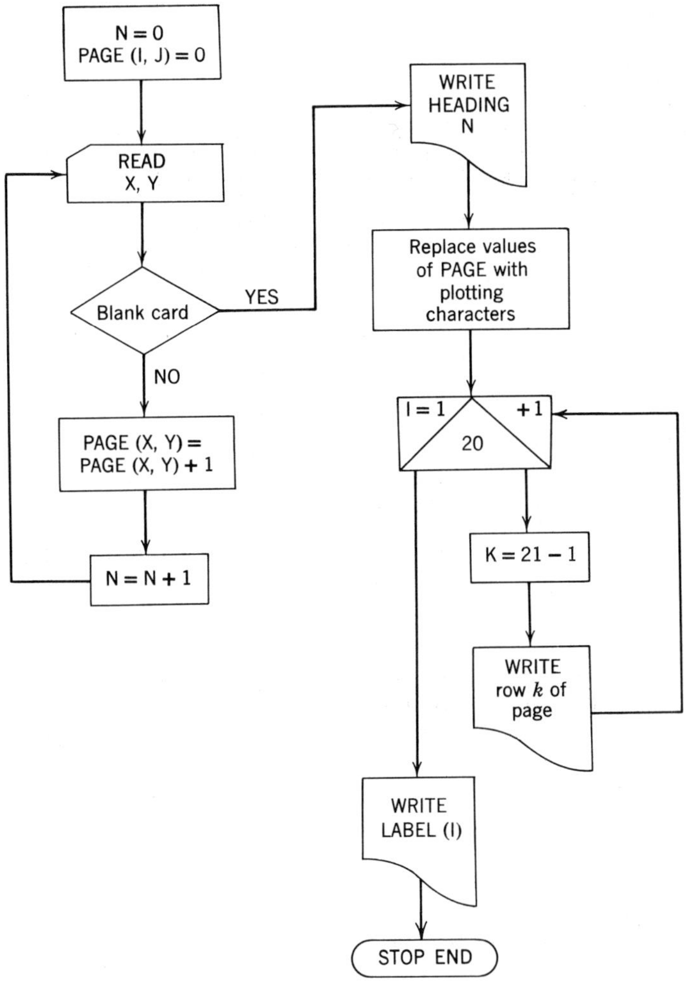

Figure B.8 Flow chart for Project 7.

the function return is +99. If the value of X is blank, then its sign is placed on the value of END, and the return is −99. The difference between these two values can be easily checked with the arithmetic IF statement.

If X and Y are not blank, they are used as subscripts locating a particular point in the array PAGE. The frequency of this point is increased by 1. When all of the values of X and Y have been counted, the numerical values in the cells of PAGE, the frequencies, are replaced with alphameric plotting characters from the array P. This replacement is done to avoid printing zero where there is a zero frequency. Printing the array in a numeric mode does not permit suppressing the numeric character corresponding to the contents of a word. The alphameric blank is used instead—all of the other frequencies are printed in alphameric as well, in order to maintain programming simplicity.

When array PAGE is printed, the values of Y are printed along the left border. The identification of these values as values of Y is accomplished by printing the character Y on the 10th row to the left of the array. This is done with a logical IF in the DO printing the rows of the array.

PROJECT 11. RANDOM SAMPLER (RSAMP)

This program departs slightly from the suggestion in Chapter 3 that programs not be written for general use. The program here is very general in its usefulness. The program will form random samples of any size (up to 100) from a population of up to 100 elements. In addition, up to 100 independent random samples of the same size may be formed. As a

```
C  PROJECT NUMBER 7
      DIMENSION PAGE(20,20),LABEL(20),P(100),APAGE(20,20)
      INTEGER X,Y,PAGE,END
      DATA END/99/
      DATA (P(I),I=1,100)/1H ,1H*,1H2,1H3,1H4,1H5,1H6,1H7,1H8,1H9,2H10,
     12H11,2H12,2H13,2H14,2H15,2H16,2H17,2H18,2H19,2H20,2H21,2H22,2H23,
     22H24,2H25,2H26,2H27,2H28,2H29,2H30,2H31,2H32,2H33,2H34,2H35,2H36,
     32H37,2H38,2H39,2H40,2H41,2H42,2H43,2H44,2H45,2H46,2H47,2H48,2H49,
     42H50,2H51,2H52,2H53,2H54,2H55,2H56,2H57,2H58,2H59,2H60,2H61,2H62,
     52H63,2H64,2H65,2H66,2H67,2H68,2H69,2H70,2H71,2H72,2H73,2H74,2H75,
     62H76,2H77,2H78,2H79,2H80,2H81,2H82,2H83,2H84,2H85,2H86,2H87,2H88,
     72H89,2H90,2H91,2H92,2H93,2H94,2H95,2H96,2H97,2H98,2H99/
    3 N = 0
C
C   SET PLOTTING ARRAY PAGE TO ZERO.
C
      DO 1 I=1,20
      DO 1 J=1,20
    1 PAGE(I,J)=0
C  READ A PAIR OF VALUES.
    7 READ(5,102)X,Y
  102 FORMAT(2I2)
C  CHECK TO SEE IF THIS IS A BLANK CARD.
      IF(SIGN(END,X))6,6,4
C   IF NOT, PLOT THE VALUES OF X AND Y BY INCREASING THE COUNT AT
C    THAT CELL OF PAGE.
    4 PAGE (Y,X) = PAGE(Y,X)+1
      N = N + 1
      GO TO 7
    6 WRITE(6,103) N
  103 FORMAT (1H1,2(/1H0),37X,30HSCATTER PLOT OF X AND Y  WITH  ,
     1 I4,24H PAIRS OF OBSERVATIONS.   /1H0/1H0)
C  RELACE NUMERICAL VALUES IN PAGE WITH PLOTTING CHARACTERS FROM P.
      DO 2 I = 1,20
      DO 2 J = 1,20
      K = PAGE(I,J)+1
      APAGE(I,J)=P(K)
    2 CONTINUE
C   BEGIN OUTPUT
      DO 5 I=1,20
      K=21-I
      IF(I.EQ.10) GO TO 10
      WRITE(6,104)K,(APAGE(K,J),J=1,20)
      GO TO 5
  104 FORMAT(1H0,29X,I2,20(2X,A2))
  105 FORMAT(1H0,14X,1HY,14X,I2,20(2X,A2))
   10 WRITE(6,105)K,(APAGE(K,J),J=1,20)
    5 CONTINUE
      DO 8 I=1,20
    8 LABEL(I)=I
      WRITE(6,106)(LABEL(I),I=1,20)
  106 FORMAT(1H0,31X,20(I4)/// 70X,1HX)
      GO TO 3
      END
```

Figure B.9 Listing of the program for Project 7.

check on the sampling procedure, a large number of samples may be selected, the first printed for use, and all remaining printing suppressed. The program will calculate the relative frequency with which each element in the population has been selected and print those frequencies. Theoretically, each element in the population is equally likely to appear in each sample. Therefore the relative frequencies of all elements over a large number of selections should be approximately equal, and each equal to 1/M where M is the number of elements in the population.

The program may also be used to arrange the M population elements into a random order by letting the sample size be as large as the population size. In short, the program selects K independent random samples of size N from a population of M elements. The restrictions on K, M, and N are that they may not exceed 100. These restrictions may be removed by changing DIMENSION statements and the diagnostics dealing with K, M, and N.

The Use of RSAMP. Elements of the population to be sampled are given names (i.e., business establishments, people, etc.) and each name is punched on a separate card begining in column 1. The name may be as long as 18 characters—i.e., it may be punched in columns 1–18. The remainder of the card should be blank. There will be M of these cards, one for each member of the population.

A control card giving several parameters must be placed before the cards containing the names of the population elements. Columns 1–5 of this card contain a value that is used as a starting value for the random number generator that is a part of the program. This must be a five digit *odd* number. The user of RSAMP is cautioned to use *different values* for this number for different executions of the program, as the use of the same number will result in the same samples being formed.

Columns 6–8 of the control card contain the number of elements in the population, M. This is a number not greater than 100, and must be punched packed right. That is, if there are 40 elements in the population, punch 040 or b40 where b is a blank column. If this value is greater than 100, the program prints a diagnostic error message and terminates. Columns 9–11 contain the sample size N. This is punched in the same manner as M. Again, the program will terminate if this value is larger than 100. Columns 12–14 contain the number of samples K, punched in the same way as M and N. The program terminates if this value is larger than 100.

The value punched in column 15 controls the output of the program. If column 15 contains a 1, only the first sample will be printed. This option is useful for checking the sampling procedure, since the remaining K−1 samples will be generated, and the relative frequencies printed. If column 15 contains a 2, all samples will be printed. If a number other than 1 or 2 appears in column 15, an error message is printed and the program terminates.

RSAMP allows any number of different sampling problems to be executed sequentially. If the user has a population of size 50 and wants to select a sample of 15 and he also wants to arrange a group of 12 items in random order, he can make up two data decks, the first containing 51 cards for the first problem. The second deck contains 13 cards and is placed immediately following the last card of the first deck. In this case the total input deck will contain 51 + 13 = 64 cards.

The use of RSAMP is illustrated in Figures B.10 through B.13. Figure B.10 illustrates the use of RSAMP as required by the description of Project 11. The names of 40 business establishments are input as the population and 100 samples of size 10 are drawn. Only the first sample is printed but the relative frequency distribution indicates that, over 100 samples, each of the 40 has a relative frequency of nearly 1/40. Figure B.11 illustrates the use of RSAMP in its most common application—simply picking one sample with

Input Deck:

```
123450400101001
JOES BAR AND GRILL
TITEFIT CORSETS
TULE COFFEE SHOPPE
GIFTS, INC.
HULDYS TAVERN
A AND B STEAK SHOP
HERMANS MENS STORE
THE BOOK RACK
FISHERS TESTS
APPLE REST HOME
R. H. FINE FOODS
FUZZYS BARBER SHOP
TWEETERS HI FI
FERRITE STORAGE CO
SHANNONS TRANSFER
PUFF PUFF PIPES
ALADDINS LAMPS
FILLINGS TAXIDERMY
DAVY JONES BOATS
PLAYGIRL MAGAZINE
CHRISTOPHERS MAPS
HOMERS TRAVEL
GINNS LIQUOR
SO AND SO TAILORS
ROOTS TREE SERVICE
PLAYMORE TOYS, LTD
IBM HARDWARE
TIMELY CLOCKS
D.O.STEEL CO.
PIPS PETS
PERT ANALYSIS, INC
BERNOULLIS TRIALS
STEVENS RESEARCH
OSGOOD LINGUISTICS
HOLLERITH PRINTING
CDC HARDWARE
JOHNS PLUMBING
BINETS PUZZLE SHOP
PLACEBOS DRUGS
GLAMOUR JEWELERS
```

Figure B.10 The use of RSAMP as required by Project 11.

Output:

```
STARTING VALUE FOR RANDOM NUMBER GENERATOR =  12345.

POPULATION SIZE =   40

SAMPLE SIZE =   10

NUMBER OF SAMPLES =  100

ALL SAMPLES WILL NOT BE PRINTED.




                    SAMPLE     1.

SELECTIONS FROM THE POPULATION IN THIS SAMPLE ARE

                    OSGOOD LINGUISTICS

                    FUZZYS BARBER SHOP

                    JOES BAR AND GRILL

                    BINETS PUZZLE SHOP

                    HOMERS TRAVEL

                    IBM HARDWARE

                    THE BOOK RACK

                    STEVENS RESEARCH

                    D.O.STEEL CO.

                    FISHERS TESTS
```

Figure B.10 (continued)

no concern for checking the relative frequencies over a long series of trials.

The formation of three independent random samples from the same population is illustrated in Figure B.12. Figure B.13 illustrates cards and output produced by using RSAMP to arrange a set of 10 items in random order.

Technical Aspects of the Program. For simplicity in the preceding discussion several parameters were given one-letter symbolic designations. In the remainder of this discussion variables will be referred to by the names used in RSAMP. In terms of RSAMP variable names, the program selects NSAMP independent random samples of size SAMSIZ from a population of POPSIZ elements. A complete definition of all of the variables used in RSAMP is given in Table B.4. The program is listed in Figure B.14, and a flowchart appears in Figure B.15.

RSAMP consists of a main program, a subroutine SAMPLE, and a function RANDOM. The main program reads the parameter values on the control card. All parameters are printed and checked for correctness. If any value is incorrect the program terminates without reading any additional cards. Assuming that all parameters are correct, the names of the POPSIZ elements of the population are read. The main program then calls SAMPLE to form a sample of size SAMSIZ. When each sample has been generated, the main program accumulates the frequencies of each

```
RELATIVE FREQUENCIES OF THE
SELECTIONS IN THE  100 SAMPLES.


JOES BAR AND GRILL             0.0230
TITEFIT CORSETS                0.0230
TULE COFFEE SHOPPE             0.0250
GIFTS, INC.                    0.0180
HULDYS TAVERN                  0.0150
A AND B STEAK SHOP             0.0200
HERMANS MENS STORE             0.0330
THE BOOK RACK                  0.0290
FISHERS TESTS                  0.0260
APPLE REST HOME                0.0240
R. H. FINE FOODS               0.0260
FUZZYS BARBER SHOP             0.0280
TWEETERS HI FI                 0.0270
FERRITE STORAGE CO             0.0290
SHANNONS TRANSFER              0.0170
PUFF PUFF PIPES                0.0300
ALADDINS LAMPS                 0.0330
FILLINGS TAXIDERMY             0.0330
DAVY JONES BOATS               0.0260
PLAYGIRL MAGAZINE              0.0260
CHRISTOPHERS MAPS              0.0300
HOMERS TRAVEL                  0.0270
GINNS LIQUOR                   0.0200
SO AND SO TAILORS              0.0250
ROOTS TREE SERVICE             0.0240
PLAYMORE TOYS, LTD             0.0260
IBM HARDWARE                   0.0190
TIMELY CLOCKS                  0.0250
D.O.STEEL CO.                  0.0350
PIPS PETS                      0.0290
PERT ANALYSIS, INC             0.0180
BERNOULLIS TRIALS              0.0240
STEVENS RESEARCH               0.0330
OSGOOD LINGUISTICS             0.0190
HOLLERITH PRINTING             0.0170
CDC HARDWARE                   0.0260
JOHNS PLUMBING                 0.0260
BINETS PUZZLE SHOP             0.0210
PLACEBOS DRUGS                 0.0220
GLAMOUR JEWELERS               0.0230
```

Figure B.10 (continued)

element chosen so that relative frequencies may be calculated. When all samples have been generated the main program calculates the relative frequencies, prints them, and terminates. The subroutine SAMPLE forms samples and prints them, if the print option specifies printing. In the process of forming a sample, SAMPLE calls upon the function RANDOM. RANDOM produces a REAL number between zero and one from a uniform probability distribution.

There are at least two general ways in which a random sample might be formed. Brief consideration of them is illustrative of the planning of an efficient program. Suppose that there are 10 elements in the population and we are to sample 2 of them. Each element in the population may be designated by a subscript, say I. Now we may obtain a random number between 1 and 10 and let that be the first member of our sample. Suppose that there is another array WHICH, for example, keeping track of the elements in the sample. We could let WHICH (I) equal 0 if the element was not in the sample and 1 if it was. Thus, having generated a random number J between 1 and 10, the statement WHICH(J) = 1 defines the Jth element of the population as being in the sample. The next step would be to generate another random number between 1 and 10 defining the second member of the sample. If the second number picked was the same as the first, we would have to generate another number to pick a different element, since the problem does not allow sampling with replacement.

This computing routine or algorithm is in-

```
Input:

543210120050011
SUBJECT G22
SUBJECT F11
SUBJECT F12
SUBJECT F13
SUBJECT F14
SUBJECT F16
SUBJECT M10
SUBJECT M11
SUBJECT M12
SUBJECT M14
SUBJECT M16
SUBJECT M17
```

Figure B.11 Using RSAMP to pick a single sample.

Output:

```
STARTING VALUE FOR RANDOM NUMBER GENERATOR =  54321.
POPULATION SIZE =   12
SAMPLE SIZE =    5
NUMBER OF SAMPLES =    1
ALL SAMPLES WILL NOT BE PRINTED.


                    SAMPLE    1.
 SELECTIONS FROM THE POPULATION IN THIS SAMPLE ARE
                 SUBJECT F16
                 SUBJECT F13
                 SUBJECT F11
                 SUBJECT M12
                 SUBJECT M11


       RELATIVE FREQUENCIES OF THE
       SELECTIONS IN THE    1 SAMPLES.



       SUBJECT G22              0.0000
       SUBJECT F11              0.2000
       SUBJECT F12              0.0000
       SUBJECT F13              0.2000
       SUBJECT F14              0.0000
       SUBJECT F16              0.2000
       SUBJECT M10              0.0000
       SUBJECT M11              0.2000
       SUBJECT M12              0.2000
       SUBJECT M14              0.0000
       SUBJECT M16              0.0000
       SUBJECT M17              0.0000
```

Figure B.11 (continued)

Input:

```
115230150050032
SUBJECT A55
SUBJECT B285
SUBJECT X15
SUBJECT J28
SUBJECT F36
SUBJECT S98
SUBJECT A19
SUBJECT C58
SUBJECT H53
SUBJECT H77
SUBJECT R23
SUBJECT B01
SUBJECT Y30
SUBJECT H11
SUBJECT  G22
```

adequate when the sample size is nearly the same as the population. Consider what would happen if we were to form a sample of 9 from a population of 10. The first element in the sample would be picked with no difficulty as illustrated above. But as more and more of the elements were placed into the sample, fewer and fewer of the random numbers between 1 and 10 could be used. For example, if the first 8 elements had been placed in the sample, then only the numbers J = 9 and J = 10 could be used. But it is a characteristic of the random number generator that it will continue to generate numbers between 1 and 10 with equal frequency, so that it may take a large number of trials to produce a 9 or 10.

The matter becomes even worse if RSAMP were to be used to arrange the elements of the population in random order. This involves

Output:

```
STARTING VALUE FOR RANDOM NUMBER GENERATOR =   11523.

POPULATION SIZE =    15

SAMPLE SIZE =     5

NUMBER OF SAMPLES =     3

ALL SAMPLES WILL       BE PRINTED.

                    SAMPLE     1.

 SELECTIONS FROM THE POPULATION IN THIS SAMPLE ARE

                 SUBJECT H77

                 SUBJECT H11

                 SUBJECT Y30

                 SUBJECT  G22

                 SUBJECT F36

                    SAMPLE     2.

 SELECTIONS FROM THE POPULATION IN THIS SAMPLE ARE

                 SUBJECT H11

                 SUBJECT Y30

                 SUBJECT B285

                 SUBJECT B01

                 SUBJECT X15
```

Figure B.12 Use of RSAMP to pick multiple samples.

```
SAMPLE    3.

SELECTIONS FROM THE POPULATION IN THIS SAMPLE ARE

SUBJECT H11

SUBJECT J28

SUBJECT A55

SUBJECT C58

SUBJECT F36


RELATIVE FREQUENCIES OF THE

SELECTIONS IN THE    3 SAMPLES.



SUBJECT A55               0.0667

SUBJECT B285              0.0667

SUBJECT X15               0.0667

SUBJECT J28               0.0667

SUBJECT F36               0.1333

SUBJECT S98               0.0000

SUBJECT A19               0.0000

SUBJECT C58               0.0667

SUBJECT H53               0.0000

SUBJECT H77               0.0667

SUBJECT R23               0.0000

SUBJECT B01               0.0667

SUBJECT Y30               0.1333

SUBJECT H11               0.2000

SUBJECT  G22              0.0667
```

Figure B.12 (continued)

drawing a sample of the same size as the population. When the population size is larger, the problem is further enlarged. For example, to randomize 100 elements, a sample of size 100 is formed. To locate the 100th element, on the average, 100 random numbers must be generated. But this is, of course, no guarantee that the 100th element will be located in 100 trials, it may take many more, or many less.

Another approach to random sampling is considerably more efficient. When the first element in the sample is drawn, a random number J between 1 and POPSIZ is generated. The Jth element in the population is thereby selected as the first member of the sample. When this has been done, the element is removed from the population, leaving POPSIZ-1 elements. The element in the last location of the population array is transferred to the location just "emptied." To place the second element in the sample, a random number between 1 and POPSIZ-1 is generated and the indicated element is placed in the sample and removed from the population. The selected element is replaced by the last remaining element in the population array. This process may be repeated until all of the elements of the population have been removed with no decrease in the efficiency of the program. For each population element to be placed in the sample, exactly one random number need be generated. This algorithm is used in RSAMP.

The Main Program. The main program begins by testing each of the values read from the parameter card. All values are printed, with the notation "TOO LARGE" when a value exceeds the legal limits. At the end of the diagnostic routine, the program termi-

Input:

```
773510100100011
PETER JONES
JOHN SMITH
SAM JOHNSON
BETTY BLANK
H. HOLLERITH
IBM COMPUTER
DAN BAILEY
DICK LEHMAN
JAMES BOND
ELSE SCHULTZ
```

Output:

```
STARTING VALUE FOR RANDOM NUMBER GENERATOR =  77351.

POPULATION SIZE =    10

SAMPLE SIZE =    10

NUMBER OF SAMPLES =     1

ALL SAMPLES WILL NOT BE PRINTED.


                   SAMPLE     1.

  SELECTIONS FROM THE POPULATION IN THIS SAMPLE ARE

                 DICK LEHMAN

                 JOHN SMITH

                 JAMES BOND

                 H. HOLLERITH

                 IBM COMPUTER

                 SAM JOHNSON

                 PETER JONES

                 ELSE SCHULTZ

                 DAN BAILEY

                 BETTY BLANK
```

Figure B.13 Using RSAMP to arrange 10 items in random order.

RELATIVE FREQUENCIES OF THE SELECTIONS IN THE 1 SAMPLES.	
PETER JONES	0.1000
JOHN SMITH	0.1000
SAM JOHNSON	0.1000
BETTY BLANK	0.1000
H. HOLLERITH	0.1000
IBM COMPUTER	0.1000
DAN BAILEY	0.1000
DICK LEHMAN	0.1000
JAMES BOND	0.1000
ELSE SCHULTZ	0.1000

Figure B.13 (continued)

nates if an illegal or missing value has been detected.

Assuming that no input error was found, the POPSIZ elements of the population are read and the numbers 1, 2, ..., POPSIZ are stored in ORDNO1. These values are used to identify which population elements are selected for a sample. The actual element names are not manipulated by the sampling routine—only the order numbers in ORDNO1, which stand for population entities, are moved in memory.

The next statements call upon SAMPLE to form a total of NSAMP different samples. Upon each return from SAMPLE, ORDNO2 contains the identifying indices (order numbers) of the population elements in the sample. For example, if ORDNO2(1) = 10 and ORDNO2(2) = 7, this indicates the population element 10 is the first member of the sample, and the item 7 in the population is the second member of the sample. The subscript K is set equal to a value of ORDNO2, and IFREQ(K) is increased by 1, indicating that the Kth population entity has been chosen, and the frequency of that element is thus increased.

When NSAMP samples have been generated, the main program calculates and prints the relative frequencies corresponding to the elements in the population. The program terminates by reading another card. If another set of data is to be processed, the parameter card is read, and the entire process repeats.

FUNCTION RANDOM. RANDOM is called from SAMPLE. Upon its return, it replaces the value of RFIRST with another randomly selected value. The program statements in RANDOM are essentially those listed in Chapter 3 in the discussion of Project 8, except for the division by 100000 which scales the number properly. Random number generation is also discussed in Chapter 11. The specific output illustrated here is dependent on the specific generator and initial values used. Better generators are discussed in Chapter 11.

SUBROUTINE SAMPLE. SAMPLE is the heart of the program RSAMP. It is here that samples are selected and printed. The main program calls SAMPLE and does summary computations, but SAMPLE does the work of the program.

The main loop in SAMPLE (DO 2) is executed SAMSIZ times, each time selecting one element from the population as a member of the sample. As indicated previously, the sampling is done from a population the size of which decreases by one each time an element is placed in the sample. The variables FL and JJ are used to keep track of the number of elements remaining in the population at any point. A number between zero and FL is generated and called J. This number then desig-

Table B.4

Glossary of variables for RSAMP

Variable	Meaning
COMMON	
BUSNES(100,3)	Each row (three words) contains the name of a population element
IPRINT	The print option: = 1 if only the first sample is to be printed, = 2 if all samples are to be printed
ORDNO1(100)	The initial ordering of elements in BUSNES
ORDNO2(100)	The order numbers, moved from ORDNO1, of elements in the sample. An entry identifies the population element whose subscript is given as ORDNO2(J) as the Jth element in the sample
POPSIZ	INTEGER variable giving the number of elements in the population—the number of columns of BUSNES actually used
RFIRST	The starting value for the random number generator—assumes different values during execution as succeeding random numbers are generated
SAMSIZ	INTEGER variable giving the size of the samples to be formed
Main program	
BL	Contains characters 1Hb
F	The REAL equivalent of NSAMP—used to calculate relative frequencies
I	A general looping index—frequently refers to the Ith sample
IFREQ(100)	The frequency with which each of the elements in BUSNES was chosen over the NSAMP samples
J	A general looping index—used in a loop to represent an entry in ORDNO2
K	A subscript for IFREQ—set equal to the value of ORDNO2(J) for accumulating frequencies
LARG1	Contains characters 6HbTOObb
LARG2	Contains characters 6HLARGEb
NSAMP	The number of samples to be formed

nates one of the FL elements in the population. The Jth entry in ORDNO1 is placed in ORDNO2(I), indicating that the Jth population entity has been chosen as the Ith member of the sample.

The final step in sampling is moving ORDNO1(JJ) to the spot just vacated by the removal of ORDNO1(J) by placing it in the sample. This procedure moves the last element in the population into the "slot" left vacant by removing one of the population elements. This procedure insures that only the first FL elements of ORDNO1 will represent entities still remaining in the population.

When all of the SAMSIZ members of the sample have been chosen, ORDNO1 is restored so that it contains, once more, the numbers 1, ..., POPSIZ. This step is necessary so that additional samples may be drawn in the same manner.

Table B.4 (continued)

RELF	A relative frequency—equal to an element of IFREQ divided by NSAMP
Argument to SAMPLE - I	

SUBROUTINE SAMPLE

Dummy argument name - KK	
FL	REAL variable equal to the number of elements remaining in the population at a particular stage in sampling
I	A general looping index—a position in a sample
J	A randomly selected value between one and FL
JJ	INTEGER equivalent of FL
JJJ	A value taken from ORDNO2 which is used as a subscript identifying a row (population element) of BUSNES for printing
KK	The number of the sample—this sample is number KK
NO	Contains characters 3HNOT
RANDNO	A random number between zero and one
Argument to RANDOM - RFIRST	

The restoration of ORDNO1 completed, the program returns if this sample is not to be printed. If the print option indicates printing, the names in BUSNES corresponding to the order numbers listed in ORDNO2 are printed, thus forming the list of elements in the sample. When printing is complete, the subroutine returns to the main program, to be called again to form the next sample.

```
CPROJ11
C RSAMP--A RANDOM SAMPLER
C
C    MAIN PROGRAM
C
C
      DIMENSION IFREQ(100),BUSNES(100,3),ORDNO1(100),ORDNO2(100)
      COMMON BUSNES,RFIRST,IPRINT,POPSIZ,SAMSIZ,ORDNO1,ORDNO2
      INTEGER POPSIZ, SAMSIZ
  999 READ(5,101)RFIRST,POPSIZ,SAMSIZ,NSAMP,IPRINT
  101 FORMAT(F5.0,3I3,I1)
C  READS STARTING VALUE FOR RANDOM NUMBER GENERATOR, POPULATION SIZE,
C     SAMPLE SIZE, NUMBER OF SAMPLES, AND THE PRINT OPTION.
C
C
C  DIAGNOSTIC ROUTINE, CHECKS PARAMETER
C      VALUES AND TERMINATES ON AN INPUT
C      ERROR
C
      DATA BL,LARG1,LARG2,NO/1H ,6H TOO   ,6H LARGE,3HNOT/
      WRITE(6,1001)RFIRST
 1001 FORMAT(1H1,45HSTARTING VALUE FOR RANDOM NUMBER GENERATOR =   ,
     1  F7.0)
      IERR=0
      IF(POPSIZ-100)1051,1051,1052
 1051 WRITE(6,1003)POPSIZ,BL,BL
      GO TO 1058
 1052 WRITE(6,1003)POPSIZ,LARG1,LARG2
      IERR=1
 1003 FORMAT(1H0,18HPOPULATION SIZE = ,I4,      4X,2A6)
 1058 IF(SAMSIZ-100)1053,1053,1054
 1053 WRITE(6,1006)SAMSIZ,BL,BL
      GO TO 1057
 1054 WRITE(6,1006)SAMSIZ,LARG1,LARG2
      IERR=1
 1006 FORMAT(1H0,14HSAMPLE SIZE = ,I4,      4X,2A6)
 1057 IF(NSAMP-100)1059,1059,1060
 1059 WRITE(6,1007)NSAMP,BL,BL
      GO TO 1061
 1060 WRITE(6,1007)NSAMP,LARG1,LARG2
      IERR=1
 1007 FORMAT(1H0,20HNUMBER OF SAMPLES = ,I4,      4X,2A6)
 1061 IF(IPRINT-1)1062,1063,1064
 1062 WRITE(6,1008)
 1008 FORMAT(1H0,31HMISSING VALUE FOR PRINT OPTION.)
      IERR=1
      GO TO 1070
 1063 WRITE(6,1009) NO
      GO TO 1070
 1064 WRITE(6,1009) BL
 1009 FORMAT(1H0,17HALL SAMPLES WILL ,A4,11HBE PRINTED. )
 1070 IF(IERR.EQ.1)STOP
C
C   END OF DIAGNOSTIC ROUTINE.
C
      DO 1 I=1,POPSIZ
      ORDNO1(I) = I
    1 READ(5,102)(BUSNES(I,J),J=1,3)
  102 FORMAT(3A6)
C

C  READS NAMES OF POPSIZ ELEMENT
```

Figure B.14 Listing of the program for project 11.

```
C
      DO 2 I=1,POPSIZ
    2 IFREQ(I)=0
      DO 3 I=1,NSAMP
C  CALLS SAMPLE NSAMP TIMES
      CALL SAMPLE (I)
      DO 3 J = 1, SAMSIZ
      K = ORDNO2(J)
    3 IFREQ(K) = IFREQ(K) + 1
      WRITE(6,103)NSAMP
  103 FORMAT(1H1,24X,28HRELATIVE FREQUENCIES OF THE ,
     1/1H0,24X,18HSELECTIONS IN THE ,I4,9H SAMPLES./////)
      F=NSAMP*SAMSIZ
      DO 10 I=1,POPSIZ
      RELF=IFREQ(I)
      RELF=RELF/F
   10 WRITE(6,104)(BUSNES(I,J),J=1,3),RELF
  104 FORMAT(1H0,24X,3A6,5X,F8.4)
      GO TO 999
      END


      FUNCTION RANDOM(START)
      START=23.*START
      III=START/100001.
      F = III
      RANDOM = START-100001.*F
      RETURN
      END


C
C  SUBROUTINE SAMPLE
C
      SUBROUTINE SAMPLE (KK)
      DIMENSION BUSNES(100,3),ORDNO1(100),ORDNO2(100)
      COMMON BUSNES,RFIRST,IPRINT,POPSIZ,SAMSIZ,ORDNO1,ORDNO2
      INTEGER SAMSIZ,POPSIZ
      DO 2 I=1,SAMSIZ
      RFIRST=RANDOM(RFIRST)
      RANDNO = RFIRST/100000.
      FL = POPSIZ - I + 1
      J = (FL*RANDNO) + 1.0
      JJ = FL
      ORDNO2(I) = ORDNO1(J)
      ORDNO1(J) = ORDNO1(JJ)
    2 CONTINUE
      DO 6 I = 1, POPSIZ
    6 ORDNO1(I)=I
      IF(IPRINT.EQ.2.OR.(IPRINT.EQ.1.AND.KK.EQ.1)) GO TO 5
      RETURN
    5 WRITE(6,1)KK
    1 FORMAT(1H1,53X,8HSAMPLE  ,I3,1H. /1H0,
     135X,49HSELECTIONS FROM THE POPULATION IN THIS SAMPLE ARE    )
      DO 3 J=1,SAMSIZ
      JJJ = ORDNO2(J)
    3 WRITE(6,4) (BUSNES(JJJ,K),K=1,3)
    4 FORMAT(1H0,50X,3A6)
      RETURN
      END
```

Figure B.14 (continued)

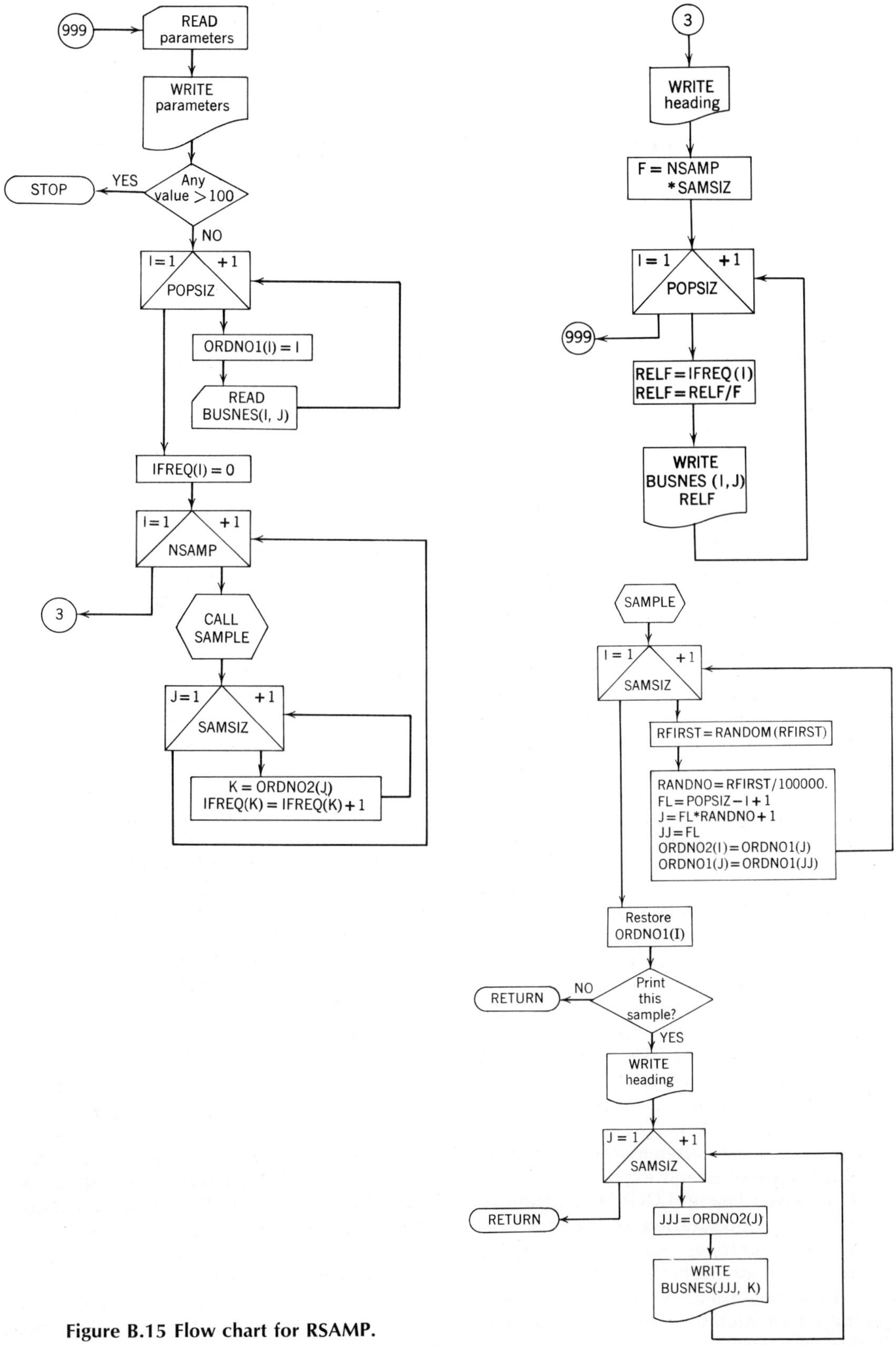

Figure B.15 Flow chart for RSAMP.

APPENDIX C **FORTRAN IMPLEMENTATIONS**

VARIATIONS IN FORTRAN IV

In this Appendix, the Fortran language as it is implemented on several computer systems is discussed. Throughout the text, reference has been made to the fact that different computer systems have somewhat different rules. It is not our purpose here to present a complete listing of all rules for all existing systems. Rather, the major categories of statements will be summarized, briefly, with an indication of how the rules might be expected to vary. The following computing systems have been chosen as representative: Burroughs B5500, Control Data 6600, GE 635, IBM 7090, IBM 1130, and UNIVAC 1108.

Mechanics. For all systems, the organization of the Fortran statement is standard. The systems vary in the maximum statement number that may be used—for all but GE and Burroughs, the maximum is 32767; for the others it is 99999. For most systems, the maximum number of continuation cards for one statement is 20, although there is no limitation for Burroughs.

Expressions and Constants. The usual limit on the magnitude of an INTEGER constant is 2^{35}, but several systems vary; the IBM 1130 is notably low with 2^{15} and the CDC 6600 permits 2^{48}; for REAL constants the limit is commonly $10^{\pm 38}$ although CDC allows $10^{\pm 308}$. Most variable names have six character limits—the 1130 allows 5 and CDC permits 7. All implementations except UNIVAC and Burroughs have a three subscript limit for arrays—UNIVAC allows 7, and Burroughs defines no limit. All systems allow LOGICAL variables, constants, and expressions, except the 1130 which has no LOGICAL capability.

Declarations. Declaration statements exist in all implementations, and there is very little about the statements that can be modified. Some implementations do not permit dimensioning information to be conveyed in type or COMMON statements.

Control Statements. These statements exist in all implementations, except that the 1130 does not allow the logical IF. There may be variations in the values that can be attained by the indexing values in a DO—these generally, but not universally, follow the rules for limits on INTEGER values. In the IBM 7090, for example, the limit is 2^{15}.

Input/Output. The executable I/O statements exist in all implementations as discussed, so long as the equipment is present. For example, the 1130 does not have tape manipulation statements since tape units are not available. A special form of READ and WRITE is employed on the 1130 for use of the disc. The standard FORMAT specifications (I, F, E, A, H, X) are available on all. Some systems allow other specifications for special purposes. The L specification is not allowed on the 1130.

Subprograms. CALL, SUBROUTINE, FUNCTION, and RETURN statements are available in all implementations. Arithmetic statement functions are not allowed on the 1130, nor are LOGICAL functions. Nonstandard returns and multiple entry points for subroutines are allowed on Burroughs, UNIVAC, GE, IBM 7090. Multiple entries are permissable on the CDC. Neither are permitted on the 1130.

DIFFERENCES BETWEEN FORTRAN II AND IV

There are not only a number of implementations of Fortran IV, but the Fortran II language offers another variant in the programming languages available to the behavioral scientist. Some computing centers offer both Fortrans II and IV; unless an existing Fortran II program is to be run, there is little point in using that langage. Some programmers may find themselves at an installation that offers only Fortran II. The following material is an introduction to the differences between the two languages.

The following features, discussed in the preceding chapters as aspects of the Fortran IV language, are not available in Fortran II:

Relational operators.
Logical operators, variables, and expressions.
Logical IF statements.
Type declarations.
DATA statements.
BLOCK DATA subprograms.
Labeled COMMON blocks.
COMMON statements containing dimensioning information.
Multiple entry points to subroutines.
Variable returns from subroutines.

The input/output statements are different between Fortrans II and IV. The following tabulation shows the two forms.

	Fortran II	*Fortran IV*
BCD input	READ INPUT TAPE *i, n, list*	READ (*i,n*) *list*
Binary input	READ TAPE *i, list*	READ (*i*) *list*
	READ DRUM *i, list*	READ (*i*) *list*
	READ DISK *i, list*	READ (*i*) *list*
BCD output	WRITE OUTPUT TAPE *i, n, list*	WRITE (*i,n*) *list*
Binary output	WRITE TAPE *i, list*	WRITE (*i*) *list*
	WRITE DRUM *i, list*	WRITE (*i*) *list*
	WRITE DISK *i, list*	WRITE (*i*) *list*

APPENDIX D TABLES

Table of Powers of Two

2^n	n	2^{-n}
1	0	1.0
2	1	0.5
4	2	0.25
8	3	0.125
16	4	0.062 5
32	5	0.031 25
64	6	0.015 625
128	7	0.007 812 5
256	8	0.003 906 25
512	9	0.001 953 125
1 024	10	0.000 976 562 5
2 048	11	0.000 488 281 25
4 096	12	0.000 244 140 625
8 192	13	0.000 122 070 312 5
16 384	14	0.000 061 035 156 25
32 768	15	0.000 030 517 578 125
65 536	16	0.000 015 258 789 062 5
131 072	17	0.000 007 629 394 531 25
262 144	18	0.000 003 814 697 265 625
524 288	19	0.000 001 907 348 632 812 5
1 048 576	20	0.000 000 953 674 316 406 25
2 097 152	21	0.000 000 476 837 158 203 125
4 194 304	22	0.000 000 238 418 579 101 562 5
8 388 608	23	0.000 000 119 209 289 550 781 25
16 777 216	24	0.000 000 059 604 644 775 390 625
33 554 432	25	0.000 000 029 802 322 387 695 312 5
67 108 864	26	0.000 000 014 901 161 193 847 656 25
134 217 728	27	0.000 000 007 450 580 596 923 828 125
268 435 456	28	0.000 000 003 725 290 298 461 914 062 5
536 870 912	29	0.000 000 001 862 645 149 230 957 031 25
1 073 741 824	30	0.000 000 000 931 322 574 615 478 515 625
2 147 483 648	31	0.000 000 000 465 661 287 307 739 257 812 5
4 294 967 296	32	0.000 000 000 232 830 643 653 869 628 906 25
8 589 934 592	33	0.000 000 000 116 415 321 826 934 814 453 125
17 179 869 184	34	0.000 000 000 058 207 660 913 467 407 226 562 5
34 359 738 368	35	0.000 000 000 029 103 830 456 733 703 613 281 25
68 719 476 736	36	0.000 000 000 014 551 915 228 366 851 806 640 625
137 438 953 472	37	0.000 000 000 007 275 957 614 183 425 903 320 312 5
274 877 906 944	38	0.000 000 000 003 637 978 807 091 712 951 660 156 25
549 755 813 888	39	0.000 000 000 001 818 989 403 545 856 475 830 078 125

Octal-Decimal Integer Conversion Table

0000 to 0777 (Octal)	0000 to 0511 (Decimal)

Octal	Decimal
10000	4096
20000	8192
30000	12288
40000	16384
50000	20480
60000	24576
70000	28672

	0	1	2	3	4	5	6	7
0000	0000	0001	0002	0003	0004	0005	0006	0007
0010	0008	0009	0010	0011	0012	0013	0014	0015
0020	0016	0017	0018	0019	0020	0021	0022	0023
0030	0024	0025	0026	0027	0028	0029	0030	0031
0040	0032	0033	0034	0035	0036	0037	0038	0039
0050	0040	0041	0042	0043	0044	0045	0046	0047
0060	0048	0049	0050	0051	0052	0053	0054	0055
0070	0056	0057	0058	0059	0060	0061	0062	0063
0100	0064	0065	0066	0067	0068	0069	0070	0071
0110	0072	0073	0074	0075	0076	0077	0078	0079
0120	0080	0081	0082	0083	0084	0085	0086	0087
0130	0088	0089	0090	0091	0092	0093	0094	0095
0140	0096	0097	0098	0099	0100	0101	0102	0103
0150	0104	0105	0106	0107	0108	0109	0110	0111
0160	0112	0113	0114	0115	0116	0117	0118	0119
0170	0120	0121	0122	0123	0124	0125	0126	0127
0200	0128	0129	0130	0131	0132	0133	0134	0135
0210	0136	0137	0138	0139	0140	0141	0142	0143
0220	0144	0145	0146	0147	0148	0149	0150	0151
0230	0152	0153	0154	0155	0156	0157	0158	0159
0240	0160	0161	0162	0163	0164	0165	0166	0167
0250	0168	0169	0170	0171	0172	0173	0174	0175
0260	0176	0177	0178	0179	0180	0181	0182	0183
0270	0184	0185	0186	0187	0188	0189	0190	0191
0300	0192	0193	0194	0195	0196	0197	0198	0199
0310	0200	0201	0202	0203	0204	0205	0206	0207
0320	0208	0209	0210	0211	0212	0213	0214	0215
0330	0216	0217	0218	0219	0220	0221	0222	0223
0340	0224	0225	0226	0227	0228	0229	0230	0231
0350	0232	0233	0234	0235	0236	0237	0238	0239
0360	0240	0241	0242	0243	0244	0245	0246	0247
0370	0248	0249	0250	0251	0252	0253	0254	0255

	0	1	2	3	4	5	6	7
0400	0256	0257	0258	0259	0260	0261	0262	0263
0410	0264	0265	0266	0267	0268	0269	0270	0271
0420	0272	0273	0274	0275	0276	0277	0278	0279
0430	0280	0281	0282	0283	0284	0285	0286	0287
0440	0288	0289	0290	0291	0292	0293	0294	0295
0450	0296	0297	0298	0299	0300	0301	0302	0303
0460	0304	0305	0306	0307	0308	0309	0310	0311
0470	0312	0313	0314	0315	0316	0317	0318	0319
0500	0320	0321	0322	0323	0324	0325	0326	0327
0510	0328	0329	0330	0331	0332	0333	0334	0335
0520	0336	0337	0338	0339	0340	0341	0342	0343
0530	0344	0345	0346	0347	0348	0349	0350	0351
0540	0352	0353	0354	0355	0356	0357	0358	0359
0550	0360	0361	0362	0363	0364	0365	0366	0367
0560	0368	0369	0370	0371	0372	0373	0374	0375
0570	0376	0377	0378	0379	0380	0381	0382	0383
0600	0384	0385	0386	0387	0388	0389	0390	0391
0610	0392	0393	0394	0395	0396	0397	0398	0399
0620	0400	0401	0402	0403	0404	0405	0406	0407
0630	0408	0409	0410	0411	0412	0413	0414	0415
0640	0416	0417	0418	0419	0420	0421	0422	0423
0650	0424	0425	0426	0427	0428	0429	0430	0431
0660	0432	0433	0434	0435	0436	0437	0438	0439
0670	0440	0441	0442	0443	0444	0445	0446	0447
0700	0448	0449	0450	0451	0452	0453	0454	0455
0710	0456	0457	0458	0459	0460	0461	0462	0463
0720	0464	0465	0466	0467	0468	0469	0470	0471
0730	0472	0473	0474	0475	0476	0477	0478	0479
0740	0480	0481	0482	0483	0484	0485	0486	0487
0750	0488	0489	0490	0491	0492	0493	0494	0495
0760	0496	0497	0498	0499	0500	0501	0502	0503
0770	0504	0505	0506	0507	0508	0509	0510	0511

1000 to 1777 (Octal)	0512 to 1023 (Decimal)

	0	1	2	3	4	5	6	7
1000	0512	0513	0514	0515	0516	0517	0518	0519
1010	0520	0521	0522	0523	0524	0525	0526	0527
1020	0528	0529	0530	0531	0532	0533	0534	0535
1030	0536	0537	0538	0539	0540	0541	0542	0543
1040	0544	0545	0546	0547	0548	0549	0550	0551
1050	0552	0553	0554	0555	0556	0557	0558	0559
1060	0560	0561	0562	0563	0564	0565	0566	0567
1070	0568	0569	0570	0571	0572	0573	0574	0575
1100	0576	0577	0578	0579	0580	0581	0582	0583
1110	0584	0585	0586	0587	0588	0589	0590	0591
1120	0592	0593	0594	0595	0596	0597	0598	0599
1130	0600	0601	0602	0603	0604	0605	0606	0607
1140	0608	0609	0610	0611	0612	0613	0614	0615
1150	0616	0617	0618	0619	0620	0621	0622	0623
1160	0624	0625	0626	0627	0628	0629	0630	0631
1170	0632	0633	0634	0635	0636	0637	0638	0639
1200	0640	0641	0642	0643	0644	0645	0646	0647
1210	0648	0649	0650	0651	0652	0653	0654	0655
1220	0656	0657	0658	0659	0660	0661	0662	0663
1230	0664	0665	0666	0667	0668	0669	0670	0671
1240	0672	0673	0674	0675	0676	0677	0678	0679
1250	0680	0681	0682	0683	0684	0685	0686	0687
1260	0688	0689	0690	0691	0692	0693	0694	0695
1270	0696	0697	0698	0699	0700	0701	0702	0703
1300	0704	0705	0706	0707	0708	0709	0710	0711
1310	0712	0713	0714	0715	0716	0717	0718	0719
1320	0720	0721	0722	0723	0724	0725	0726	0727
1330	0728	0729	0730	0731	0732	0733	0734	0735
1340	0736	0737	0738	0739	0740	0741	0742	0743
1350	0744	0745	0746	0747	0748	0749	0750	0751
1360	0752	0753	0754	0755	0756	0757	0758	0759
1370	0760	0761	0762	0763	0764	0765	0766	0767

	0	1	2	3	4	5	6	7
1400	0768	0769	0770	0771	0772	0773	0774	0775
1410	0776	0777	0778	0779	0780	0781	0782	0783
1420	0784	0785	0786	0787	0788	0789	0790	0791
1430	0792	0793	0794	0795	0796	0797	0798	0799
1440	0800	0801	0802	0803	0804	0805	0806	0807
1450	0808	0809	0810	0811	0812	0813	0814	0815
1460	0816	0817	0818	0819	0820	0821	0822	0823
1470	0824	0825	0826	0827	0828	0829	0830	0831
1500	0832	0833	0834	0835	0836	0837	0838	0839
1510	0840	0841	0842	0843	0844	0845	0846	0847
1520	0848	0849	0850	0851	0852	0853	0854	0855
1530	0856	0857	0858	0859	0860	0861	0862	0863
1540	0864	0865	0866	0867	0868	0869	0870	0871
1550	0872	0873	0874	0875	0876	0877	0878	0879
1560	0880	0881	0882	0883	0884	0885	0886	0887
1570	0888	0889	0890	0891	0892	0893	0894	0895
1600	0896	0897	0898	0899	0900	0901	0902	0903
1610	0904	0905	0906	0907	0908	0909	0910	0911
1620	0912	0913	0914	0915	0916	0917	0918	0919
1630	0920	0921	0922	0923	0924	0925	0926	0927
1640	0928	0929	0930	0931	0932	0933	0934	0935
1650	0936	0937	0938	0939	0940	0941	0942	0943
1660	0944	0945	0946	0947	0948	0949	0950	0951
1670	0952	0953	0954	0955	0956	0957	0958	0959
1700	0960	0961	0962	0963	0964	0965	0966	0967
1710	0968	0969	0970	0971	0972	0973	0974	0975
1720	0976	0977	0978	0979	0980	0981	0982	0983
1730	0984	0985	0986	0987	0988	0989	0990	0991
1740	0992	0993	0994	0995	0996	0997	0998	0999
1750	1000	1001	1002	1003	1004	1005	1006	1007
1760	1008	1009	1010	1011	1012	1013	1014	1015
1770	1016	1017	1018	1019	1020	1021	1022	1023

This table is reproduced with the permission of the International Business Machines Corporation.

Octal-Decimal Integer Conversion Table

	0	1	2	3	4	5	6	7
2000	1024	1025	1026	1027	1028	1029	1030	1031
2010	1032	1033	1034	1035	1036	1037	1038	1039
2020	1040	1041	1042	1043	1044	1045	1046	1047
2030	1048	1049	1050	1051	1052	1053	1054	1055
2040	1056	1057	1058	1059	1060	1061	1062	1063
2050	1064	1065	1066	1067	1068	1069	1070	1071
2060	1072	1073	1074	1075	1076	1077	1078	1079
2070	1080	1081	1082	1083	1084	1085	1086	1087
2100	1088	1089	1090	1091	1092	1093	1094	1095
2110	1096	1097	1098	1099	1100	1101	1102	1103
2120	1104	1105	1106	1107	1108	1109	1110	1111
2130	1112	1113	1114	1115	1116	1117	1118	1119
2140	1120	1121	1122	1123	1124	1125	1126	1127
2150	1128	1129	1130	1131	1132	1133	1134	1135
2160	1136	1137	1138	1139	1140	1141	1142	1143
2170	1144	1145	1146	1147	1148	1149	1150	1151
2200	1152	1153	1154	1155	1156	1157	1158	1159
2210	1160	1161	1162	1163	1164	1165	1166	1167
2220	1168	1169	1170	1171	1172	1173	1174	1175
2230	1176	1177	1178	1179	1180	1181	1182	1183
2240	1184	1185	1186	1187	1188	1189	1190	1191
2250	1192	1193	1194	1195	1196	1197	1198	1199
2260	1200	1201	1202	1203	1204	1205	1206	1207
2270	1208	1209	1210	1211	1212	1213	1214	1215
2300	1216	1217	1218	1219	1220	1221	1222	1223
2310	1224	1225	1226	1227	1228	1229	1230	1231
2320	1232	1233	1234	1235	1236	1237	1238	1239
2330	1240	1241	1242	1243	1244	1245	1246	1247
2340	1248	1249	1250	1251	1252	1253	1254	1255
2350	1256	1257	1258	1259	1260	1261	1262	1263
2360	1264	1265	1266	1267	1268	1269	1270	1271
2370	1272	1273	1274	1275	1276	1277	1278	1279

	0	1	2	3	4	5	6	7
2400	1280	1281	1282	1283	1284	1285	1286	1287
2410	1288	1289	1290	1291	1292	1293	1294	1295
2420	1296	1297	1298	1299	1300	1301	1302	1303
2430	1304	1305	1306	1307	1308	1309	1310	1311
2440	1312	1313	1314	1315	1316	1317	1318	1319
2450	1320	1321	1322	1323	1324	1325	1326	1327
2460	1328	1329	1330	1331	1332	1333	1334	1335
2470	1336	1337	1338	1339	1340	1341	1342	1343
2500	1344	1345	1346	1347	1348	1349	1350	1351
2510	1352	1353	1354	1355	1356	1357	1358	1359
2520	1360	1361	1362	1363	1364	1365	1366	1367
2530	1368	1369	1370	1371	1372	1373	1374	1375
2540	1376	1377	1378	1379	1380	1381	1382	1383
2550	1384	1385	1386	1387	1388	1389	1390	1391
2560	1392	1393	1394	1395	1396	1397	1398	1399
2570	1400	1401	1402	1403	1404	1405	1406	1407
2600	1408	1409	1410	1411	1412	1413	1414	1415
2610	1416	1417	1418	1419	1420	1421	1422	1423
2620	1424	1425	1426	1427	1428	1429	1430	1431
2630	1432	1433	1434	1435	1436	1437	1438	1439
2640	1440	1441	1442	1443	1444	1445	1446	1447
2650	1448	1449	1450	1451	1452	1453	1454	1455
2660	1456	1457	1458	1459	1460	1461	1462	1463
2670	1464	1465	1466	1467	1468	1469	1470	1471
2700	1472	1473	1474	1475	1476	1477	1478	1479
2710	1480	1481	1482	1483	1484	1485	1486	1487
2720	1488	1489	1490	1491	1492	1493	1494	1495
2730	1496	1497	1498	1499	1500	1501	1502	1503
2740	1504	1505	1506	1507	1508	1509	1510	1511
2750	1512	1513	1514	1515	1516	1517	1518	1519
2760	1520	1521	1522	1523	1524	1525	1526	1527
2770	1528	1529	1530	1531	1532	1533	1534	1535

2000 to 2777 (Octal) | 1024 to 1535 (Decimal)

Octal	Decimal
10000 -	4096
20000 -	8192
30000 -	12288
40000 -	16384
50000 -	20480
60000 -	24576
70000 -	28672

	0	1	2	3	4	5	6	7
3000	1536	1537	1538	1539	1540	1541	1542	1543
3010	1544	1545	1546	1547	1548	1549	1550	1551
3020	1552	1553	1554	1555	1556	1557	1558	1559
3030	1560	1561	1562	1563	1564	1565	1566	1567
3040	1568	1569	1570	1571	1572	1573	1574	1575
3050	1576	1577	1578	1579	1580	1581	1582	1583
3060	1584	1585	1586	1587	1588	1589	1590	1591
3070	1592	1593	1594	1595	1596	1597	1598	1599
3100	1600	1601	1602	1603	1604	1605	1606	1607
3110	1608	1609	1610	1611	1612	1613	1614	1615
3120	1616	1617	1618	1619	1620	1621	1622	1623
3130	1624	1625	1626	1627	1628	1629	1630	1631
3140	1632	1633	1634	1635	1636	1637	1638	1639
3150	1640	1641	1642	1643	1644	1645	1646	1647
3160	1648	1649	1650	1651	1652	1653	1654	1655
3170	1656	1657	1658	1659	1660	1661	1662	1663
3200	1664	1665	1666	1667	1668	1669	1670	1671
3210	1672	1673	1674	1675	1676	1677	1678	1679
3220	1680	1681	1682	1683	1684	1685	1686	1687
3230	1688	1689	1690	1691	1692	1693	1694	1695
3240	1696	1697	1698	1699	1700	1701	1702	1703
3250	1704	1705	1706	1707	1708	1709	1710	1711
3260	1712	1713	1714	1715	1716	1717	1718	1719
3270	1720	1721	1722	1723	1724	1725	1726	1727
3300	1728	1729	1730	1731	1732	1733	1734	1735
3310	1736	1737	1738	1739	1740	1741	1742	1743
3320	1744	1745	1746	1747	1748	1749	1750	1751
3330	1752	1753	1754	1755	1756	1757	1758	1759
3340	1760	1761	1762	1763	1764	1765	1766	1767
3350	1768	1769	1770	1771	1772	1773	1774	1775
3360	1776	1777	1778	1779	1780	1781	1782	1783
3370	1784	1785	1786	1787	1788	1789	1790	1791

	0	1	2	3	4	5	6	7
3400	1792	1793	1794	1795	1796	1797	1798	1799
3410	1800	1801	1802	1803	1804	1805	1806	1807
3420	1808	1809	1810	1811	1812	1813	1814	1815
3430	1816	1817	1818	1819	1820	1821	1822	1823
3440	1824	1825	1826	1827	1828	1829	1830	1831
3450	1832	1833	1834	1835	1836	1837	1838	1839
3460	1840	1841	1842	1843	1844	1845	1846	1847
3470	1848	1849	1850	1851	1852	1853	1854	1855
3500	1856	1857	1858	1859	1860	1861	1862	1863
3510	1864	1865	1866	1867	1868	1869	1870	1871
3520	1872	1873	1874	1875	1876	1877	1878	1879
3530	1880	1881	1882	1883	1884	1885	1886	1887
3540	1888	1889	1890	1891	1892	1893	1894	1895
3550	1896	1897	1898	1899	1900	1901	1902	1903
3560	1904	1905	1906	1907	1908	1909	1910	1911
3570	1912	1913	1914	1915	1916	1917	1918	1919
3600	1920	1921	1922	1923	1924	1925	1926	1927
3610	1928	1929	1930	1931	1932	1933	1934	1935
3620	1936	1937	1938	1939	1940	1941	1942	1943
3630	1944	1945	1946	1947	1948	1949	1950	1951
3640	1952	1953	1954	1955	1956	1957	1958	1959
3650	1960	1961	1962	1963	1964	1965	1966	1967
3660	1968	1969	1970	1971	1972	1973	1974	1975
3670	1976	1977	1978	1979	1980	1981	1982	1983
3700	1984	1985	1986	1987	1988	1989	1990	1991
3710	1992	1993	1994	1995	1996	1997	1998	1999
3720	2000	2001	2002	2003	2004	2005	2006	2007
3730	2008	2009	2010	2011	2012	2013	2014	2015
3740	2016	2017	2018	2019	2020	2021	2022	2023
3750	2024	2025	2026	2027	2028	2029	2030	2031
3760	2032	2033	2034	2035	2036	2037	2038	2039
3770	2040	2041	2042	2043	2044	2045	2046	2047

3000 to 3777 (Octal) | 1536 to 2047 (Decimal)

Octal-Decimal Integer Conversion Table

4000 to 4777 (Octal) | 2048 to 2559 (Decimal)

Octal Decimal
10000 - 4096
20000 - 8192
30000 - 12288
40000 - 16384
50000 - 20480
60000 - 24576
70000 - 28672

	0	1	2	3	4	5	6	7
4000	2048	2049	2050	2051	2052	2053	2054	2055
4010	2056	2057	2058	2059	2060	2061	2062	2063
4020	2064	2065	2066	2067	2068	2069	2070	2071
4030	2072	2073	2074	2075	2076	2077	2078	2079
4040	2080	2081	2082	2083	2084	2085	2086	2087
4050	2088	2089	2090	2091	2092	2093	2094	2095
4060	2096	2097	2098	2099	2100	2101	2102	2103
4070	2104	2105	2106	2107	2108	2109	2110	2111
4100	2112	2113	2114	2115	2116	2117	2118	2119
4110	2120	2121	2122	2123	2124	2125	2126	2127
4120	2128	2129	2130	2131	2132	2133	2134	2135
4130	2136	2137	2138	2139	2140	2141	2142	2143
4140	2144	2145	2146	2147	2148	2149	2150	2151
4150	2152	2153	2154	2155	2156	2157	2158	2159
4160	2160	2161	2162	2163	2164	2165	2166	2167
4170	2168	2169	2170	2171	2172	2173	2174	2175
4200	2176	2177	2178	2179	2180	2181	2182	2183
4210	2184	2185	2186	2187	2188	2189	2190	2191
4220	2192	2193	2194	2195	2196	2197	2198	2199
4230	2200	2201	2202	2203	2204	2205	2206	2207
4240	2208	2209	2210	2211	2212	2213	2214	2215
4250	2216	2217	2218	2219	2220	2221	2222	2223
4260	2224	2225	2226	2227	2228	2229	2230	2231
4270	2232	2233	2234	2235	2236	2237	2238	2239
4300	2240	2241	2242	2243	2244	2245	2246	2247
4310	2248	2249	2250	2251	2252	2253	2254	2255
4320	2256	2257	2258	2259	2260	2261	2262	2263
4330	2264	2265	2266	2267	2268	2269	2270	2271
4340	2272	2273	2274	2275	2276	2277	2278	2279
4350	2280	2281	2282	2283	2284	2285	2286	2287
4360	2288	2289	2290	2291	2292	2293	2294	2295
4370	2296	2297	2298	2299	2300	2301	2302	2303

	0	1	2	3	4	5	6	7
4400	2304	2305	2306	2307	2308	2309	2310	2311
4410	2312	2313	2314	2315	2316	2317	2318	2319
4420	2320	2321	2322	2323	2324	2325	2326	2327
4430	2328	2329	2330	2331	2332	2333	2334	2335
4440	2336	2337	2338	2339	2340	2341	2342	2343
4450	2344	2345	2346	2347	2348	2349	2350	2351
4460	2352	2353	2354	2355	2356	2357	2358	2359
4470	2360	2361	2362	2363	2364	2365	2366	2367
4500	2368	2369	2370	2371	2372	2373	2374	2375
4510	2376	2377	2378	2379	2380	2381	2382	2383
4520	2384	2385	2386	2387	2388	2389	2390	2391
4530	2392	2393	2394	2395	2396	2397	2398	2399
4540	2400	2401	2402	2403	2404	2405	2406	2407
4550	2408	2409	2410	2411	2412	2413	2414	2415
4560	2416	2417	2418	2419	2420	2421	2422	2423
4570	2424	2425	2426	2427	2428	2429	2430	2431
4600	2432	2433	2434	2435	2436	2437	2438	2439
4610	2440	2441	2442	2443	2444	2445	2446	2447
4620	2448	2449	2450	2451	2452	2453	2454	2455
4630	2456	2457	2458	2459	2460	2461	2462	2463
4640	2464	2465	2466	2467	2468	2469	2470	2471
4650	2472	2473	2474	2475	2476	2477	2478	2479
4660	2480	2481	2482	2483	2484	2485	2486	2487
4670	2488	2489	2490	2491	2492	2493	2494	2495
4700	2496	2497	2498	2499	2500	2501	2502	2503
4710	2504	2505	2506	2507	2508	2509	2510	2511
4720	2512	2513	2514	2515	2516	2517	2518	2519
4730	2520	2521	2522	2523	2524	2525	2526	2527
4740	2528	2529	2530	2531	2532	2533	2534	2535
4750	2536	2537	2538	2539	2540	2541	2542	2543
4760	2544	2545	2546	2547	2548	2549	2550	2551
4770	2552	2553	2554	2555	2556	2557	2558	2559

5000 to 5777 (Octal) | 2560 to 3071 (Decimal)

	0	1	2	3	4	5	6	7
5000	2560	2561	2562	2563	2564	2565	2566	2567
5010	2568	2569	2570	2571	2572	2573	2574	2575
5020	2576	2577	2578	2579	2580	2581	2582	2583
5030	2584	2585	2586	2587	2588	2589	2590	2591
5040	2592	2593	2594	2595	2596	2597	2598	2599
5050	2600	2601	2602	2603	2604	2605	2606	2607
5060	2608	2609	2610	2611	2612	2613	2614	2615
5070	2616	2617	2618	2619	2620	2621	2622	2623
5100	2624	2625	2626	2627	2628	2629	2630	2631
5110	2632	2633	2634	2635	2636	2637	2638	2639
5120	2640	2641	2642	2643	2644	2645	2646	2647
5130	2648	2649	2650	2651	2652	2653	2654	2655
5140	2656	2657	2658	2659	2660	2661	2662	2663
5150	2664	2665	2666	2667	2668	2669	2670	2671
5160	2672	2673	2674	2675	2676	2677	2678	2679
5170	2680	2681	2682	2683	2684	2685	2686	2687
5200	2688	2689	2690	2691	2692	2693	2694	2695
5210	2696	2697	2698	2699	2700	2701	2702	2703
5220	2704	2705	2706	2707	2708	2709	2710	2711
5230	2712	2713	2714	2715	2716	2717	2718	2719
5240	2720	2721	2722	2723	2724	2725	2726	2727
5250	2728	2729	2730	2731	2732	2733	2734	2735
5260	2736	2737	2738	2739	2740	2741	2742	2743
5270	2744	2745	2746	2747	2748	2749	2750	2751
5300	2752	2753	2754	2755	2756	2757	2758	2759
5310	2760	2761	2762	2763	2764	2765	2766	2767
5320	2768	2769	2770	2771	2772	2773	2774	2775
5330	2776	2777	2778	2779	2780	2781	2782	2783
5340	2784	2785	2786	2787	2788	2789	2790	2791
5350	2792	2793	2794	2795	2796	2797	2798	2799
5360	2800	2801	2802	2803	2804	2805	2806	2807
5370	2808	2809	2810	2811	2812	2813	2814	2815

	0	1	2	3	4	5	6	7
5400	2816	2817	2818	2819	2820	2821	2822	2823
5410	2824	2825	2826	2827	2828	2829	2830	2831
5420	2832	2833	2834	2835	2836	2837	2838	2839
5430	2840	2841	2842	2843	2844	2845	2846	2847
5440	2848	2849	2850	2851	2852	2853	2854	2855
5450	2856	2857	2858	2859	2860	2861	2862	2863
5460	2864	2865	2866	2867	2868	2869	2870	2871
5470	2872	2873	2874	2875	2876	2877	2878	2879
5500	2880	2881	2882	2883	2884	2885	2886	2887
5510	2888	2889	2890	2891	2892	2893	2894	2895
5520	2896	2897	2898	2899	2900	2901	2902	2903
5530	2904	2905	2906	2907	2908	2909	2910	2911
5540	2912	2913	2914	2915	2916	2917	2918	2919
5550	2920	2921	2922	2923	2924	2925	2926	2927
5560	2928	2929	2930	2931	2932	2933	2934	2935
5570	2936	2937	2938	2939	2940	2941	2942	2943
5600	2944	2945	2946	2947	2948	2949	2950	2951
5610	2952	2953	2954	2955	2956	2957	2958	2959
5620	2960	2961	2962	2963	2964	2965	2966	2967
5630	2968	2969	2970	2971	2972	2973	2974	2975
5640	2976	2977	2978	2979	2980	2981	2982	2983
5650	2984	2985	2986	2987	2988	2989	2990	2991
5660	2992	2993	2994	2995	2996	2997	2998	2999
5670	3000	3001	3002	3003	3004	3005	3006	3007
5700	3008	3009	3010	3011	3012	3013	3014	3015
5710	3016	3017	3018	3019	3020	3021	3022	3023
5720	3024	3025	3026	3027	3028	3029	3030	3031
5730	3032	3033	3034	3035	3036	3037	3038	3039
5740	3040	3041	3042	3043	3044	3045	3046	3047
5750	3048	3049	3050	3051	3052	3053	3054	3055
5760	3056	3057	3058	3059	3060	3061	3062	3063
5770	3064	3065	3066	3067	3068	3069	3070	3071

Octal-Decimal Integer Conversion Table

	0	1	2	3	4	5	6	7
6000	3072	3073	3074	3075	3076	3077	3078	3079
6010	3080	3081	3082	3083	3084	3085	3086	3087
6020	3088	3089	3090	3091	3092	3093	3094	3095
6030	3096	3097	3098	3099	3100	3101	3102	3103
6040	3104	3105	3106	3107	3108	3109	3110	3111
6050	3112	3113	3114	3115	3116	3117	3118	3119
6060	3120	3121	3122	3123	3124	3125	3126	3127
6070	3128	3129	3130	3131	3132	3133	3134	3135
6100	3136	3137	3138	3139	3140	3141	3142	3143
6110	3144	3145	3146	3147	3148	3149	3150	3151
6120	3152	3153	3154	3155	3156	3157	3158	3159
6130	3160	3161	3162	3163	3164	3165	3166	3167
6140	3168	3169	3170	3171	3172	3173	3174	3175
6150	3176	3177	3178	3179	3180	3181	3182	3183
6160	3184	3185	3186	3187	3188	3189	3190	3191
6170	3192	3193	3194	3195	3196	3197	3198	3199
6200	3200	3201	3202	3203	3204	3205	3206	3207
6210	3208	3209	3210	3211	3212	3213	3214	3215
6220	3216	3217	3218	3219	3220	3221	3222	3223
6230	3224	3225	3226	3227	3228	3229	3230	3231
6240	3232	3233	3234	3235	3236	3237	3238	3239
6250	3240	3241	3242	3243	3244	3245	3246	3247
6260	3248	3249	3250	3251	3252	3253	3254	3255
6270	3256	3257	3258	3259	3260	3261	3262	3263
6300	3264	3265	3266	3267	3268	3269	3270	3271
6310	3272	3273	3274	3275	3276	3277	3278	3279
6320	3280	3281	3282	3283	3284	3285	3286	3287
6330	3288	3289	3290	3291	3292	3293	3294	3295
6340	3296	3297	3298	3299	3300	3301	3302	3303
6350	3304	3305	3306	3307	3308	3309	3310	3311
6360	3312	3313	3314	3315	3316	3317	3318	3319
6370	3320	3321	3322	3323	3324	3325	3326	3327

	0	1	2	3	4	5	6	7
6400	3328	3329	3330	3331	3332	3333	3334	3335
6410	3336	3337	3338	3339	3340	3341	3342	3343
6420	3344	3345	3346	3347	3348	3349	3350	3351
6430	3352	3353	3354	3355	3356	3357	3358	3359
6440	3360	3361	3362	3363	3364	3365	3366	3367
6450	3368	3369	3370	3371	3372	3373	3374	3375
6460	3376	3377	3378	3379	3380	3381	3382	3383
6470	3384	3385	3386	3387	3388	3389	3390	3391
6500	3392	3393	3394	3395	3396	3397	3398	3399
6510	3400	3401	3402	3403	3404	3405	3406	3407
6520	3408	3409	3410	3411	3412	3413	3414	3415
6530	3416	3417	3418	3419	3420	3421	3422	3423
6540	3424	3425	3426	3427	3428	3429	3430	3431
6550	3432	3433	3434	3435	3436	3437	3438	3439
6560	3440	3441	3442	3443	3444	3445	3446	3447
6570	3448	3449	3450	3451	3452	3453	3454	3455
6600	3456	3457	3458	3459	3460	3461	3462	3463
6610	3464	3465	3466	3467	3468	3469	3470	3471
6620	3472	3473	3474	3475	3476	3477	3478	3479
6630	3480	3481	3482	3483	3484	3485	3486	3487
6640	3488	3489	3490	3491	3492	3493	3494	3495
6650	3496	3497	3498	3499	3500	3501	3502	3503
6660	3504	3505	3506	3507	3508	3509	3510	3511
6670	3512	3513	3514	3515	3516	3517	3518	3519
6700	3520	3521	3522	3523	3524	3525	3526	3527
6710	3528	3529	3530	3531	3532	3533	3534	3535
6720	3536	3537	3538	3539	3540	3541	3542	3543
6730	3544	3545	3546	3547	3548	3549	3550	3551
6740	3552	3553	3554	3555	3556	3557	3558	3559
6750	3560	3561	3562	3563	3564	3565	3566	3567
6760	3568	3569	3570	3571	3572	3573	3574	3575
6770	3576	3577	3578	3579	3580	3581	3582	3583

6000 to 6777 (Octal) | 3072 to 3583 (Decimal)

Octal	Decimal
10000 -	4096
20000 -	8192
30000 -	12288
40000 -	16384
50000 -	20480
60000 -	24576
70000 -	28672

	0	1	2	3	4	5	6	7
7000	3584	3585	3586	3587	3588	3589	3590	3591
7010	3592	3593	3594	3595	3596	3597	3598	3599
7020	3600	3601	3602	3603	3604	3605	3606	3607
7030	3608	3609	3610	3611	3612	3613	3614	3615
7040	3616	3617	3618	3619	3620	3621	3622	3623
7050	3624	3625	3626	3627	3628	3629	3630	3631
7060	3632	3633	3634	3635	3636	3637	3638	3639
7070	3640	3641	3642	3643	3644	3645	3646	3647
7100	3648	3649	3650	3651	3652	3653	3654	3655
7110	3656	3657	3658	3659	3660	3661	3662	3663
7120	3664	3665	3666	3667	3668	3669	3670	3671
7130	3672	3673	3674	3675	3676	3677	3678	3679
7140	3680	3681	3682	3683	3684	3685	3686	3687
7150	3688	3689	3690	3691	3692	3693	3694	3695
7160	3696	3697	3698	3699	3700	3701	3702	3703
7170	3704	3705	3706	3707	3708	3709	3710	3711
7200	3712	3713	3714	3715	3716	3717	3718	3719
7210	3720	3721	3722	3723	3724	3725	3726	3727
7220	3728	3729	3730	3731	3732	3733	3734	3735
7230	3736	3737	3738	3739	3740	3741	3742	3743
7240	3744	3745	3746	3747	3748	3749	3750	3751
7250	3752	3753	3754	3755	3756	3757	3758	3759
7260	3760	3761	3762	3763	3764	3765	3766	3767
7270	3768	3769	3770	3771	3772	3773	3774	3775
7300	3776	3777	3778	3779	3780	3781	3782	3783
7310	3784	3785	3786	3787	3788	3789	3790	3791
7320	3792	3793	3794	3795	3796	3797	3798	3799
7330	3800	3801	3802	3803	3804	3805	3806	3807
7340	3808	3809	3810	3811	3812	3813	3814	3815
7350	3816	3817	3818	3819	3820	3821	3822	3823
7360	3824	3825	3826	3827	3828	3829	3830	3831
7370	3832	3833	3834	3835	3836	3837	3838	3839

	0	1	2	3	4	5	6	7
7400	3840	3841	3842	3843	3844	3845	3846	3847
7410	3848	3849	3850	3851	3852	3853	3854	3855
7420	3856	3857	3858	3859	3860	3861	3862	3863
7430	3864	3865	3866	3867	3868	3869	3870	3871
7440	3872	3873	3874	3875	3876	3877	3878	3879
7450	3880	3881	3882	3883	3884	3885	3886	3887
7460	3888	3889	3890	3891	3892	3893	3894	3895
7470	3896	3897	3898	3899	3900	3901	3902	3903
7500	3904	3905	3906	3907	3908	3909	3910	3911
7510	3912	3913	3914	3915	3916	3917	3918	3919
7520	3920	3921	3922	3923	3924	3925	3926	3927
7530	3928	3929	3930	3931	3932	3933	3934	3935
7540	3936	3937	3938	3939	3940	3941	3942	3943
7550	3944	3945	3946	3947	3948	3949	3950	3951
7560	3952	3953	3954	3955	3956	3957	3958	3959
7570	3960	3961	3962	3963	3964	3965	3966	3967
7600	3968	3969	3970	3971	3972	3973	3974	3975
7610	3976	3977	3978	3979	3980	3981	3982	3983
7620	3984	3985	3986	3987	3988	3989	3990	3991
7630	3992	3993	3994	3995	3996	3997	3998	3999
7640	4000	4001	4002	4003	4004	4005	4006	4007
7650	4008	4009	4010	4011	4012	4013	4014	4015
7660	4016	4017	4018	4019	4020	4021	4022	4023
7670	4024	4025	4026	4027	4028	4029	4030	4031
7700	4032	4033	4034	4035	4036	4037	4038	4039
7710	4040	4041	4042	4043	4044	4045	4046	4047
7720	4048	4049	4050	4051	4052	4053	4054	4055
7730	4056	4057	4058	4059	4060	4061	4062	4063
7740	4064	4065	4066	4067	4068	4069	4070	4071
7750	4072	4073	4074	4075	4076	4077	4078	4079
7760	4080	4081	4082	4083	4084	4085	4086	4087
7770	4088	4089	4090	4091	4092	4093	4094	4095

7000 to 7777 (Octal) | 3584 to 4095 (Decimal)

Octal-Decimal Fraction Conversion Table

OCTAL	DEC.	OCTAL	DEC.	OCTAL	DEC.	OCTAL	DEC.
.000	.000000	.100	.125000	.200	.250000	.300	.375000
.001	.001953	.101	.126953	.201	.251953	.301	.376953
.002	.003906	.102	.128906	.202	.253906	.302	.378906
.003	.005859	.103	.130859	.203	.255859	.303	.380859
.004	.007812	.104	.132812	.204	.257812	.304	.382812
.005	.009765	.105	.134765	.205	.259765	.305	.384765
.006	.011718	.106	.136718	.206	.261718	.306	.386718
.007	.013671	.107	.138671	.207	.263671	.307	.388671
.010	.015625	.110	.140625	.210	.265625	.310	.390625
.011	.017578	.111	.142578	.211	.267578	.311	.392578
.012	.019531	.112	.144531	.212	.269531	.312	.394531
.013	.021484	.113	.146484	.213	.271484	.313	.396484
.014	.023437	.114	.148437	.214	.273437	.314	.398437
.015	.025390	.115	.150390	.215	.275390	.315	.400390
.016	.027343	.116	.152343	.216	.277343	.316	.402343
.017	.029296	.117	.154296	.217	.279296	.317	.404296
.020	.031250	.120	.156250	.220	.281250	.320	.406250
.021	.033203	.121	.158203	.221	.283203	.321	.408203
.022	.035156	.122	.160156	.222	.285156	.322	.410156
.023	.037109	.123	.162109	.223	.287109	.323	.412109
.024	.039062	.124	.164062	.224	.289062	.324	.414062
.025	.041015	.125	.166015	.225	.291015	.325	.416015
.026	.042968	.126	.167968	.226	.292968	.326	.417968
.027	.044921	.127	.169921	.227	.294921	.327	.419921
.030	.046875	.130	.171875	.230	.296875	.330	.421875
.031	.048828	.131	.173828	.231	.298828	.331	.423828
.032	.050781	.132	.175781	.232	.300781	.332	.425781
.033	.052734	.133	.177734	.233	.302734	.333	.427734
.034	.054687	.134	.179687	.234	.304687	.334	.429687
.035	.056640	.135	.181640	.235	.306640	.335	.431640
.036	.058593	.136	.183593	.236	.308593	.336	.433593
.037	.060546	.137	.185546	.237	.310546	.337	.435546
.040	.062500	.140	.187500	.240	.312500	.340	.437500
.041	.064453	.141	.189453	.241	.314453	.341	.439453
.042	.066406	.142	.191406	.242	.316406	.342	.441406
.043	.068359	.143	.193359	.243	.318359	.343	.443359
.044	.070312	.144	.195312	.244	.320312	.344	.445312
.045	.072265	.145	.197265	.245	.322265	.345	.447265
.046	.074218	.146	.199218	.246	.324218	.346	.449218
.047	.076171	.147	.201171	.247	.326171	.347	.451171
.050	.078125	.150	.203125	.250	.328125	.350	.453125
.051	.080078	.151	.205078	.251	.330078	.351	.455078
.052	.082031	.152	.207031	.252	.332031	.352	.457031
.053	.083984	.153	.208984	.253	.333984	.353	.458984
.054	.085937	.154	.210937	.254	.335937	.354	.460937
.055	.087890	.155	.212890	.255	.337890	.355	.462890
.056	.089843	.156	.214843	.256	.339843	.356	.464843
.057	.091796	.157	.216796	.257	.341796	.357	.466796
.060	.093750	.160	.218750	.260	.343750	.360	.468750
.061	.095703	.161	.220703	.261	.345703	.361	.470703
.062	.097656	.162	.222656	.262	.347656	.362	.472656
.063	.099609	.163	.224609	.263	.349609	.363	.474609
.064	.101562	.164	.226562	.264	.351562	.364	.476562
.065	.103515	.165	.228515	.265	.353515	.365	.478515
.066	.105468	.166	.230468	.266	.355468	.366	.480468
.067	.107421	.167	.232421	.267	.357421	.367	.482421
.070	.109375	.170	.234375	.270	.359375	.370	.484375
.071	.111328	.171	.236328	.271	.361328	.371	.486328
.072	.113281	.172	.238281	.272	.363281	.372	.488281
.073	.115234	.173	.240234	.273	.365234	.373	.490234
.074	.117187	.174	.242187	.274	.367187	.374	.492187
.075	.119140	.175	.244140	.275	.369140	.375	.494140
.076	.121093	.176	.246093	.276	.371093	.376	.496093
.077	.123046	.177	.248046	.277	.373046	.377	.498046

Octal-Decimal Fraction Conversion Table

OCTAL	DEC.	OCTAL	DEC.	OCTAL	DEC.	OCTAL	DEC.
.000000	.000000	.000100	.000244	.000200	.000488	.000300	.000732
.000001	.000003	.000101	.000247	.000201	.000492	.000301	.000736
.000002	.000007	.000102	.000251	.000202	.000495	.000302	.000740
.000003	.000011	.000103	.000255	.000203	.000499	.000303	.000743
.000004	.000015	.000104	.000259	.000204	.000503	.000304	.000747
.000005	.000019	.000105	.000263	.000205	.000507	.000305	.000751
.000006	.000022	.000106	.000267	.000206	.000511	.000306	.000755
.000007	.000026	.000107	.000270	.000207	.000514	.000307	.000759
.000010	.000030	.000110	.000274	.000210	.000518	.000310	.000762
.000011	.000034	.000111	.000278	.000211	.000522	.000311	.000766
.000012	.000038	.000112	.000282	.000212	.000526	.000312	.000770
.000013	.000041	.000113	.000286	.000213	.000530	.000313	.000774
.000014	.000045	.000114	.000289	.000214	.000534	.000314	.000778
.000015	.000049	.000115	.000293	.000215	.000537	.000315	.000782
.000016	.000053	.000116	.000297	.000216	.000541	.000316	.000785
.000017	.000057	.000117	.000301	.000217	.000545	.000317	.000789
.000020	.000061	.000120	.000305	.000220	.000549	.000320	.000793
.000021	.000064	.000121	.000308	.000221	.000553	.000321	.000797
.000022	.000068	.000122	.000312	.000222	.000556	.000322	.000801
.000023	.000072	.000123	.000316	.000223	.000560	.000323	.000805
.000024	.000076	.000124	.000320	.000224	.000564	.000324	.000808
.000025	.000080	.000125	.000324	.000225	.000568	.000325	.000812
.000026	.000083	.000126	.000328	.000226	.000572	.000326	.000816
.000027	.000087	.000127	.000331	.000227	.000576	.000327	.000820
.000030	.000091	.000130	.000335	.000230	.000579	.000330	.000823
.000031	.000095	.000131	.000339	.000231	.000583	.000331	.000827
.000032	.000099	.000132	.000343	.000232	.000587	.000332	.000831
.000033	.000102	.000133	.000347	.000233	.000591	.000333	.000835
.000034	.000106	.000134	.000350	.000234	.000595	.000334	.000839
.000035	.000110	.000135	.000354	.000235	.000598	.000335	.000843
.000036	.000114	.000136	.000358	.000236	.000602	.000336	.000846
.000037	.000118	.000137	.000362	.000237	.000606	.000337	.000850
.000040	.000122	.000140	.000366	.000240	.000610	.000340	.000854
.000041	.000125	.000141	.000370	.000241	.000614	.000341	.000858
.000042	.000129	.000142	.000373	.000242	.000617	.000342	.000862
.000043	.000133	.000143	.000377	.000243	.000621	.000343	.000865
.000044	.000137	.000144	.000381	.000244	.000625	.000344	.000869
.000045	.000141	.000145	.000385	.000245	.000629	.000345	.000873
.000046	.000144	.000146	.000389	.000246	.000633	.000346	.000877
.000047	.000148	.000147	.000392	.000247	.000637	.000347	.000881
.000050	.000152	.000150	.000396	.000250	.000640	.000350	.000885
.000051	.000156	.000151	.000400	.000251	.000644	.000351	.000888
.000052	.000160	.000152	.000404	.000252	.000648	.000352	.000892
.000053	.000164	.000153	.000408	.000253	.000652	.000353	.000896
.000054	.000167	.000154	.000411	.000254	.000656	.000354	.000900
.000055	.000171	.000155	.000415	.000255	.000659	.000355	.000904
.000056	.000175	.000156	.000419	.000256	.000663	.000356	.000907
.000057	.000179	.000157	.000423	.000257	.000667	.000357	.000911
.000060	.000183	.000160	.000427	.000260	.000671	.000360	.000915
.000061	.000186	.000161	.000431	.000261	.000675	.000361	.000919
.000062	.000190	.000162	.000434	.000262	.000679	.000362	.000923
.000063	.000194	.000163	.000438	.000263	.000682	.000363	.000926
.000064	.000198	.000164	.000442	.000264	.000686	.000364	.000930
.000065	.000202	.000165	.000446	.000265	.000690	.000365	.000934
.000066	.000205	.000166	.000450	.000266	.000694	.000366	.000938
.000067	.000209	.000167	.000453	.000267	.000698	.000367	.000942
.000070	.000213	.000170	.000457	.000270	.000701	.000370	.000946
.000071	.000217	.000171	.000461	.000271	.000705	.000371	.000949
.000072	.000221	.000172	.000465	.000272	.000709	.000372	.000953
.000073	.000225	.000173	.000469	.000273	.000713	.000373	.000957
.000074	.000228	.000174	.000473	.000274	.000717	.000374	.000961
.000075	.000232	.000175	.000476	.000275	.000720	.000375	.000965
.000076	.000236	.000176	.000480	.000276	.000724	.000376	.000968
.000077	.000240	.000177	.000484	.000277	.000728	.000377	.000972

Octal-Decimal Fraction Conversion Table

OCTAL	DEC.	OCTAL	DEC.	OCTAL	DEC.	OCTAL	DEC.
.000400	.000976	.000500	.001220	.000600	.001464	.000700	.001708
.000401	.000980	.000501	.001224	.000601	.001468	.000701	.001712
.000402	.000984	.000502	.001228	.000602	.001472	.000702	.001716
.000403	.000988	.000503	.001232	.000603	.001476	.000703	.001720
.000404	.000991	.000504	.001235	.000604	.001480	.000704	.001724
.000405	.000995	.000505	.001239	.000605	.001483	.000705	.001728
.000406	.000999	.000506	.001243	.000606	.001487	.000706	.001731
.000407	.001003	.000507	.001247	.000607	.001491	.000707	.001735
.000410	.001007	.000510	.001251	.000610	.001495	.000710	.001739
.000411	.001010	.000511	.001255	.000611	.001499	.000711	.001743
.000412	.001014	.000512	.001258	.000612	.001502	.000712	.001747
.000413	.001018	.000513	.001262	.000613	.001506	.000713	.001750
.000414	.001022	.000514	.001266	.000614	.001510	.000714	.001754
.000415	.001026	.000515	.001270	.000615	.001514	.000715	.001758
.000416	.001029	.000516	.001274	.000616	.001518	.000716	.001762
.000417	.001033	.000517	.001277	.000617	.001522	.000717	.001766
.000420	.001037	.000520	.001281	.000620	.001525	.000720	.001770
.000421	.001041	.000521	.001285	.000621	.001529	.000721	.001773
.000422	.001045	.000522	.001289	.000622	.001533	.000722	.001777
.000423	.001049	.000523	.001293	.000623	.001537	.000723	.001781
.000424	.001052	.000524	.001296	.000624	.001541	.000724	.001785
.000425	.001056	.000525	.001300	.000625	.001544	.000725	.001789
.000426	.001060	.000526	.001304	.000626	.001548	.000726	.001792
.000427	.001064	.000527	.001308	.000627	.001552	.000727	.001796
.000430	.001068	.000530	.001312	.000630	.001556	.000730	.001800
.000431	.001071	.000531	.001316	.000631	.001560	.000731	.001804
.000432	.001075	.000532	.001319	.000632	.001564	.000732	.001808
.000433	.001079	.000533	.001323	.000633	.001567	.000733	.001811
.000434	.001083	.000534	.001327	.000634	.001571	.000734	.001815
.000435	.001087	.000535	.001331	.000635	.001575	.000735	.001819
.000436	.001091	.000536	.001335	.000636	.001579	.000736	.001823
.000437	.001094	.000537	.001338	.000637	.001583	.000737	.001827
.000440	.001098	.000540	.001342	.000640	.001586	.000740	.001831
.000441	.001102	.000541	.001346	.000641	.001590	.000741	.001834
.000442	.001106	.000542	.001350	.000642	.001594	.000742	.001838
.000443	.001110	.000543	.001354	.000643	.001598	.000743	.001842
.000444	.001113	.000544	.001358	.000644	.001602	.000744	.001846
.000445	.001117	.000545	.001361	.000645	.001605	.000745	.001850
.000446	.001121	.000546	.001365	.000646	.001609	.000746	.001853
.000447	.001125	.000547	.001369	.000647	.001613	.000747	.001857
.000450	.001129	.000550	.001373	.000650	.001617	.000750	.001861
.000451	.001132	.000551	.001377	.000651	.001621	.000751	.001865
.000452	.001136	.000552	.001380	.000652	.001625	.000752	.001869
.000453	.001140	.000553	.001384	.000653	.001628	.000753	.001873
.000454	.001144	.000554	.001388	.000654	.001632	.000754	.001876
.000455	.001148	.000555	.001392	.000655	.001636	.000755	.001880
.000456	.001152	.000556	.001396	.000656	.001640	.000756	.001884
.000457	.001155	.000557	.001399	.000657	.001644	.000757	.001888
.000460	.001159	.000560	.001403	.000660	.001647	.000760	.001892
.000461	.001163	.000561	.001407	.000661	.001651	.000761	.001895
.000462	.001167	.000562	.001411	.000662	.001655	.000762	.001899
.000463	.001171	.000563	.001415	.000663	.001659	.000763	.001903
.000464	.001174	.000564	.001419	.000664	.001663	.000764	.001907
.000465	.001178	.000565	.001422	.000665	.001667	.000765	.001911
.000466	.001182	.000566	.001426	.000666	.001670	.000766	.001914
.000467	.001186	.000567	.001430	.000667	.001674	.000767	.001918
.000470	.001190	.000570	.001434	.000670	.001678	.000770	.001922
.000471	.001194	.000571	.001438	.000671	.001682	.000771	.001926
.000472	.001197	.000572	.001441	.000672	.001686	.000772	.001930
.000473	.001201	.000573	.001445	.000673	.001689	.000773	.001934
.000474	.001205	.000574	.001449	.000674	.001693	.000774	.001937
.000475	.001209	.000575	.001453	.000675	.001697	.000775	.001941
.000476	.001213	.000576	.001457	.000676	.001701	.000776	.001945
.000477	.001216	.000577	.001461	.000677	.001705	.000777	.001949

Decimal/ Hexadecimal Conversion Chart

The tables printed below are used to convert decimal numbers to hexadecimal and hexadecimal numbers to decimal. In the descriptions that follow, the explanation of each step is followed by an example in parentheses.

Decimal to Hexadecimal Conversion. Locate the decimal number (0489) in the body of the table. The two high-order digits (1E) of the hexadecimal number are in the left column on the same line, and the low-order digit (9) is at the top of the column. Thus, the hexadecimal number 1E9 is equal to the decimal number 0489.

Hexadecimal to Decimal Conversion. Locate the first two digits (1E) of the hexadecimal number (1E9) in the left column. Follow the line of figures across the page to the column headed by the low-order digit (9). The decimal number (0489) located at the junction of the horizontal line and the vertical column is the equivalent of the hexadecimal number.

	0	1	2	3	4	5	6	7	8	9	A	B	C	D	E	F
00	0000	0001	0002	0003	0004	0005	0006	0007	0008	0009	0010	0011	0012	0013	0014	0015
01	0016	0017	0018	0019	0020	0021	0022	0023	0024	0025	0026	0027	0028	0029	0030	0031
02	0032	0033	0034	0035	0036	0037	0038	0039	0040	0041	0042	0043	0044	0045	0046	0047
03	0048	0049	0050	0051	0052	0053	0054	0055	0056	0057	0058	0059	0060	0061	0062	0063
04	0064	0065	0066	0067	0068	0069	0070	0071	0072	0073	0074	0075	0076	0077	0078	0079
05	0080	0081	0082	0083	0084	0085	0086	0087	0088	0089	0090	0091	0092	0093	0094	0095
06	0096	0097	0098	0099	0100	0101	0102	0103	0104	0105	0106	0107	0108	0109	0110	0111
07	0112	0113	0114	0115	0116	0117	0118	0119	0120	0121	0122	0123	0124	0125	0126	0127
08	0128	0129	0130	0131	0132	0133	0134	0135	0136	0137	0138	0139	0140	0141	0142	0143
09	0144	0145	0146	0147	0148	0149	0150	0151	0152	0153	0154	0155	0156	0157	0158	0159
0A	0160	0161	0162	0163	0164	0165	0166	0167	0168	0169	0170	0171	0172	0173	0174	0175
0B	0176	0177	0178	0179	0180	0181	0182	0183	0184	0185	0186	0187	0188	0189	0190	0191
0C	0192	0193	0194	0195	0196	0197	0198	0199	0200	0201	0202	0203	0204	0205	0206	0207
0D	0208	0209	0210	0211	0212	0213	0214	0215	0216	0217	0218	0219	0220	0221	0222	0223
0E	0224	0225	0226	0227	0228	0229	0230	0231	0232	0233	0234	0235	0236	0237	0238	0239
0F	0240	0241	0242	0243	0244	0245	0246	0247	0248	0249	0250	0251	0252	0253	0254	0255
10	0256	0257	0258	0259	0260	0261	0262	0263	0264	0265	0266	0267	0268	0269	0270	0271
11	0272	0273	0274	0275	0276	0277	0278	0279	0280	0281	0282	0283	0284	0285	0286	0287
12	0288	0289	0290	0291	0292	0293	0294	0295	0296	0297	0298	0299	0300	0301	0302	0303
13	0304	0305	0306	0307	0308	0309	0310	0311	0312	0313	0314	0315	0316	0317	0318	0319
14	0320	0321	0322	0323	0324	0325	0326	0327	0328	0329	0330	0331	0332	0333	0334	0335
15	0336	0337	0338	0339	0340	0341	0342	0343	0344	0345	0346	0347	0348	0349	0350	0351
16	0352	0353	0354	0355	0356	0357	0358	0359	0360	0361	0362	0363	0364	0365	0366	0367
17	0368	0369	0370	0371	0372	0373	0374	0375	0376	0377	0378	0379	0380	0381	0382	0383
18	0384	0385	0386	0387	0388	0389	0390	0391	0392	0393	0394	0395	0396	0397	0398	0399
19	0400	0401	0402	0403	0404	0405	0406	0407	0408	0409	0410	0411	0412	0413	0414	0415
1A	0416	0417	0418	0419	0420	0421	0422	0423	0424	0425	0426	0427	0428	0429	0430	0431
1B	0432	0433	0434	0435	0436	0437	0438	0439	0440	0441	0442	0443	0444	0445	0446	0447
1C	0448	0449	0450	0451	0452	0453	0454	0455	0456	0457	0458	0459	0460	0461	0462	0463
1D	0464	0465	0466	0467	0468	0469	0470	0471	0472	0473	0474	0475	0476	0477	0478	0479
1E	0480	0481	0482	0483	0484	0485	0486	0487	0488	0489	0490	0491	0492	0493	0494	0495
1F	0496	0497	0498	0499	0500	0501	0502	0503	0504	0505	0506	0507	0508	0509	0510	0511
20	0512	0513	0514	0515	0516	0517	0518	0519	0520	0521	0522	0523	0524	0525	0526	0527
21	0528	0529	0530	0531	0532	0533	0534	0535	0536	0537	0538	0539	0540	0541	0542	0543
22	0544	0545	0546	0547	0548	0549	0550	0551	0552	0553	0554	0555	0556	0557	0558	0559
23	0560	0561	0562	0563	0564	0565	0566	0567	0568	0569	0570	0571	0572	0573	0574	0575
24	0576	0577	0578	0579	0580	0581	0582	0583	0584	0585	0586	0587	0588	0589	0590	0591
25	0592	0593	0594	0595	0596	0597	0598	0599	0600	0601	0602	0603	0604	0605	0606	0607
26	0608	0609	0610	0611	0612	0613	0614	0615	0616	0617	0618	0619	0620	0621	0622	0623
27	0624	0625	0626	0627	0628	0629	0630	0631	0632	0633	0634	0635	0636	0637	0638	0639
28	0640	0641	0642	0643	0644	0645	0646	0647	0648	0649	0650	0651	0652	0653	0654	0655
29	0656	0657	0658	0659	0660	0661	0662	0663	0664	0665	0666	0667	0668	0669	0670	0671
2A	0672	0673	0674	0675	0676	0677	0678	0679	0680	0681	0682	0683	0684	0685	0686	0687
2B	0688	0689	0690	0691	0692	0693	0694	0695	0696	0697	0698	0699	0700	0701	0702	0703
2C	0704	0705	0706	0707	0708	0709	0710	0711	0712	0713	0714	0715	0716	0717	0718	0719
2D	0720	0721	0722	0723	0724	0725	0726	0727	0728	0729	0730	0731	0732	0733	0734	0735
2E	0736	0737	0738	0739	0740	0741	0742	0743	0744	0745	0746	0747	0748	0749	0750	0751
2F	0752	0753	0754	0755	0756	0757	0758	0759	0760	0761	0762	0763	0764	0765	0766	0767
30	0768	0769	0770	0771	0772	0773	0774	0775	0776	0777	0778	0779	0780	0781	0782	0783
31	0784	0785	0786	0787	0788	0789	0790	0791	0792	0793	0794	0795	0796	0797	0798	0799
32	0800	0801	0802	0803	0804	0805	0806	0807	0808	0809	0810	0811	0812	0813	0814	0815
33	0816	0817	0818	0819	0820	0821	0822	0823	0824	0825	0826	0827	0828	0829	0830	0831
34	0832	0833	0834	0835	0836	0837	0838	0839	0840	0841	0842	0843	0844	0845	0846	0847
35	0848	0849	0850	0851	0852	0853	0854	0855	0856	0857	0858	0859	0860	0861	0862	0863
36	0864	0865	0866	0867	0868	0869	0870	0871	0872	0873	0874	0875	0876	0877	0878	0879
37	0880	0881	0882	0883	0884	0885	0886	0887	0888	0889	0890	0891	0892	0893	0894	0895
38	0896	0897	0898	0899	0900	0901	0902	0903	0904	0905	0906	0907	0908	0909	0910	0911
39	0912	0913	0914	0915	0916	0917	0918	0919	0920	0921	0922	0923	0924	0925	0926	0927
3A	0928	0929	0930	0931	0932	0933	0934	0935	0936	0937	0938	0939	0940	0941	0942	0943
3B	0944	0945	0946	0947	0948	0949	0950	0951	0952	0953	0954	0955	0956	0957	0958	0959
3C	0960	0961	0962	0963	0964	0965	0966	0967	0968	0969	0970	0971	0972	0973	0974	0975
3D	0976	0977	0978	0979	0980	0981	0982	0983	0984	0985	0986	0987	0988	0989	0990	0991
3E	0992	0993	0994	0995	0996	0997	0998	0999	1000	1001	1002	1003	1004	1005	1006	1007
3F	1008	1009	1010	1011	1012	1013	1014	1015	1016	1017	1018	1019	1020	1021	1022	1023
40	1024	1025	1026	1027	1028	1029	1030	1031	1032	1033	1034	1035	1036	1037	1038	1039
41	1040	1041	1042	1043	1044	1045	1046	1047	1048	1049	1050	1051	1052	1053	1054	1055
42	1056	1057	1058	1059	1060	1061	1062	1063	1064	1065	1066	1067	1068	1069	1070	1071
43	1072	1073	1074	1075	1076	1077	1078	1079	1080	1081	1082	1083	1084	1085	1086	1087
44	1088	1089	1090	1091	1092	1093	1094	1095	1096	1097	1098	1099	1100	1101	1102	1103
45	1104	1105	1106	1107	1108	1109	1110	1111	1112	1113	1114	1115	1116	1117	1118	1119
46	1120	1121	1122	1123	1124	1125	1126	1127	1128	1129	1130	1131	1132	1133	1134	1135
47	1136	1137	1138	1139	1140	1141	1142	1143	1144	1145	1146	1147	1148	1149	1150	1151
48	1152	1153	1154	1155	1156	1157	1158	1159	1160	1161	1162	1163	1164	1165	1166	1167
49	1168	1169	1170	1171	1172	1173	1174	1175	1176	1177	1178	1179	1180	1181	1182	1183
4A	1184	1185	1186	1187	1188	1189	1190	1191	1192	1193	1194	1195	1196	1197	1198	1199
4B	1200	1201	1202	1203	1204	1205	1206	1207	1208	1209	1210	1211	1212	1213	1214	1215
4C	1216	1217	1218	1219	1220	1221	1222	1223	1224	1225	1226	1227	1228	1229	1230	1231
4D	1232	1233	1234	1235	1236	1237	1238	1239	1240	1241	1242	1243	1244	1245	1246	1247
4E	1248	1249	1250	1251	1252	1253	1254	1255	1256	1257	1258	1259	1260	1261	1262	1263
4F	1264	1265	1266	1267	1268	1269	1270	1271	1272	1273	1274	1275	1276	1277	1278	1279
50	1280	1281	1282	1283	1284	1285	1286	1287	1288	1289	1290	1291	1292	1293	1294	1295
51	1296	1297	1298	1299	1300	1301	1302	1303	1304	1305	1306	1307	1308	1309	1310	1311
52	1312	1313	1314	1315	1316	1317	1318	1319	1320	1321	1322	1323	1324	1325	1326	1327
53	1328	1329	1330	1331	1332	1333	1334	1335	1336	1337	1338	1339	1340	1341	1342	1343
54	1344	1345	1346	1347	1348	1349	1350	1351	1352	1353	1354	1355	1356	1357	1358	1359
55	1360	1361	1362	1363	1364	1365	1366	1367	1368	1369	1370	1371	1372	1373	1374	1375
56	1376	1377	1378	1379	1380	1381	1382	1383	1384	1385	1386	1387	1388	1389	1390	1391
57	1392	1393	1394	1395	1396	1397	1398	1399	1400	1401	1402	1403	1404	1405	1406	1407
58	1408	1409	1410	1411	1412	1413	1414	1415	1416	1417	1418	1419	1420	1421	1422	1423
59	1424	1425	1426	1427	1428	1429	1430	1431	1432	1433	1434	1435	1436	1437	1438	1439
5A	1440	1441	1442	1443	1444	1445	1446	1447	1448	1449	1450	1451	1452	1453	1454	1455
5B	1456	1457	1458	1459	1460	1461	1462	1463	1464	1465	1466	1467	1468	1469	1470	1471
5C	1472	1473	1474	1475	1476	1477	1478	1479	1480	1481	1482	1483	1484	1485	1486	1487
5D	1488	1489	1490	1491	1492	1493	1494	1495	1496	1497	1498	1499	1500	1501	1502	1503
5E	1504	1505	1506	1507	1508	1509	1510	1511	1512	1513	1514	1515	1516	1517	1518	1519
5F	1520	1521	1522	1523	1524	1525	1526	1527	1528	1529	1530	1531	1532	1533	1534	1535
60	1536	1537	1538	1539	1540	1541	1542	1543	1544	1545	1546	1547	1548	1549	1550	1551
61	1552	1553	1554	1555	1556	1557	1558	1559	1560	1561	1562	1563	1564	1565	1566	1567
62	1568	1569	1570	1571	1572	1573	1574	1575	1576	1577	1578	1579	1580	1581	1582	1583
63	1584	1585	1586	1587	1588	1589	1590	1591	1592	1593	1594	1595	1596	1597	1598	1599
64	1600	1601	1602	1603	1604	1605	1606	1607	1608	1609	1610	1611	1612	1613	1614	1615
65	1616	1617	1618	1619	1620	1621	1622	1623	1624	1625	1626	1627	1628	1629	1630	1631
66	1632	1633	1634	1635	1636	1637	1638	1639	1640	1641	1642	1643	1644	1645	1646	1647
67	1648	1649	1650	1651	1652	1653	1654	1655	1656	1657	1658	1659	1660	1661	1662	1663
68	1664	1665	1666	1667	1668	1669	1670	1671	1672	1673	1674	1675	1676	1677	1678	1679
69	1680	1681	1682	1683	1684	1685	1686	1687	1688	1689	1690	1691	1692	1693	1694	1695
6A	1696	1697	1698	1699	1700	1701	1702	1703	1704	1705	1706	1707	1708	1709	1710	1711
6B	1712	1713	1714	1715	1716	1717	1718	1719	1720	1721	1722	1723	1724	1725	1726	1727
6C	1728	1729	1730	1731	1732	1733	1734	1735	1736	1737	1738	1739	1740	1741	1742	1743
6D	1744	1745	1746	1747	1748	1749	1750	1751	1752	1753	1754	1755	1756	1757	1758	1759
6E	1760	1761	1762	1763	1764	1765	1766	1767	1768	1769	1770	1771	1772	1773	1774	1775
6F	1776	1777	1778	1779	1780	1781	1782	1783	1784	1785	1786	1787	1788	1789	1790	1791
70	1792	1793	1794	1795	1796	1797	1798	1799	1800	1801	1802	1803	1804	1805	1806	1807
71	1808	1809	1810	1811	1812	1813	1814	1815	1816	1817	1818	1819	1820	1821	1822	1823
72	1824	1825	1826	1827	1828	1829	1830	1831	1832	1833	1834	1835	1836	1837	1838	1839
73	1840	1841	1842	1843	1844	1845	1846	1847	1848	1849	1850	1851	1852	1853	1854	1855
74	1856	1857	1858	1859	1860	1861	1862	1863	1864	1865	1866	1867	1868	1869	1870	1871
75	1872	1873	1874	1875	1876	1877	1878	1879	1880	1881	1882	1883	1884	1885	1886	1887
76	1888	1889	1890	1891	1892	1893	1894	1895	1896	1897	1898	1899	1900	1901	1902	1903
77	1904	1905	1906	1907	1908	1909	1910	1911	1912	1913	1914	1915	1916	1917	1918	1919
78	1920	1921	1922	1923	1924	1925	1926	1927	1928	1929	1930	1931	1932	1933	1934	1935
79	1936	1937	1938	1939	1940	1941	1942	1943	1944	1945	1946	1947	1948	1949	1950	1951
7A	1952	1953	1954	1955	1956	1957	1958	1959	1960	1961	1962	1963	1964	1965	1966	1967
7B	1968	1969	1970	1971	1972	1973	1974	1975	1976	1977	1978	1979	1980	1981	1982	1983
7C	1984	1985	1986	1987	1988	1989	1990	1991	1992	1993	1994	1995	1996	1997	1998	1999
7D	2000	2001	2002	2003	2004	2005	2006	2007	2008	2009	2010	2011	2012	2013	2014	2015
7E	2016	2017	2018	2019	2020	2021	2022	2023	2024	2025	2026	2027	2028	2029	2030	2031
7F	2032	2033	2034	2035	2036	2037	2038	2039	2040	2041	2042	2043	2044	2045	2046	2047

	0	1	2	3	4	5	6	7	8	9	A	B	C	D	E	F
80-	2048	2049	2050	2051	2052	2053	2054	2055	2056	2057	2058	2059	2060	2061	2062	2063
81-	2064	2065	2066	2067	2068	2069	2070	2071	2072	2073	2074	2075	2076	2077	2078	2079
82-	2080	2081	2082	2083	2084	2085	2086	2087	2088	2089	2090	2091	2092	2093	2094	2095
83-	2096	2097	2098	2099	2100	2101	2102	2103	2104	2105	2106	2107	2108	2109	2110	2111
84-	2112	2113	2114	2115	2116	2117	2118	2119	2120	2121	2122	2123	2124	2125	2126	2127
85-	2128	2129	2130	2131	2132	2133	2134	2135	2136	2137	2138	2139	2140	2141	2142	2143
86-	2144	2145	2146	2147	2148	2149	2150	2151	2152	2153	2154	2155	2156	2157	2158	2159
87-	2160	2161	2162	2163	2164	2165	2166	2167	2168	2169	2170	2171	2172	2173	2174	2175
88-	2176	2177	2178	2179	2180	2181	2182	2183	2184	2185	2186	2187	2188	2189	2190	2191
89-	2192	2193	2194	2195	2196	2197	2198	2199	2200	2201	2202	2203	2204	2205	2206	2207
8A-	2208	2209	2210	2211	2212	2213	2214	2215	2216	2217	2218	2219	2220	2221	2222	2223
8B-	2224	2225	2226	2227	2228	2229	2230	2231	2232	2233	2234	2235	2236	2237	2238	2239
8C-	2240	2241	2242	2243	2244	2245	2246	2247	2248	2249	2250	2251	2252	2253	2254	2255
8D-	2256	2257	2258	2259	2260	2261	2262	2263	2264	2265	2266	2267	2268	2269	2270	2271
8E-	2272	2273	2274	2275	2276	2277	2278	2279	2280	2281	2282	2283	2284	2285	2286	2287
8F-	2288	2289	2290	2291	2292	2293	2294	2295	2296	2297	2298	2299	2300	2301	2302	2303
90-	2304	2305	2306	2307	2308	2309	2310	2311	2312	2313	2314	2315	2316	2317	2318	2319
91-	2320	2321	2322	2323	2324	2325	2326	2327	2328	2329	2330	2331	2332	2333	2334	2335
92-	2336	2337	2338	2339	2340	2341	2342	2343	2344	2345	2346	2347	2348	2349	2350	2351
93-	2352	2353	2354	2355	2356	2357	2358	2359	2360	2361	2362	2363	2364	2365	2366	2367
94-	2368	2369	2370	2371	2372	2373	2374	2375	2376	2377	2378	2379	2380	2381	2382	2383
95-	2384	2385	2386	2387	2388	2389	2390	2391	2392	2393	2394	2395	2396	2397	2398	2399
96-	2400	2401	2402	2403	2404	2405	2406	2407	2408	2409	2410	2411	2412	2413	2414	2415
97-	2416	2417	2418	2419	2420	2421	2422	2423	2424	2425	2426	2427	2428	2429	2430	2431
98-	2432	2433	2434	2435	2436	2437	2438	2439	2440	2441	2442	2443	2444	2445	2446	2447
99-	2448	2449	2450	2451	2452	2453	2454	2455	2456	2457	2458	2459	2460	2461	2462	2463
9A-	2464	2465	2466	2467	2468	2469	2470	2471	2472	2473	2474	2475	2476	2477	2478	2479
9B-	2480	2481	2482	2483	2484	2485	2486	2487	2488	2489	2490	2491	2492	2493	2494	2495
9C-	2496	2497	2498	2499	2500	2501	2502	2503	2504	2505	2506	2507	2508	2509	2510	2511
9D-	2512	2513	2514	2515	2516	2517	2518	2519	2520	2521	2522	2523	2524	2525	2526	2527
9E-	2528	2529	2530	2531	2532	2533	2534	2535	2536	2537	2538	2539	2540	2541	2542	2543
9F-	2544	2545	2546	2547	2548	2549	2550	2551	2552	2553	2554	2555	2556	2557	2558	2559
A0-	2560	2561	2562	2563	2564	2565	2566	2567	2568	2569	2570	2571	2572	2573	2574	2575
A1-	2576	2577	2578	2579	2580	2581	2582	2583	2584	2585	2586	2587	2588	2589	2590	2591
A2-	2592	2593	2594	2595	2596	2597	2598	2599	2600	2601	2602	2603	2604	2605	2606	2607
A3-	2608	2609	2610	2611	2612	2613	2614	2615	2616	2617	2618	2619	2620	2621	2622	2623
A4-	2624	2625	2626	2627	2628	2629	2630	2631	2632	2633	2634	2635	2636	2637	2638	2639
A5-	2640	2641	2642	2643	2644	2645	2646	2647	2648	2649	2650	2651	2652	2653	2654	2655
A6-	2656	2657	2658	2659	2660	2661	2662	2663	2664	2665	2666	2667	2668	2669	2670	2671
A7-	2672	2673	2674	2675	2676	2677	2678	2679	2680	2681	2682	2683	2684	2685	2686	2687
A8-	2688	2689	2690	2691	2692	2693	2694	2695	2696	2697	2698	2699	2700	2701	2702	2703
A9-	2704	2705	2706	2707	2708	2709	2710	2711	2712	2713	2714	2715	2716	2717	2718	2719
AA-	2720	2721	2722	2723	2724	2725	2726	2727	2728	2729	2730	2731	2732	2733	2734	2735
AB-	2736	2737	2738	2739	2740	2741	2742	2743	2744	2745	2746	2747	2748	2749	2750	2751
AC-	2752	2753	2754	2755	2756	2757	2758	2759	2760	2761	2762	2763	2764	2765	2766	2767
AD-	2768	2769	2770	2771	2772	2773	2774	2775	2776	2777	2778	2779	2780	2781	2782	2783
AE-	2784	2785	2786	2787	2788	2789	2790	2791	2792	2793	2794	2795	2796	2797	2798	2799
AF-	2800	2801	2802	2803	2804	2805	2806	2807	2808	2809	2810	2811	2812	2813	2814	2815
B0-	2816	2817	2818	2819	2820	2821	2822	2823	2824	2825	2826	2827	2828	2829	2830	2831
B1-	2832	2833	2834	2835	2836	2837	2838	2839	2840	2841	2842	2843	2844	2845	2846	2847
B2-	2848	2849	2850	2851	2852	2853	2854	2855	2856	2857	2858	2859	2860	2861	2862	2863
B3-	2864	2865	2866	2867	2868	2869	2870	2871	2872	2873	2874	2875	2876	2877	2878	2879
B4-	2880	2881	2882	2883	2884	2885	2886	2887	2888	2889	2890	2891	2892	2893	2894	2895
B5-	2896	2897	2898	2899	2900	2901	2902	2903	2904	2905	2906	2907	2908	2909	2910	2911
B6-	2912	2913	2914	2915	2916	2917	2918	2919	2920	2921	2922	2923	2924	2925	2926	2927
B7-	2928	2929	2930	2931	2932	2933	2934	2935	2936	2937	2938	2939	2940	2941	2942	2943
B8-	2944	2945	2946	2947	2948	2949	2950	2951	2952	2953	2954	2955	2956	2957	2958	2959
B9-	2960	2961	2962	2963	2964	2965	2966	2967	2968	2969	2970	2971	2972	2973	2974	2975
BA-	2976	2977	2978	2979	2980	2981	2982	2983	2984	2985	2986	2987	2988	2989	2990	2991
BB-	2992	2993	2994	2995	2996	2997	2998	2999	3000	3001	3002	3003	3004	3005	3006	3007
BC-	3008	3009	3010	3011	3012	3013	3014	3015	3016	3017	3018	3019	3020	3021	3022	3023
BD-	3024	3025	3026	3027	3028	3029	3030	3031	3032	3033	3034	3035	3036	3037	3038	3039
BE-	3040	3041	3042	3043	3044	3045	3046	3047	3048	3049	3050	3051	3052	3053	3054	3055
BF-	3056	3057	3058	3059	3060	3061	3062	3063	3064	3065	3066	3067	3068	3069	3070	3071

	0	1	2	3	4	5	6	7	8	9	A	B	C	D	E	F
C0-	3072	3073	3074	3075	3076	3077	3078	3079	3080	3081	3082	3083	3084	3085	3086	3087
C1-	3088	3089	3090	3091	3092	3093	3094	3095	3096	3097	3098	3099	3100	3101	3102	3103
C2-	3104	3105	3106	3107	3108	3109	3110	3111	3112	3113	3114	3115	3116	3117	3118	3119
C3-	3120	3121	3122	3123	3124	3125	3126	3127	3128	3129	3130	3131	3132	3133	3134	3135
C4-	3136	3137	3138	3139	3140	3141	3142	3143	3144	3145	3146	3147	3148	3149	3150	3151
C5-	3152	3153	3154	3155	3156	3157	3158	3159	3160	3161	3162	3163	3164	3165	3166	3167
C6-	3168	3169	3170	3171	3172	3173	3174	3175	3176	3177	3178	3179	3180	3181	3182	3183
C7-	3184	3185	3186	3187	3188	3189	3190	3191	3192	3193	3194	3195	3196	3197	3198	3199
C8-	3200	3201	3202	3203	3204	3205	3206	3207	3208	3209	3210	3211	3212	3213	3214	3215
C9-	3216	3217	3218	3219	3220	3221	3222	3223	3224	3225	3226	3227	3228	3229	3230	3231
CA-	3232	3233	3234	3235	3236	3237	3238	3239	3240	3241	3242	3243	3244	3245	3246	3247
CB-	3248	3249	3250	3251	3252	3253	3254	3255	3256	3257	3258	3259	3260	3261	3262	3263
CC-	3264	3265	3266	3267	3268	3269	3270	3271	3272	3273	3274	3275	3276	3277	3278	3279
CD-	3280	3281	3282	3283	3284	3285	3286	3287	3288	3289	3290	3291	3292	3293	3294	3295
CE-	3296	3297	3298	3299	3300	3301	3302	3303	3304	3305	3306	3307	3308	3309	3310	3311
CF-	3312	3313	3314	3315	3316	3317	3318	3319	3320	3321	3322	3323	3324	3325	3326	3327
D0-	3328	3329	3330	3331	3332	3333	3334	3335	3336	3337	3338	3339	3340	3341	3342	3343
D1-	3344	3345	3346	3347	3348	3349	3350	3351	3352	3353	3354	3355	3356	3357	3358	3359
D2-	3360	3361	3362	3363	3364	3365	3366	3367	3368	3369	3370	3371	3372	3373	3374	3375
D3-	3376	3377	3378	3379	3380	3381	3382	3383	3384	3385	3386	3387	3388	3389	3390	3391
D4-	3392	3393	3394	3395	3396	3397	3398	3399	3400	3401	3402	3403	3404	3405	3406	3407
D5-	3408	3409	3410	3411	3412	3413	3414	3415	3416	3417	3418	3419	3420	3421	3422	3423
D6-	3424	3425	3426	3427	3428	3429	3430	3431	3432	3433	3434	3435	3436	3437	3438	3439
D7-	3440	3441	3442	3443	3444	3445	3446	3447	3448	3449	3450	3451	3452	3453	3454	3455
D8-	3456	3457	3458	3459	3460	3461	3462	3463	3464	3465	3466	3467	3468	3469	3470	3471
D9-	3472	3473	3474	3475	3476	3477	3478	3479	3480	3481	3482	3483	3484	3485	3486	3487
DA-	3488	3489	3490	3491	3492	3493	3494	3495	3496	3497	3498	3499	3500	3501	3502	3503
DB-	3504	3505	3506	3507	3508	3509	3510	3511	3512	3513	3514	3515	3516	3517	3518	3519
DC-	3520	3521	3522	3523	3524	3525	3526	3527	3528	3529	3530	3531	3532	3533	3534	3535
DD-	3536	3537	3538	3539	3540	3541	3542	3543	3544	3545	3546	3547	3548	3549	3550	3551
DE-	3552	3553	3554	3555	3556	3557	3558	3559	3560	3561	3562	3563	3564	3565	3566	3567
DF-	3568	3569	3570	3571	3572	3573	3574	3575	3576	3577	3578	3579	3580	3581	3582	3583
E0-	3584	3585	3586	3587	3588	3589	3590	3591	3592	3593	3594	3595	3596	3597	3598	3599
E1-	3600	3601	3602	3603	3604	3605	3606	3607	3608	3609	3610	3611	3612	3613	3614	3615
E2-	3616	3617	3618	3619	3620	3621	3622	3623	3624	3625	3626	3627	3628	3629	3630	3631
E3-	3632	3633	3634	3635	3636	3637	3638	3639	3640	3641	3642	3643	3644	3645	3646	3647
E4-	3648	3649	3650	3651	3652	3653	3654	3655	3656	3657	3658	3659	3660	3661	3662	3663
E5-	3664	3665	3666	3667	3668	3669	3670	3671	3672	3673	3674	3675	3676	3677	3678	3679
E6-	3680	3681	3682	3683	3684	3685	3686	3687	3688	3689	3690	3691	3692	3693	3694	3695
E7-	3696	3697	3698	3699	3700	3701	3702	3703	3704	3705	3706	3707	3708	3709	3710	3711
E8-	3712	3713	3714	3715	3716	3717	3718	3719	3720	3721	3722	3723	3724	3725	3726	3727
E9-	3728	3729	3730	3731	3732	3733	3734	3735	3736	3737	3738	3739	3740	3741	3742	3743
EA-	3744	3745	3746	3747	3748	3749	3750	3751	3752	3753	3754	3755	3756	3757	3758	3759
EB-	3760	3761	3762	3763	3764	3765	3766	3767	3768	3769	3770	3771	3772	3773	3774	3775
EC-	3776	3777	3778	3779	3780	3781	3782	3783	3784	3785	3786	3787	3788	3789	3790	3791
ED-	3792	3793	3794	3795	3796	3797	3798	3799	3800	3801	3802	3803	3804	3805	3806	3807
EE-	3808	3809	3810	3811	3812	3813	3814	3815	3816	3817	3818	3819	3820	3821	3822	3823
EF-	3824	3825	3826	3827	3828	3829	3830	3831	3832	3833	3834	3835	3836	3837	3838	3839
F0-	3840	3841	3842	3843	3844	3845	3846	3847	3848	3849	3850	3851	3852	3853	3854	3855
F1-	3856	3857	3858	3859	3860	3861	3862	3863	3864	3865	3866	3867	3868	3869	3870	3871
F2-	3872	3873	3874	3875	3876	3877	3878	3879	3880	3881	3882	3883	3884	3885	3886	3887
F3-	3888	3889	3890	3891	3892	3893	3894	3895	3896	3897	3898	3899	3900	3901	3902	3903
F4-	3904	3905	3906	3907	3908	3909	3910	3911	3912	3913	3914	3915	3916	3917	3918	3919
F5-	3920	3921	3922	3923	3924	3925	3926	3927	3928	3929	3930	3931	3932	3933	3934	3935
F6-	3936	3937	3938	3939	3940	3941	3942	3943	3944	3945	3946	3947	3948	3949	3950	3951
F7-	3952	3953	3954	3955	3956	3957	3958	3959	3960	3961	3962	3963	3964	3965	3966	3967
F8-	3968	3969	3970	3971	3972	3973	3974	3975	3976	3977	3978	3979	3980	3981	3982	3983
F9-	3984	3985	3986	3987	3988	3989	3990	3991	3992	3993	3994	3995	3996	3997	3998	3999
FA-	4000	4001	4002	4003	4004	4005	4006	4007	4008	4009	4010	4011	4012	4013	4014	4015
FB-	4016	4017	4018	4019	4020	4021	4022	4023	4024	4025	4026	4027	4028	4029	4030	4031
FC-	4032	4033	4034	4035	4036	4037	4038	4039	4040	4041	4042	4043	4044	4045	4046	4047
FD-	4048	4049	4050	4051	4052	4053	4054	4055	4056	4057	4058	4059	4060	4061	4062	4063
FE-	4064	4065	4066	4067	4068	4069	4070	4071	4072	4073	4074	4075	4076	4077	4078	4079
FF-	4080	4081	4082	4083	4084	4085	4086	4087	4088	4089	4090	4091	4092	4093	4094	4095

Dec	Bin	Hex	Dec	Bin	Hex
0	0000	0	8	1000	8
1	0001	1	9	1001	9
2	0010	2	10	1010	A
3	0011	3	11	1011	B
4	0100	4	12	1100	C
5	0101	5	13	1101	D
6	0110	6	14	1110	E
7	0111	7	15	1111	F

The table to the left gives the decimal, binary, and hexadecimal coding for the full range of four binary bits, from zero through F_{16} and 15_{10}.

To convert a four-digit hexadecimal number to decimal, determine the decimal value of the three low-order hexadecimal digits in the main table, and add the value for the high-order digit, as shown in the extended chart to the right.

For conversion of decimal values beyond the main table, deduct the largest number in the table at the right that will yield a positive result. The related digit is the high-order hexadecimal digit. Determine the three remaining hexadecimal digits by converting the product of the above subtraction in the main table.

Hex	Dec	Hex	Dec
1000	4096	9000	36864
2000	8192	A000	40960
3000	12288	B000	45056
4000	16384	C000	49152
5000	20480	D000	53248
6000	24576	E000	57344
7000	28672	F000	61440
8000	32768		

DECIMAL/HEXADECIMAL CONVERSION CHART – FRACTIONS

Decimal to Hexadecimal Conversion. Locate the decimal fraction (.1973) in the table. If the exact figure is not shown, locate the next higher and lower fractions (.19726563, .19750977). The first two digits of the hexadecimal fraction are at the top of the column (.32). To locate the third digit, determine by observation or subtraction the smaller difference between the known fraction and each of the found fractions. The smaller difference identifies the correct line (.008). The hexadecimal equivalent is .328.
If the hexadecimal fraction is required to more places, multiply the decimal fraction by 16 and develop integers as successive terms of the hexadecimal fraction. Using the previous sample decimal fraction:

```
  .1973
    x16
 3.1568
    x16
 2.5085
    x16
 8.1360
    x16
 2.1760
```

$.1973_{10} = .3282_{16}$

Hexadecimal to Decimal Conversion. Locate the first two digits (.1E) of the hexadecimal fraction (.1E9) in the horizontal row of column headings. Locate the third digit (.009) in the leftmost column of the table. Follow the .009 line horizontally to the right to the .1E column. The decimal equivalent is .11938477.
The decimal fractions in the table were carried to eight places and rounded. If 12 places are required, or if the hexadecimal fraction exceeds the capacity of the table, express the hexadecimal fraction as powers of 16 (expansion). For example:

$$.1E94_{16} = 1(16^{-1}) + 14(16^{-2}) + 9(16^{-3}) + 4(16^{-4})$$
$$= 1(.0625) + 14(.00390625) + 9(.000244140625) + 4(.0000152587890625)$$
$$= .119445800781250_{10}$$

	.00	.01	.02	.03	.04	.05	.06	.07	.08	.09	.0A	.0B	.0C	.0D	.0E	.0F
.000	.00000000	.00390625	.00781250	.01171875	.01562500	.01953125	.02343750	.02734375	.03125000	.03515625	.03906250	.04296875	.04687500	.05078125	.05468750	.05859375
.001	.00024414	.00415039	.00805664	.01196289	.01586914	.01977539	.02368164	.02758789	.03149414	.03540039	.03930664	.04321289	.04711914	.05102539	.05493164	.05883789
.002	.00048828	.00439453	.00830078	.01220703	.01611328	.02001953	.02392578	.02783203	.03173828	.03564453	.03955078	.04345703	.04736328	.05126953	.05517578	.05908203
.003	.00073242	.00463867	.00854492	.01245117	.01635742	.02026367	.02416992	.02807617	.03198242	.03588867	.03979492	.04370117	.04760742	.05151367	.05541992	.05932617
.004	.00097656	.00488281	.00878906	.01269531	.01660156	.02050781	.02441406	.02832031	.03222656	.03613281	.04003906	.04394531	.04785156	.05175781	.05566406	.05957031
.005	.00122070	.00512695	.00903320	.01293945	.01684570	.02075195	.02465820	.02856445	.03247070	.03637695	.04028320	.04418945	.04809570	.05200195	.05590820	.05981445
.006	.00146484	.00537109	.00927734	.01318359	.01708984	.02099609	.02490234	.02880859	.03271484	.03662109	.04052734	.04443359	.04833984	.05224609	.05615234	.06005859
.007	.00170898	.00561523	.00952148	.01342773	.01733398	.02124023	.02514648	.02905273	.03295898	.03686523	.04077148	.04467773	.04858398	.05249023	.05639648	.06030273
.008	.00195313	.00585938	.00976563	.01367188	.01757813	.02148438	.02539063	.02929688	.03320313	.03710938	.04101563	.04492188	.04882813	.05273438	.05664063	.06054688
.009	.00219727	.00610352	.01000977	.01391602	.01782227	.02172852	.02563477	.02954102	.03344727	.03735352	.04125977	.04516602	.04907227	.05297852	.05688477	.06079102
.00A	.00244141	.00634766	.01025391	.01416016	.01806641	.02197266	.02587891	.02978516	.03369141	.03759766	.04150391	.04541016	.04931641	.05322266	.05712891	.06103516
.00B	.00268555	.00659180	.01049805	.01440430	.01831055	.02221680	.02612305	.03002930	.03393555	.03784180	.04174805	.04565430	.04956055	.05346680	.05737305	.06127930
.00C	.00292969	.00683594	.01074219	.01464844	.01855469	.02246094	.02636719	.03027344	.03417969	.03808594	.04199219	.04589844	.04980469	.05371094	.05761719	.06152344
.00D	.00317383	.00708008	.01098633	.01489258	.01879883	.02270508	.02661133	.03051758	.03442383	.03833008	.04223633	.04614258	.05004883	.05395508	.05786133	.06176758
.00E	.00341797	.00732422	.01123047	.01513672	.01904297	.02294922	.02685547	.03076172	.03466797	.03857422	.04248047	.04638672	.05029297	.05419922	.05810547	.06201172
.00F	.00366211	.00756836	.01147461	.01538086	.01928711	.02319336	.02709961	.03100586	.03491211	.03881836	.04272461	.04663086	.05053711	.05444336	.05834961	.06225586

	.10	.11	.12	.13	.14	.15	.16	.17	.18	.19	.1A	.1B	.1C	.1D	.1E	.1F
.000	.06250000	.06640625	.07031250	.07421875	.07812500	.08203125	.08593750	.08984375	.09375000	.09765625	.10156250	.10546875	.10937500	.11328125	.11718750	.12109375
.001	.06274414	.06665039	.07055664	.07446289	.07836914	.08227539	.08618164	.09008789	.09399414	.09790039	.10180664	.10571289	.10961914	.11352539	.11743164	.12133789
.002	.06298828	.06689453	.07080078	.07470703	.07861328	.08251953	.08642578	.09033203	.09423828	.09814453	.10205078	.10595703	.10986328	.11376953	.11767578	.12158203
.003	.06323242	.06713867	.07104492	.07495117	.07885742	.08276367	.08666992	.09057617	.09448242	.09838867	.10229492	.10620117	.11010742	.11401367	.11791992	.12182617
.004	.06347656	.06738281	.07128906	.07519531	.07910156	.08300781	.08691406	.09082031	.09472656	.09863281	.10253906	.10644531	.11035156	.11425781	.11816406	.12207031
.005	.06372070	.06762695	.07153320	.07543945	.07934570	.08325195	.08715820	.09106445	.09497070	.09887695	.10278320	.10668945	.11059570	.11450195	.11840820	.12231445
.006	.06396484	.06787109	.07177734	.07568359	.07958984	.08349609	.08740234	.09130859	.09521484	.09912109	.10302734	.10693359	.11083984	.11474609	.11865234	.12255859
.007	.06420898	.06811523	.07202148	.07592773	.07983398	.08374023	.08764648	.09155273	.09545898	.09936523	.10327148	.10717773	.11108398	.11499023	.11889648	.12280273
.008	.06445313	.06835938	.07226563	.07617188	.08007813	.08398438	.08789063	.09179688	.09570313	.09960938	.10351563	.10742188	.11132813	.11523438	.11914063	.12304688
.009	.06469727	.06860352	.07250977	.07641602	.08032227	.08422852	.08813477	.09204102	.09594727	.09985352	.10375977	.10766602	.11157227	.11547852	.11938477	.12329102
.00A	.06494141	.06884766	.07275391	.07666016	.08056641	.08447266	.08837891	.09228516	.09619141	.10009766	.10400391	.10791016	.11181641	.11572266	.11962891	.12353516
.00B	.06518555	.06909180	.07299805	.07690430	.08081055	.08471680	.08862305	.09252930	.09643555	.10034180	.10424805	.10815430	.11206055	.11596680	.11987305	.12377930
.00C	.06542969	.06933594	.07324219	.07714844	.08105469	.08496094	.08886719	.09277344	.09667969	.10058594	.10449219	.10839844	.11230469	.11621094	.12011719	.12402344
.00D	.06567383	.06958008	.07348633	.07739258	.08129883	.08520508	.08911133	.09301758	.09692383	.10083008	.10473633	.10864258	.11254883	.11645508	.12036133	.12426758
.00E	.06591797	.06982422	.07373047	.07763672	.08154297	.08544922	.08935547	.09326172	.09716797	.10107422	.10498047	.10888672	.11279297	.11669922	.12060547	.12451172
.C0F	.06616211	.07006836	.07397461	.07788086	.08178711	.08569336	.08959961	.09350586	.09741211	.10131836	.10522461	.10913086	.11303711	.11694336	.12084961	.12475586

	.20	.21	.22	.23	.24	.25	.26	.27	.28	.29	.2A	.2B	.2C	.2D	.2E	.2F
.000	.12500000	.12890625	.13281250	.13671875	.14062500	.14453125	.14843750	.15234375	.15625000	.16015625	.16406250	.16796875	.17187500	.17578125	.17968750	.18359375
.001	.12524414	.12915039	.13305664	.13696289	.14086914	.14477539	.14868164	.15258789	.15649414	.16040039	.16430664	.16821289	.17211914	.17602539	.17993164	.18383789
.002	.12548828	.12939453	.13330078	.13720703	.14111328	.14501953	.14892578	.15283203	.15673828	.16064453	.16455078	.16845703	.17236328	.17626953	.18017578	.18408203
.003	.12573242	.12963867	.13354492	.13745117	.14135742	.14526367	.14916992	.15307617	.15698242	.16088867	.16479492	.16870117	.17260742	.17651367	.18041992	.18432617
.004	.12597656	.12988281	.13378906	.13769531	.14160156	.14550781	.14941406	.15332031	.15722656	.16113281	.16503906	.16894531	.17285156	.17675781	.18066406	.18457031
.005	.12622070	.13012695	.13403320	.13793945	.14184570	.14575195	.14965820	.15356445	.15747070	.16137695	.16528320	.16918945	.17309570	.17700195	.18090820	.18481445
.006	.12646484	.13037109	.13427734	.13818359	.14208984	.14599609	.14990234	.15380859	.15771484	.16162109	.16552734	.16943359	.17333984	.17724609	.18115234	.18505859
.007	.12670898	.13061523	.13452148	.13842773	.14233398	.14624023	.15014648	.15405273	.15795898	.16186523	.16577148	.16967773	.17358398	.17749023	.18139648	.18530273
.008	.12695313	.13085938	.13476563	.13867188	.14257813	.14648438	.15039063	.15429688	.15820313	.16210938	.16601563	.16992188	.17382813	.17773438	.18164063	.18554688
.009	.12719727	.13110352	.13500977	.13891602	.14282227	.14672852	.15063477	.15454102	.15844727	.16235352	.16625977	.17016602	.17407227	.17797852	.18188477	.18579102
.00A	.12744141	.13134766	.13525391	.13916016	.14306641	.14697266	.15087891	.15478516	.15869141	.16259766	.16650391	.17041016	.17431641	.17822266	.18212891	.18603516
.00B	.12768555	.13159180	.13549805	.13940430	.14331055	.14721680	.15112305	.15502930	.15893555	.16284180	.16674805	.17065430	.17456055	.17846680	.18237305	.18627930
.00C	.12792969	.13183594	.13574219	.13964844	.14355469	.14746094	.15136719	.15527344	.15917969	.16308594	.16699219	.17089844	.17480469	.17871094	.18261719	.18652344
.00D	.12817383	.13208008	.13598633	.13989258	.14379883	.14770508	.15161133	.15551758	.15942383	.16333008	.16723633	.17114258	.17504883	.17895508	.18286133	.18676758
.00E	.12841797	.13232422	.13623047	.14013672	.14404297	.14794922	.15185547	.15576172	.15966797	.16357422	.16748047	.17138672	.17529297	.17919922	.18310547	.18701172
.00F	.12866211	.13256836	.13647461	.14038086	.14428711	.14819336	.15209961	.15600586	.15991211	.16381836	.16772461	.17163086	.17553711	.17944336	.18334961	.18725586

	.30	.31	.32	.33	.34	.35	.36	.37	.38	.39	.3A	.3B	.3C	.3D	.3E	.3F
.000	.18750000	.19140625	.19531250	.19921875	.20312500	.20703125	.21093750	.21484375	.21875000	.22265625	.22656250	.23046875	.23437500	.23828125	.24218750	.24609375
.001	.18774414	.19165039	.19555664	.19946289	.20336914	.20727539	.21118164	.21508789	.21899414	.22290039	.22680664	.23071289	.23461914	.23852539	.24243164	.24633789
.002	.18798828	.19189453	.19580078	.19970703	.20361328	.20751953	.21142578	.21533203	.21923828	.22314453	.22705078	.23095703	.23486328	.23876953	.24267578	.24658203
.003	.18823242	.19213867	.19604492	.19995117	.20385742	.20776367	.21166992	.21557617	.21948242	.22338867	.22729492	.23120117	.23510742	.23901367	.24291992	.24682617
.004	.18847656	.19238281	.19628906	.20019531	.20410156	.20800781	.21191406	.21582031	.21972656	.22363281	.22753906	.23144531	.23535156	.23925781	.24316406	.24707031
.005	.18872070	.19262695	.19653320	.20043945	.20434570	.20825195	.21215820	.21606445	.21997070	.22387695	.22778320	.23168945	.23559570	.23950195	.24340820	.24731445
.006	.18896484	.19287109	.19677734	.20068359	.20458984	.20849609	.21240234	.21630859	.22021484	.22412109	.22802734	.23193359	.23583984	.23974609	.24365234	.24755859
.007	.18920898	.19311523	.19702148	.20092773	.20483398	.20874023	.21264648	.21655273	.22045898	.22436523	.22827148	.23217773	.23608398	.23999023	.24389648	.24780273
.008	.18945313	.19335938	.19726563	.20117188	.20507813	.20898438	.21289063	.21679688	.22070313	.22460938	.22851563	.23242188	.23632813	.24023438	.24414063	.24804688
.009	.18969727	.19360352	.19750977	.20141602	.20532227	.20922852	.21313477	.21704102	.22094727	.22485352	.22875977	.23266602	.23657227	.24047852	.24438477	.24829102
.00A	.18994141	.19384766	.19775391	.20166016	.20556641	.20947266	.21337891	.21728516	.22119141	.22509766	.22900391	.23291016	.23681641	.24072266	.24462891	.24853516
.00B	.19018555	.19409180	.19799805	.20190430	.20581055	.20971680	.21362305	.21752930	.22143555	.22534180	.22924805	.23315430	.23706055	.24096680	.24487305	.24877930
.00C	.19042969	.19433594	.19824219	.20214844	.20605469	.20996094	.21386719	.21777344	.22167969	.22558594	.22949219	.23339844	.23730469	.24121094	.24511719	.24902344
.00D	.19067383	.19458008	.19848633	.20239258	.20629883	.21020508	.21411133	.21801758	.22192383	.22583008	.22973633	.23364258	.23754883	.24145508	.24536133	.24926758
.00E	.19091797	.19482422	.19873047	.20263672	.20654297	.21044922	.21435547	.21826172	.22216797	.22607422	.22998047	.23388672	.23779297	.24169922	.24560547	.24951172
.00F	.19116211	.19506836	.19897461	.20288086	.20678711	.21069336	.21459961	.21850586	.22241211	.22631836	.23022461	.23413086	.23803711	.24194336	.24584961	.24975586

	.40	.41	.42	.43	.44	.45	.46	.47	.48	.49	.4A	.4B	.4C	.4D	.4E	.4F
.000	.25000000	.25390625	.25781250	.26171875	.26562500	.26953125	.27343750	.27734375	.28125000	.28515625	.28906250	.29296875	.29687500	.30078125	.30468750	.30859375
.001	.25024414	.25415039	.25805664	.26196289	.26586914	.26977539	.27368164	.27758789	.28149414	.28540039	.28930664	.29321289	.29711914	.30102539	.30493164	.30883789
.002	.25048828	.25439453	.25830078	.26220703	.26611328	.27001953	.27392578	.27783203	.28173828	.28564453	.28955078	.29345703	.29736328	.30126953	.30517578	.30908203
.003	.25073242	.25463867	.25854492	.26245117	.26635742	.27026367	.27416992	.27807617	.28198242	.28588867	.28979492	.29370117	.29760742	.30151367	.30541992	.30932617
.004	.25097656	.25488281	.25878906	.26269531	.26660156	.27050781	.27441406	.27832031	.28222656	.28613281	.29003906	.29394531	.29785156	.30175781	.30566406	.30957031
.005	.25122070	.25512695	.25903320	.26293945	.26684570	.27075195	.27465820	.27856445	.28247070	.28637695	.29028320	.29418945	.29809570	.30200195	.30590820	.30981445
.006	.25146484	.25537109	.25927734	.26318359	.26708984	.27099609	.27490234	.27880859	.28271484	.28662109	.29052734	.29443359	.29833984	.30224609	.30615234	.31005859
.007	.25170898	.25561523	.25952148	.26342773	.26733398	.27124023	.27514648	.27905273	.28295898	.28686523	.29077148	.29467773	.29858398	.30249023	.30639648	.31030273
.008	.25195313	.25585938	.25976563	.26367188	.26757813	.27148438	.27539063	.27929688	.28320313	.28710938	.29101563	.29492188	.29882813	.30273438	.30664063	.31054688
.009	.25219727	.25610352	.26000977	.26391602	.26782227	.27172852	.27563477	.27954102	.28344727	.28735352	.29125977	.29516602	.29907227	.30297852	.30688477	.31079102
.00A	.25244141	.25634766	.26025391	.26416016	.26806641	.27197266	.27587891	.27978516	.28369141	.28759766	.29150391	.29541016	.29931641	.30322266	.30712891	.31103516
.00B	.25268555	.25659180	.26049805	.26440430	.26831055	.27221680	.27612305	.28002930	.28393555	.28784180	.29174805	.29565430	.29956055	.30346680	.30737305	.31127930
.00C	.25292969	.25683594	.26074219	.26464844	.26855469	.27246094	.27636719	.28027344	.28417969	.28808594	.29199219	.29589844	.29980469	.30371094	.30761719	.31152344
.00D	.25317383	.25708008	.26098633	.26489258	.26879883	.27270508	.27661133	.28051758	.28442383	.28833008	.29223633	.29614258	.30004883	.30395508	.30786133	.31176758
.00E	.25341797	.25732422	.26123047	.26513672	.26904297	.27294922	.27685547	.28076172	.28466797	.28857422	.29248047	.29638672	.30029297	.30419922	.30810547	.31201172
.00F	.25366211	.25756836	.26147461	.26538086	.26928711	.27319336	.27709961	.28100586	.28491211	.28881836	.29272461	.29663086	.30053711	.30444336	.30834961	.31225586

	.50	.51	.52	.53	.54	.55	.56	.57	.58	.59	.5A	.5B	.5C	.5D	.5E	.5F
.000	.31250000	.31640625	.32031250	.32421875	.32812500	.33203125	.33593750	.33984375	.34375000	.34765625	.35156250	.35546875	.35937500	.36328125	.36718750	.37109375
.001	.31274414	.31665039	.32055664	.32446289	.32836914	.33227539	.33618164	.34008789	.34399414	.34790039	.35180664	.35571289	.35961914	.36352539	.36743164	.37133789
.002	.31298828	.31689453	.32080078	.32470703	.32861328	.33251953	.33642578	.34033203	.34423828	.34814453	.35205078	.35595703	.35986328	.36376953	.36767578	.37158203
.003	.31323242	.31713867	.32104492	.32495117	.32885742	.33276367	.33666992	.34057617	.34448242	.34838867	.35229492	.35620117	.36010742	.36401367	.36791992	.37182617
.004	.31347656	.31738281	.32128906	.32519531	.32910156	.33300781	.33691406	.34082031	.34472656	.34863281	.35253906	.35644531	.36035156	.36425781	.36816406	.37207031
.005	.31372070	.31762695	.32153320	.32543945	.32934570	.33325195	.33715820	.34106445	.34497070	.34887695	.35278320	.35668945	.36059570	.36450195	.36840820	.37231445
.006	.31396484	.31787109	.32177734	.32568359	.32958984	.33349609	.33740234	.34130859	.34521484	.34912109	.35302734	.35693359	.36083984	.36474609	.36865234	.37255859
.007	.31420898	.31811523	.32202148	.32592773	.32983398	.33374023	.33764648	.34155273	.34545898	.34936523	.35327148	.35717773	.36108398	.36499023	.36889648	.37280273
.008	.31445313	.31835938	.32226563	.32617188	.33007813	.33398438	.33789063	.34179688	.34570313	.34960938	.35351563	.35742188	.36132813	.36523438	.36914063	.37304688
.009	.31469727	.31860352	.32250977	.32641602	.33032227	.33422852	.33813477	.34204102	.34594727	.34985352	.35375977	.35766602	.36157227	.36547852	.36938477	.37329102
.00A	.31494141	.31884766	.32275391	.32666016	.33056641	.33447266	.33837891	.34228516	.34619141	.35009766	.35400391	.35791016	.36181641	.36572266	.36962891	.37353516
.00B	.31518555	.31909180	.32299805	.32690430	.33081055	.33471680	.33862305	.34252930	.34643555	.35034180	.35424805	.35815430	.36206055	.36596680	.36987305	.37377930
.00C	.31542969	.31933594	.32324219	.32714844	.33105469	.33496094	.33886719	.34277344	.34667969	.35058594	.35449219	.35839844	.36230469	.36621094	.37011719	.37402344
.00D	.31567383	.31958008	.32348633	.32739258	.33129883	.33520508	.33911133	.34301758	.34692383	.35083008	.35473633	.35864258	.36254883	.36645508	.37036133	.37426758
.00E	.31591797	.31982422	.32373047	.32763672	.33154297	.33544922	.33935547	.34326172	.34716797	.35107422	.35498047	.35888672	.36279297	.36669922	.37060547	.37451172
.00F	.31616211	.32006836	.32397461	.32788086	.33178711	.33569336	.33959961	.34350586	.34741211	.35131836	.35522461	.35913086	.36303711	.36694336	.37084961	.37475586

	.60	.61	.62	.63	.64	.65	.66	.67	.68	.69	.6A	.6B	.6C	.6D	.6E	.6F
.000	.37500000	.37890625	.38281250	.38671875	.39062500	.39453125	.39843750	.40234375	.40625000	.41015625	.41406250	.41796875	.42187500	.42578125	.42968750	.43359375
.001	.37524414	.37915039	.38305664	.38696289	.39086914	.39477539	.39868164	.40258789	.40649414	.41040039	.41430664	.41821289	.42211914	.42602539	.42993164	.43383789
.002	.37548828	.37939453	.38330078	.38720703	.39111328	.39501953	.39892578	.40283203	.40673828	.41064453	.41455078	.41845703	.42236328	.42626953	.43017578	.43408203
.003	.37573242	.37963867	.38354492	.38745117	.39135742	.39526367	.39916992	.40307617	.40698242	.41088867	.41479492	.41870117	.42260742	.42651367	.43041992	.43432617
.004	.37597656	.37988281	.38378906	.38769531	.39160156	.39550781	.39941406	.40332031	.40722656	.41113281	.41503906	.41894531	.42285156	.42675781	.43066406	.43457031
.005	.37622070	.38012695	.38403320	.38793945	.39184570	.39575195	.39965820	.40356445	.40747070	.41137695	.41528320	.41918945	.42309570	.42700195	.43090820	.43481445
.006	.37646484	.38037109	.38427734	.38818359	.39208984	.39599609	.39990234	.40380859	.40771484	.41162109	.41552734	.41943359	.42333984	.42724609	.43115234	.43505859
.007	.37670898	.38061523	.38452148	.38842773	.39233398	.39624023	.40014648	.40405273	.40795898	.41186523	.41577148	.41967773	.42358398	.42749023	.43139648	.43530273
.008	.37695313	.38085938	.38476563	.38867188	.39257813	.39648438	.40039063	.40429688	.40820313	.41210938	.41601563	.41992188	.42382813	.42773438	.43164063	.43554688
.009	.37719727	.38110352	.38500977	.38891602	.39282227	.39672852	.40063477	.40454102	.40844727	.41235352	.41625977	.42016602	.42407227	.42797852	.43188477	.43579102
.00A	.37744141	.38134766	.38525391	.38916016	.39306641	.39697266	.40087891	.40478516	.40869141	.41259766	.41650391	.42041016	.42431641	.42822266	.43212891	.43603516
.00B	.37768555	.38159180	.38549805	.38940430	.39331055	.39721680	.40112305	.40502930	.40893555	.41284180	.41674805	.42065430	.42456055	.42846680	.43237305	.43627930
.00C	.37792969	.38183594	.38574219	.38964844	.39355469	.39746094	.40136719	.40527344	.40917969	.41308594	.41699219	.42089844	.42480469	.42871094	.43261719	.43652344
.00D	.37817383	.38208008	.38598633	.38989258	.39379883	.39770508	.40161133	.40551758	.40942383	.41333008	.41723633	.42114258	.42504883	.42895508	.43286133	.43676758
.00E	.37841797	.38232422	.38623047	.39013672	.39404297	.39794922	.40185547	.40576172	.40966797	.41357422	.41748047	.42138672	.42529297	.42919922	.43310547	.43701172
.00F	.37866211	.38256836	.38647461	.39038086	.39428711	.39819336	.40209961	.40600586	.40991211	.41381836	.41772461	.42163086	.42553711	.42944336	.43334961	.43725586

	.70	.71	.72	.73	.74	.75	.76	.77	.78	.79	.7A	.7B	.7C	.7D	.7E	.7F
.000	.43750000	.44140625	.44531250	.44921875	.45312500	.45703125	.46093750	.46484375	.46875000	.47265625	.47656250	.48046875	.48437500	.48828125	.49218750	.49609375
.001	.43774414	.44165039	.44555664	.44946289	.45336914	.45727539	.46118164	.46508789	.46899414	.47290039	.47680664	.48071289	.48461914	.48852539	.49243164	.49633789
.002	.43798828	.44189453	.44580078	.44970703	.45361328	.45751953	.46142578	.46533203	.46923828	.47314453	.47705078	.48095703	.48486328	.48876953	.49267578	.49658203
.003	.43823242	.44213867	.44604492	.44995117	.45385742	.45776367	.46166992	.46557617	.46948242	.47338867	.47729492	.48120117	.48510742	.48901367	.49291992	.49682617
.004	.43847656	.44238281	.44628906	.45019531	.45410156	.45800781	.46191406	.46582031	.46972656	.47363281	.47753906	.48144531	.48535156	.48925781	.49316406	.49707031
.005	.43872070	.44262695	.44653320	.45043945	.45434570	.45825195	.46215820	.46606445	.46997070	.47387695	.47778320	.48168945	.48559570	.48950195	.49340820	.49731445
.006	.43896484	.44287109	.44677734	.45068359	.45458984	.45849609	.46240234	.46630859	.47021484	.47412109	.47802734	.48193359	.48583984	.48974609	.49365234	.49755859
.007	.43920898	.44311523	.44702148	.45092773	.45483398	.45874023	.46264648	.46655273	.47045898	.47436523	.47827148	.48217773	.48608398	.48999023	.49389648	.49780273
.008	.43945313	.44335938	.44726563	.45117188	.45507813	.45898438	.46289063	.46679688	.47070313	.47460938	.47851563	.48242188	.48632813	.49023438	.49414063	.49804688
.009	.43969727	.44360352	.44750977	.45141602	.45532227	.45922852	.46313477	.46704102	.47094727	.47485352	.47875977	.48266602	.48657227	.49047852	.49438477	.49829102
.00A	.43994141	.44384766	.44775391	.45166016	.45556641	.45947266	.46337891	.46728516	.47119141	.47509766	.47900391	.48291016	.48681641	.49072266	.49462891	.49853516
.00B	.44018555	.44409180	.44799805	.45190430	.45581055	.45971680	.46362305	.46752930	.47143555	.47534180	.47924805	.48315430	.48706055	.49096680	.49487305	.49877930
.00C	.44042969	.44433594	.44824219	.45214844	.45605469	.45996094	.46386719	.46777344	.47167969	.47558594	.47949219	.48339844	.48730469	.49121094	.49511719	.49902344
.00D	.44067383	.44458008	.44848633	.45239258	.45629883	.46020508	.46411133	.46801758	.47192383	.47583008	.47973633	.48364258	.48754883	.49145508	.49536133	.49926758
.00E	.44091797	.44482422	.44873047	.45263672	.45654297	.46044922	.46435547	.46826172	.47216797	.47607422	.47998047	.48388672	.48779297	.49169922	.49560547	.49951172
.00F	.44116211	.44506836	.44897461	.45288086	.45678711	.46069336	.46459961	.46850586	.47241211	.47631836	.48022461	.48413086	.48803711	.49194336	.49584961	.49975586

	.80	.81	.82	.83	.84	.85	.86	.87	.88	.89	.8A	.8B	.8C	.8D	.8E	.8F
.000	.50000000	.50390625	.50781250	.51171875	.51562500	.51953125	.52343750	.52734375	.53125000	.53515625	.53906250	.54296875	.54687500	.55078125	.55468750	.55859375
.001	.50024414	.50415039	.50805664	.51196289	.51586914	.51977539	.52368164	.52758789	.53149414	.53540039	.53930664	.54321289	.54711914	.55102539	.55493164	.55883789
.002	.50048828	.50439453	.50830078	.51220703	.51611328	.52001953	.52392578	.52783203	.53173828	.53564453	.53955078	.54345703	.54736328	.55126953	.55517578	.55908203
.003	.50073242	.50463867	.50854492	.51245117	.51635742	.52026367	.52416992	.52807617	.53198242	.53588867	.53979492	.54370117	.54760742	.55151367	.55541992	.55932617
.004	.50097656	.50488281	.50878906	.51269531	.51660156	.52050781	.52441406	.52832031	.53222656	.53613281	.54003906	.54394531	.54785156	.55175781	.55566406	.55957031
.005	.50122070	.50512695	.50903320	.51293945	.51684570	.52075195	.52465820	.52856445	.53247070	.53637695	.54028320	.54418945	.54809570	.55200195	.55590820	.55981445
.006	.50146484	.50537109	.50927734	.51318359	.51708984	.52099609	.52490234	.52880859	.53271484	.53662109	.54052734	.54443359	.54833984	.55224609	.55615234	.56005859
.007	.50170898	.50561523	.50952148	.51342773	.51733398	.52124023	.52514648	.52905273	.53295898	.53686523	.54077148	.54467773	.54858398	.55249023	.55639648	.56030273
.008	.50195313	.50585938	.50976563	.51367188	.51757813	.52148438	.52539063	.52929688	.53320313	.53710938	.54101563	.54492188	.54882813	.55273438	.55664063	.56054688
.009	.50219727	.50610352	.51000977	.51391602	.51782227	.52172852	.52563477	.52954102	.53344727	.53735352	.54125977	.54516602	.54907227	.55297852	.55688477	.56079102
.00A	.50244141	.50634766	.51025391	.51416016	.51806641	.52197266	.52587891	.52978516	.53369141	.53759766	.54150391	.54541016	.54931641	.55322266	.55712891	.56103516
.00B	.50268555	.50659180	.51049805	.51440430	.51831055	.52221680	.52612305	.53002930	.53393555	.53784180	.54174805	.54565430	.54956055	.55346680	.55737305	.56127930
.00C	.50292969	.50683594	.51074219	.51464844	.51855469	.52246094	.52636719	.53027344	.53417969	.53808594	.54199219	.54589844	.54980469	.55371094	.55761719	.56152344
.00D	.50317383	.50708008	.51098633	.51489258	.51879883	.52270508	.52661133	.53051758	.53442383	.53833008	.54223633	.54614258	.55004883	.55395508	.55786133	.56176758
.00E	.50341797	.50732422	.51123047	.51513672	.51904297	.52294922	.52685547	.53076172	.53466797	.53857422	.54248047	.54638672	.55029297	.55419922	.55810547	.56201172
.00F	.50366211	.50756836	.51147461	.51538086	.51928711	.52319336	.52709961	.53100586	.53491211	.53881836	.54272461	.54663086	.55053711	.55444336	.55834961	.56225586

	.90	.91	.92	.93	.94	.95	.96	.97	.98	.99	.9A	.9B	.9C	.9D	.9E	.9F
.000	.56250000	.56640625	.57031250	.57421875	.57812500	.58203125	.58593750	.58984375	.59375000	.59765625	.60156250	.60546875	.60937500	.61328125	.61718750	.62109375
.001	.56274414	.56665039	.57055664	.57446289	.57836914	.58227539	.58618164	.59008789	.59399414	.59790039	.60180664	.60571289	.60961914	.61352539	.61743164	.62133789
.002	.56298828	.56689453	.57080078	.57470703	.57861328	.58251953	.58642578	.59033203	.59423828	.59814453	.60205078	.60595703	.60986328	.61376953	.61767578	.62158203
.003	.56323242	.56713867	.57104492	.57495117	.57885742	.58276367	.58666992	.59057617	.59448242	.59838867	.60229492	.60620117	.61010742	.61401367	.61791992	.62182617
.004	.56347656	.56738281	.57128906	.57519531	.57910156	.58300781	.58691406	.59082031	.59472656	.59863281	.60253906	.60644531	.61035156	.61425781	.61816406	.62207031
.005	.56372070	.56762695	.57153320	.57543945	.57934570	.58325195	.58715820	.59106445	.59497070	.59887695	.60278320	.60668945	.61059570	.61450195	.61840820	.62231445
.006	.56396484	.56787109	.57177734	.57568359	.57958984	.58349609	.58740234	.59130859	.59521484	.59912109	.60302734	.60693359	.61083984	.61474609	.61865234	.62255859
.007	.56420898	.56811523	.57202148	.57592773	.57983398	.58374023	.58764648	.59155273	.59545898	.59936523	.60327148	.60717773	.61108398	.61499023	.61889648	.62280273
.008	.56445313	.56835938	.57226563	.57617188	.58007813	.58398438	.58789063	.59179688	.59570313	.59960938	.60351563	.60742188	.61132813	.61523438	.61914063	.62304688
.009	.56469727	.56860352	.57250977	.57641602	.58032227	.58422852	.58813477	.59204102	.59594727	.59985352	.60375977	.60766602	.61157227	.61547852	.61938477	.62329102
.00A	.56494141	.56884766	.57275391	.57666016	.58056641	.58447266	.58837891	.59228516	.59619141	.60009766	.60400391	.60791016	.61181641	.61572266	.61962891	.62353516
.00B	.56518555	.56909180	.57299805	.57690430	.58081055	.58471680	.58862305	.59252930	.59643555	.60034180	.60424805	.60815430	.61206055	.61596680	.61987305	.62377930
.00C	.56542969	.56933594	.57324219	.57714844	.58105469	.58496094	.58886719	.59277344	.59667969	.60058594	.60449219	.60839844	.61230469	.61621094	.62011719	.62402344
.00D	.56567383	.56958008	.57348633	.57739258	.58129883	.58520508	.58911133	.59301758	.59692383	.60083008	.60473633	.60864258	.61254883	.61645508	.62036133	.62426758
.00E	.56591797	.56982422	.57373047	.57763672	.58154297	.58544922	.58935547	.59326172	.59716797	.60107422	.60498047	.60888672	.61279297	.61669922	.62060547	.62451172
.00F	.56616211	.57006836	.57397461	.57788086	.58178711	.58569336	.58959961	.59350586	.59741211	.60131836	.60522461	.60913086	.61303711	.61694336	.62084961	.62475586

	.A0	.A1	.A2	.A3	.A4	.A5	.A6	.A7	.A8	.A9	.AA	.AB	.AC	.AD	.AE	.AF
.000	.62500000	.62890625	.63281250	.63671875	.64062500	.64453125	.64843750	.65234375	.65625000	.66015625	.66406250	.66796875	.67187500	.67578125	.67968750	.68359375
.001	.62524414	.62915039	.63305664	.63696289	.64086914	.64477539	.64868164	.65258789	.65649414	.66040039	.66430664	.66821289	.67211914	.67602539	.67993164	.68383789
.002	.62548828	.62939453	.63330078	.63720703	.64111328	.64501953	.64892578	.65283203	.65673828	.66064453	.66455078	.66845703	.67236328	.67626953	.68017578	.68408203
.003	.62573242	.62963867	.63354492	.63745117	.64135742	.64526367	.64916992	.65307617	.65698242	.66088867	.66479492	.66870117	.67260742	.67651367	.68041992	.68432617
.004	.62597656	.62988281	.63378906	.63769531	.64160156	.64550781	.64941406	.65332031	.65722656	.66113281	.66503906	.66894531	.67285156	.67675781	.68066406	.68457031
.005	.62622070	.63012695	.63403320	.63793945	.64184570	.64575195	.64965820	.65356445	.65747070	.66137695	.66528320	.66918945	.67309570	.67700195	.68090820	.68481445
.006	.62646484	.63037109	.63427734	.63818359	.64208984	.64599609	.64990234	.65380859	.65771484	.66162109	.66552734	.66943359	.67333984	.67724609	.68115234	.68505859
.007	.62670898	.63061523	.63452148	.63842773	.64233398	.64624023	.65014648	.65405273	.65795898	.66186523	.66577148	.66967773	.67358398	.67749023	.68139648	.68530273
.008	.62695313	.63085938	.63476563	.63867188	.64257813	.64648438	.65039063	.65429688	.65820313	.66210938	.66601563	.66992188	.67382813	.67773438	.68164063	.68554688
.009	.62719727	.63110352	.63500977	.63891602	.64282227	.64672852	.65063477	.65454102	.65844727	.66235352	.66625977	.67016602	.67407227	.67797852	.68188477	.68579102
.00A	.62744141	.63134766	.63525391	.63916016	.64306641	.64697266	.65087891	.65478516	.65869141	.66259766	.66650391	.67041016	.67431641	.67822266	.68212891	.68603516
.00B	.62768555	.63159180	.63549805	.63940430	.64331055	.64721680	.65112305	.65502930	.65893555	.66284180	.66674805	.67065430	.67456055	.67846680	.68237305	.68627930
.00C	.62792969	.63183594	.63574219	.63964844	.64355469	.64746094	.65136719	.65527344	.65917969	.66308594	.66699219	.67089844	.67480469	.67871094	.68261719	.68652344
.00D	.62817383	.63208008	.63598633	.63989258	.64379883	.64770508	.65161133	.65551758	.65942383	.66333008	.66723633	.67114258	.67504883	.67895508	.68286133	.68676758
.00E	.62841797	.63232422	.63623047	.64013672	.64404297	.64794922	.65185547	.65576172	.65966797	.66357422	.66748047	.67138672	.67529297	.67919922	.68310547	.68701172
.00F	.62866211	.63256836	.63647461	.64038086	.64428711	.64819336	.65209961	.65600586	.65991211	.66381836	.66772461	.67163086	.67553711	.67944336	.68334961	.68725586

	.B0	.B1	.B2	.B3	.B4	.B5	.B6	.B7	.B8	.B9	.BA	.BB	.BC	.BD	.BE	.BF
.000	.68750000	.69140625	.69531250	.69921875	.70312500	.70703125	.71093750	.71484375	.71875000	.72265625	.72656250	.73046875	.73437500	.73828125	.74218750	.74609375
.001	.68774414	.69165039	.69555664	.69946289	.70336914	.70727539	.71118164	.71508789	.71899414	.72290039	.72680664	.73071289	.73461914	.73852539	.74243164	.74633789
.002	.68798828	.69189453	.69580078	.69970703	.70361328	.70751953	.71142578	.71533203	.71923828	.72314453	.72705078	.73095703	.73486328	.73876953	.74267578	.74658203
.003	.68823242	.69213867	.69604492	.69995117	.70385742	.70776367	.71166992	.71557617	.71948242	.72338867	.72729492	.73120117	.73510742	.73901367	.74291992	.74682617
.004	.68847656	.69238281	.69628906	.70019531	.70410156	.70800781	.71191406	.71582031	.71972656	.72363281	.72753906	.73144531	.73535156	.73925781	.74316406	.74707031
.005	.68872070	.69262695	.69653320	.70043945	.70434570	.70825195	.71215820	.71606445	.71997070	.72387695	.72778320	.73168945	.73559570	.73950195	.74340820	.74731445
.006	.68896484	.69287109	.69677734	.70068359	.70458984	.70849609	.71240234	.71630859	.72021484	.72412109	.72802734	.73193359	.73583984	.73974609	.74365234	.74755859
.007	.68920898	.69311523	.69702148	.70092773	.70483398	.70874023	.71264648	.71655273	.72045898	.72436523	.72827148	.73217773	.73608398	.73999023	.74389648	.74780273
.008	.68945313	.69335938	.69726563	.70117188	.70507813	.70898438	.71289063	.71679688	.72070313	.72460938	.72851563	.73242188	.73632813	.74023438	.74414063	.74804688
.009	.68969727	.69360352	.69750977	.70141602	.70532227	.70922852	.71313477	.71704102	.72094727	.72485352	.72875977	.73266602	.73657227	.74047852	.74438477	.74829102
.00A	.68994141	.69384766	.69775391	.70166016	.70556641	.70947266	.71337891	.71728516	.72119141	.72509766	.72900391	.73291016	.73681641	.74072266	.74462891	.74853516
.00B	.69018555	.69409180	.69799805	.70190430	.70581055	.70971680	.71362305	.71752930	.72143555	.72534180	.72924805	.73315430	.73706055	.74096680	.74487305	.74877930
.00C	.69042969	.69433594	.69824219	.70214844	.70605469	.70996094	.71386719	.71777344	.72167969	.72558594	.72949219	.73339844	.73730469	.74121094	.74511719	.74902344
.00D	.69067383	.69458008	.69848633	.70239258	.70629883	.71020508	.71411133	.71801758	.72192383	.72583008	.72973633	.73364258	.73754883	.74145508	.74536133	.74926758
.00E	.69091797	.69482422	.69873047	.70263672	.70654297	.71044922	.71435547	.71826172	.72216797	.72607422	.72998047	.73388672	.73779297	.74169922	.74560547	.74951172
.00F	.69116211	.69506836	.69897461	.70288086	.70678711	.71069336	.71459961	.71850586	.72241211	.72631836	.73022461	.73413086	.73803711	.74194336	.74584961	.74975586

	.C0	.C1	.C2	.C3	.C4	.C5	.C6	.C7	.C8	.C9	.CA	.CB	.CC	.CD	.CE	.CF
.000	.75000000	.75390625	.75781250	.76171875	.76562500	.76953125	.77343750	.77734375	.78125000	.78515625	.78906250	.79296875	.79687500	.80078125	.80468750	.80859375
.001	.75024414	.75415039	.75805664	.76196289	.76586914	.76977539	.77368164	.77758789	.78149414	.78540039	.78930664	.79321289	.79711914	.80102539	.80493164	.80883789
.002	.75048828	.75439453	.75830078	.76220703	.76611328	.77001953	.77392578	.77783203	.78173828	.78564453	.78955078	.79345703	.79736328	.80126953	.80517578	.80908203
.003	.75073242	.75463867	.75854492	.76245117	.76635742	.77026367	.77416992	.77807617	.78198242	.78588867	.78979492	.79370117	.79760742	.80151367	.80541992	.80932617
.004	.75097656	.75488281	.75878906	.76269531	.76660156	.77050781	.77441406	.77832031	.78222656	.78613281	.79003906	.79394531	.79785156	.80175781	.80566406	.80957031
.005	.75122070	.75512695	.75903320	.76293945	.76684570	.77075195	.77465820	.77856445	.78247070	.78637695	.79028320	.79418945	.79809570	.80200195	.80590820	.80981445
.006	.75146484	.75537109	.75927734	.76318359	.76708984	.77099609	.77490234	.77880859	.78271484	.78662109	.79052734	.79443359	.79833984	.80224609	.80615234	.81005859
.007	.75170898	.75561523	.75952148	.76342773	.76733398	.77124023	.77514648	.77905273	.78295898	.78686523	.79077148	.79467773	.79858398	.80249023	.80639648	.81030273
.008	.75195313	.75585938	.75976563	.76367188	.76757813	.77148438	.77539063	.77929688	.78320313	.78710938	.79101563	.79492188	.79882813	.80273438	.80664063	.81054688
.009	.75219727	.75610352	.76000977	.76391602	.76782227	.77172852	.77563477	.77954102	.78344727	.78735352	.79125977	.79516602	.79907227	.80297852	.80688477	.81079102
.00A	.75244141	.75634766	.76025391	.76416016	.76806641	.77197266	.77587891	.77978516	.78369141	.78759766	.79150391	.79541016	.79931641	.80322266	.80712891	.81103516
.00B	.75268555	.75659180	.76049805	.76440430	.76831055	.77221680	.77612305	.78002930	.78393555	.78784180	.79174805	.79565430	.79956055	.80346680	.80737305	.81127930
.00C	.75292969	.75683594	.76074219	.76464844	.76855469	.77246094	.77636719	.78027344	.78417969	.78808594	.79199219	.79589844	.79980469	.80371094	.80761719	.81152344
.00D	.75317383	.75708008	.76098633	.76489258	.76879883	.77270508	.77661133	.78051758	.78442383	.78833008	.79223633	.79614258	.80004883	.80395508	.80786133	.81176758
.00E	.75341797	.75732422	.76123047	.76513672	.76904297	.77294922	.77685547	.78076172	.78466797	.78857422	.79248047	.79638672	.80029297	.80419922	.80810547	.81201172
.00F	.75366211	.75756836	.76147461	.76538086	.76928711	.77319336	.77709961	.78100586	.78491211	.78881836	.79272461	.79663086	.80053711	.80444336	.80834961	.81225586

	.D0	.D1	.D2	.D3	.D4	.D5	.D6	.D7	.D8	.D9	.DA	.DB	.DC	.DD	.DE	.DF
.000	.81250000	.81640625	.82031250	.82421875	.82812500	.83203125	.83593750	.83984375	.84375000	.84765625	.85156250	.85546875	.85937500	.86328125	.86718750	.87109375
.001	.81274414	.81665039	.82055664	.82446289	.82836914	.83227539	.83618164	.84008789	.84399414	.84790039	.85180664	.85571289	.85961914	.86352539	.86743164	.87133789
.002	.81298828	.81689453	.82080078	.82470703	.82861328	.83251953	.83642578	.84033203	.84423828	.84814453	.85205078	.85595703	.85986328	.86376953	.86767578	.87158203
.003	.81323242	.81713867	.82104492	.82495117	.82885742	.83276367	.83666992	.84057617	.84448242	.84838867	.85229492	.85620117	.86010742	.86401367	.86791992	.87182617
.004	.81347656	.81738281	.82128906	.82519531	.82910156	.83300781	.83691406	.84082031	.84472656	.84863281	.85253906	.85644531	.86035156	.86425781	.86816406	.87207031
.005	.81372070	.81762695	.82153320	.82543945	.82934570	.83325195	.83715820	.84106445	.84497070	.84887695	.85278320	.85668945	.86059570	.86450195	.86840820	.87231445
.006	.81396484	.81787109	.82177734	.82568359	.82958984	.83349609	.83740234	.84130859	.84521484	.84912109	.85302734	.85693359	.86083984	.86474609	.86865234	.87255859
.007	.81420898	.81811523	.82202148	.82592773	.82983398	.83374023	.83764648	.84155273	.84545898	.84936523	.85327148	.85717773	.86108398	.86499023	.86889648	.87280273
.008	.81445313	.81835938	.82226563	.82617188	.83007813	.83398438	.83789063	.84179688	.84570313	.84960938	.85351563	.85742188	.86132813	.86523438	.86914063	.87304688
.009	.81469727	.81860352	.82250977	.82641602	.83032227	.83422852	.83813477	.84204102	.84594727	.84985352	.85375977	.85766602	.86157227	.86547852	.86938477	.87329102
.00A	.81494141	.81884766	.82275391	.82666016	.83056641	.83447266	.83837891	.84228516	.84619141	.85009766	.85400391	.85791016	.86181641	.86572266	.86962891	.87353516
.00B	.81518555	.81909180	.82299805	.82690430	.83081055	.83471680	.83862305	.84252930	.84643555	.85034180	.85424805	.85815430	.86206055	.86596680	.86987305	.87377930
.00C	.81542969	.81933594	.82324219	.82714844	.83105469	.83496094	.83886719	.84277344	.84667969	.85058594	.85449219	.85839844	.86230469	.86621094	.87011719	.87402344
.00D	.81567383	.81958008	.82348633	.82739258	.83129883	.83520508	.83911133	.84301758	.84692383	.85083008	.85473633	.85864258	.86254883	.86645508	.87036133	.87426758
.00E	.81591797	.81982422	.82373047	.82763672	.83154297	.83544922	.83935547	.84326172	.84716797	.85107422	.85498047	.85888672	.86279297	.86669922	.87060547	.87451172
.00F	.81616211	.82006836	.82397461	.82788086	.83178711	.83569336	.83959961	.84350586	.84741211	.85131836	.85522461	.85913086	.86303711	.86694336	.87084961	.87475586

	.E0	.E1	.E2	.E3	.E4	.E5	.E6	.E7	.E8	.E9	.EA	.EB	.EC	.ED	.EE	.EF
.000	.87500000	.87890625	.88281250	.88671875	.89062500	.89453125	.89843750	.90234375	.90625000	.91015625	.91406250	.91796875	.92187500	.92578125	.92968750	.93359375
.001	.87524414	.87915039	.88305664	.88696289	.89086914	.89477539	.89868164	.90258789	.90649414	.91040039	.91430664	.91821289	.92211914	.92602539	.92993164	.93383789
.002	.87548828	.87939453	.88330078	.88720703	.89111328	.89501953	.89892578	.90283203	.90673828	.91064453	.91455078	.91845703	.92236328	.92626953	.93017578	.93408203
.003	.87573242	.87963867	.88354492	.88745117	.89135742	.89526367	.89916992	.90307617	.90698242	.91088867	.91479492	.91870117	.92260742	.92651367	.93041992	.93432617
.004	.87597656	.87988281	.88378906	.88769531	.89160156	.89550781	.89941406	.90332031	.90722656	.91113281	.91503906	.91894531	.92285156	.92675781	.93066406	.93457031
.005	.87622070	.88012695	.88403320	.88793945	.89184570	.89575195	.89965820	.90356445	.90747070	.91137695	.91528320	.91918945	.92309570	.92700195	.93090820	.93481445
.006	.87646484	.88037109	.88427734	.88818359	.89208984	.89599609	.89990234	.90380859	.90771484	.91162109	.91552734	.91943359	.92333984	.92724609	.93115234	.93505859
.007	.87670898	.88061523	.88452148	.88842773	.89233398	.89624023	.90014648	.90405273	.90795898	.91186523	.91577148	.91967773	.92358398	.92749023	.93139648	.93530273
.008	.87695313	.88085938	.88476563	.88867188	.89257813	.89648438	.90039063	.90429688	.90820313	.91210938	.91601563	.91992188	.92382813	.92773438	.93164063	.93554688
.009	.87719727	.88110352	.88500977	.88891602	.89282227	.89672852	.90063477	.90454102	.90844727	.91235352	.91625977	.92016602	.92407227	.92797852	.93188477	.93579102
.00A	.87744141	.88134766	.88525391	.88916016	.89306641	.89697266	.90087891	.90478516	.90869141	.91259766	.91650391	.92041016	.92431641	.92822266	.93212891	.93603516
.00B	.87768555	.88159180	.88549805	.88940430	.89331055	.89721680	.90112305	.90502930	.90893555	.91284180	.91674805	.92065430	.92456055	.92846680	.93237305	.93627930
.00C	.87792969	.88183594	.88574219	.88964844	.89355469	.89746094	.90136719	.90527344	.90917969	.91308594	.91699219	.92089844	.92480469	.92871094	.93261719	.93652344
.00D	.87817383	.88208008	.88598633	.88989258	.89379883	.89770508	.90161133	.90551758	.90942383	.91333008	.91723633	.92114258	.92504883	.92895508	.93286133	.93676758
.00E	.87841797	.88232422	.88623047	.89013672	.89404297	.89794922	.90185547	.90576172	.90966797	.91357422	.91748047	.92138672	.92529297	.92919922	.93310547	.93701172
.00F	.87866211	.88256836	.88647461	.89038086	.89428711	.89819336	.90209961	.90600586	.90991211	.91381836	.91772461	.92163086	.92553711	.92944336	.93334961	.93725586

	.F0	.F1	.F2	.F3	.F4	.F5	.F6	.F7	.F8	.F9	.FA	.FB	.FC	.FD	.FE	.FF
.000	.93750000	.94140625	.94531250	.94921875	.95312500	.95703125	.96093750	.96484375	.96875000	.97265625	.97656250	.98046875	.98437500	.98828125	.99218750	.99609375
.001	.93774414	.94165039	.94555664	.94946289	.95336914	.95727539	.96118164	.96508789	.96899414	.97290039	.97680664	.98071289	.98461914	.98852539	.99243164	.99633789
.002	.93798828	.94189453	.94580078	.94970703	.95361328	.95751953	.96142578	.96533203	.96923828	.97314453	.97705078	.98095703	.98486328	.98876953	.99267578	.99658203
.003	.93823242	.94213867	.94604492	.94995117	.95385742	.95776367	.96166992	.96557617	.96948242	.97338867	.97729492	.98120117	.98510742	.98901367	.99291992	.99682617
.004	.93847656	.94238281	.94628906	.95019531	.95410156	.95800781	.96191406	.96582031	.96972656	.97363281	.97753906	.98144531	.98535156	.98925781	.99316406	.99707031
.005	.93872070	.94262695	.94653320	.95043945	.95434570	.95825195	.96215820	.96606445	.96997070	.97387695	.97778320	.98168945	.98559570	.98950195	.99340820	.99731445
.006	.93896484	.94287109	.94677734	.95068359	.95458984	.95849609	.96240234	.96630859	.97021484	.97412109	.97802734	.98193359	.98583984	.98974609	.99365234	.99755859
.007	.93920898	.94311523	.94702148	.95092773	.95483398	.95874023	.96264648	.96655273	.97045898	.97436523	.97827148	.98217773	.98608398	.98999023	.99389648	.99780273
.008	.93945313	.94335938	.94726563	.95117188	.95507813	.95898438	.96289063	.96679688	.97070313	.97460938	.97851563	.98242188	.98632813	.99023438	.99414063	.99804688
.009	.93969727	.94360352	.94750977	.95141602	.95532227	.95922852	.96313477	.96704102	.97094727	.97485352	.97875977	.98266602	.98657227	.99047852	.99438477	.99829102
.00A	.93994141	.94384766	.94775391	.95166016	.95556641	.95947266	.96337891	.96728516	.97119141	.97509766	.97900391	.98291016	.98681641	.99072266	.99462891	.99853516
.00B	.94018555	.94409180	.94799805	.95190430	.95581055	.95971680	.96362305	.96752930	.97143555	.97534180	.97924805	.98315430	.98706055	.99096680	.99487305	.99877930
.00C	.94042969	.94433594	.94824219	.95214844	.95605469	.95996094	.96386719	.96777344	.97167969	.97558594	.97949219	.98339844	.98730469	.99121094	.99511719	.99902344
.00D	.94067383	.94458008	.94848633	.95239258	.95629883	.96020508	.96411133	.96801758	.97192383	.97583008	.97973633	.98364258	.98754883	.99145508	.99536133	.99926758
.00E	.94091797	.94482422	.94873047	.95263672	.95654297	.96044922	.96435547	.96826172	.97216797	.97607422	.97998047	.98388672	.98779297	.99169922	.99560547	.99951172
.00F	.94116211	.94506836	.94897461	.95288086	.95678711	.96069336	.96459961	.96850586	.97241211	.97631836	.98022461	.98413086	.98803711	.99194336	.99584961	.99975586

INDEX